CONVERSION TABLE FOR ENERGY UNITS

Multiply	*By*	*To obtain*
Mev	1.07×10^{-3}	mass unit
	1.60×10^{-6}	erg.
	3.83×10^{-14}	gm. cal
	4.45×10^{-20}	kw. hr.
Mass units	9.31×10^{2}	Mev
	1.49×10^{-3}	erg.
	3.56×10^{-11}	gm. cal.
	4.15×10^{-17}	kw. hr.
erg.	6.71×10^{2}	mass units
	6.24×10^{5}	Mev
	2.39×10^{-8}	gm. cal.
	2.78×10^{-14}	kw. hr.
gm. cal.	2.81×10^{10}	mass units
	2.62×10^{13}	Mev
	4.18×10^{7}	erg.
	1.16×10^{-6}	kw. hr.
kw. hr.	2.41×10^{16}	mass units
	2.25×10^{19}	Mev
	3.60×10^{13}	erg.
	8.60×10^{5}	gm. cal.

From H. D. Smyth, Atomic Energy for Military Purposes, Rev. Mod. Phys., **17**, 458 (1945).

CONVERSION OF ELECTRICAL UNITS

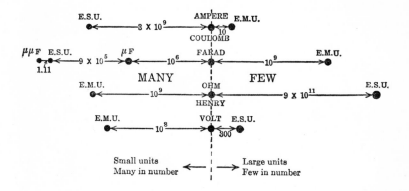

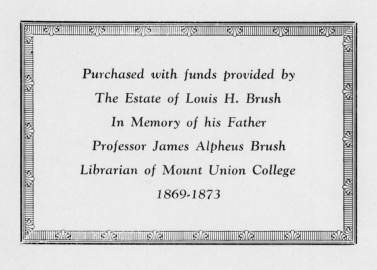

Electron

AND

Nuclear Physics

By

J. BARTON HOAG, Ph.D

PROFESSOR, WITH THE RANK OF COMMANDER, U.S.C.G.
*Fellow of the American Physical Society; Member of the
Institute of Radio Engineers;* FORMERLY, *Assistant
Professor, Dept. of Physics, Univ. of Chicago*

THIRD EDITION, NINTH PRINTING

REVISED BY

S. A. KORFF, Ph.D

*Professor of Physics
College of Engineering, New York University*

D. VAN NOSTRAND COMPANY, INC.

PRINCETON, NEW JERSEY

TORONTO   LONDON

NEW YORK

D. VAN NOSTRAND COMPANY, INC.
120 Alexander St., Princeton, New Jersey (*Principal office*)
24 West 40 Street, New York 18, New York

D. VAN NOSTRAND COMPANY, LTD.
358, Kensington High Street, London, W.14, England

D. VAN NOSTRAND COMPANY (Canada), LTD.
25 Hollinger Road, Toronto 16, Canada

PREFACE TO THIRD EDITION

The purpose of this book, to present the results of modern physics on the college student level, is best served by having the book contain as much of the latest material as contributes significantly to our current picture of physics. With this thought in mind, the present revision was carried out. The major changes and differences between this and the previous edition are the inclusion of the new material developed in the past few years, which includes the newer accelerating devices, the new experimental techniques, modern vacuum tubes, and a discussion of the neutron experiments and their bearing on the structure of the nucleus. The principal changes, therefore, are all in the latter chapters of the book. In the chapter on vacuum tubes, for example, the former section on tetrodes has been condensed, while that on pentodes, formerly mentioned but briefly, has been expanded, and a description of the properties of some of the newer gas-discharge tubes has been added. The section describing that device whose utility is constantly expanding, the counter tube or Geiger-Müller counter, is amplified, and more descriptive material is added both to the paragraphs on its construction and its use, and to the basic physics of its operation.

The section on cosmic rays has been reworked and a good bit of new material added to bring it in accord with the current point of view. Some of the recent significant experiments are quoted, the present evidence about the nature of the radiation is set forth, and a number of illustrations of cosmic rays as a source of high-energy nuclear reactions is given. In particular, mesotron production is discussed, and mesotron theory is mentioned. A new experiment has been added, in using coincidence counters, by means of which the student may familiarize himself both with the use of counters as a measuring device, and also with some of the properties of cosmic radiation.

The section on nuclear physics is the portion which has been most completely rewritten and revised. The types of nuclear reactions have been rearranged and are discussed in the order in which they appear in Bethe's famous article. Thus the content and the arrange-

iii

ment of Chapter 14 is almost entirely new. First the effects produced by charged particles are discussed. Then the discovery of the neutron is described, and the transmutations produced by its use, the neutron scattering experiments, and the phenomena of artificial radioactivity are brought in. Artificial transmutations and the physical optics of neutrons are discussed.

No attempt has been made to use the methods of quantum mechanics in this text, because it is assumed that the student is not familiar with these procedures. The degree of sophistication expected of the reader and the level of the treatment are the same as in the previous edition.

S.A.K.

New York, N. Y.
November, 1947

PREFACE TO FIRST EDITION

The student of physics at the senior college or early graduate level is confronted with a vast array of physical concepts, interpretative theories and experimental techniques, all of which have expanded rapidly in recent years. In addition to an extension of the earlier knowledge of alpha, beta, gamma, cosmic and x-rays, electrons, protons, photons, gas-filled and vacuum tubes, photoelectric effects, radioactivity, etc., new entities such as the positron and neutron have been discovered. The development of magnificent devices for the acceleration of elementary particles to high energies, as well as the use of projectiles from radioactive substances, has opened the door to the transmutation of elements and to a fuller knowledge of the nature of the nucleus of the atom. Radioactive substances have been produced by artificial means.

The underlying purpose of this book is to present the experimental evidence for those concepts which lie in the domain of *electron and nuclear physics*. Simple statements of the experimental facts and physical principles of both the newer and older concepts are recognized as being of great help in bridging the gap between the early study of physics and the specialization of advanced research.

A strenuous effort has been made to develop the subjects in such a sequence as to avoid reference at any point to discussions which appear later in the book. The early chapters treat of the electron, its charge, mass, wave-length and emission from hot and cold surfaces. These are followed by chapters dealing with electrical phenomena specific to the outer parts of the atom. In succeeding chapters there are discussions of the phenomena involving the nuclei of atoms, such as positive rays, natural and artificial radioactivity, transmutations, etc. This large amount of material has been presented in one book, because many basic relations and experimental techniques are common to several of these fields of study.

At the end of each chapter there is a detailed description of experiments, by means of which the student is brought to recognize the concepts involved as necessary abstractions of his own experience. The apparatus has been simplified from the original research form to an extent which avoids the expenditure of too much time or effort, yet permits a degree of accuracy which leaves conviction. Anyone with a taste for experimentation will be fascinated by watching the changes of velocity of an oil drop in a condenser, as it picks up or loses charges, or by observing the scintillations produced on a screen by particles thrown out of an atom during its transmutation.

Among the simpler experiments described may be mentioned those numbered 1–1, 4–1, 4–2, 5–1, 6–1, 6–2, 8–5, 11–1 and 12–4, while the following should be attempted only by the more advanced students: 3–1, 4–4, 8–4, 9–3 and 10–1. Experiments 14–1 and 15–1 require considerable previous training and should serve as a challenge to the best of students. Many of the experiments, in their modified form, are published here for the first time.

Many details of laboratory technique have been woven into the experiments. In addition, the last four chapters of the book are entirely devoted to the techniques which are applicable in common to several fields of modern physics. Parts of this material have not been published before.

The problems at the end have been found to be of great assistance to the student in grasping the subject matter.

The author wishes to express his thanks to Professor A. J. Dempster, who has continued to give invaluable advice, suggesting improvements and new experiments; to Professor A. H. Compton for his valuable criticism of the chapters on x-rays and cosmic rays; to Dr. L. W. Alvarez who has read much of the manuscript; to the various members of the faculty at Ryerson Laboratory for occasional advice; and especially to the groups of students who have so eagerly tested and rearranged the experiments during the past twelve years.

J. Barton Hoag.

Ryerson Physical Laboratory,
The University of Chicago,
January, 1938.

CONTENTS

ELECTRON PHYSICS

NUCLEAR PHYSICS

LABORATORY TECHNIQUES

EXPERIMENTS

CHAPTER 1

THE CHARGE OF THE ELECTRON

1-1. Introduction.—The granular structure of electricity has been observed in widely different fields of physics by many different methods. For example, the individual charges emitted by the hot filament in a radio tube are always of a definite, small amount, regardless of the material or the temperature of the filament. The particles spontaneously emitted by radioactive substances carry either one or two times this small amount. Again, the electrified particles in the air around us carry an integral multiple of this natural unit of electrical charge. Further, the frictional electricity on drops of water or oil sprayed from an atomizer is found to have this same granular structure.

The name *electron* was first applied to the smallest amount of electricity found in nature, in 1874 by C. J. Stoney. Since then additional properties have been associated with this charge, such as mass and wave-length, so that it has become an entity in itself instead of a unit of electricity. It is a common constituent of all atoms. Extensive studies have been made of the energy required to shift electrons from their normal condition and even to remove them from the atoms of various elements. In this research, new laws and properties of Nature have been discovered.

The electrons which carry a negative charge are by far the most common and accessible and will be referred to throughout this book simply as electrons. The rarer, positively charged electrons are called "positrons." In the first three chapters, methods of measuring the charge, the mass and the wave-length of the electron will be presented.

The charge of the electron is only a small part of one electrostatic unit. It is equal to 4.8×10^{-10} e.s.u.

1-2. An Early Method of Measuring the Charge of the Electron.—If a gas, saturated with water vapor, is suddenly expanded, its temperature falls below the dew point. Small drops of water then form on condensation centers such as dust or electrically charged particles, called "ions," and appear as a cloud which slowly settles to the bottom of the containing chamber under the force of gravity. The weight of this cloud can be determined by blowing it into a drying tube, which is weighed before and after the arrival of the cloud. The average weight of one of the water drops may be estimated by observing the rate of fall of the top surface of the cloud and applying Stokes' theoretical law for the velocity of fall of a small body through a gas. Dividing the total weight of the cloud by the average weight of one drop then gives the total number of drops in the cloud. This is also equal to the number of charged particles, provided only one water drop forms on one ion. Next, the total electrical charge of the cloud is measured by passing it into a chamber or allowing it to fall upon a metal plate connected to a sensitive electrical instrument such as an electrometer. Dividing the total charge by the number of ions in the cloud gives the charge on each ion.

In 1897, Townsend used this method and found the charge of the electron to be $e = 3.4 \times 10^{-10}$ e.s.u. In 1903, H. A. Wilson used this method with the addition of an electrical field. His method is essentially that described in the next section, except that he used water drops, which evaporate during the experiment, and that he made his measurements on the entire cloud instead of on a single drop. He found $e = 3.1 \times 10^{-10}$ e.s.u. Both of these early values are of the right order of magnitude only.

1–3. The Oil-drop Method.—An accurate method of measuring the charge of the electron was developed during the years 1909–1913 by R. A. Millikan. He made many measurements of the electrical charge on a *single* drop of oil located between the plates

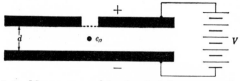

Fig. 1–1. Measurement of the electrical charge on small drops.

of a condenser, as in figure 1–1, and found that the charge was always an integral multiple of a certain small amount. Oil was used to prevent loss of weight by evaporation. The oil is charged as it is sprayed from an atomizer and falls through small holes in the center of the top plate of the condenser. The plates have smooth inner surfaces and are parallel to each other. Air currents are carefully avoided.

Let m be the mass of the drop and g the acceleration of gravity. The downward force, mg, does not cause the drop to accelerate, as might be expected, but to fall with a constant velocity, as may be seen by watching its motion with a long focus microscope containing a scale in its eyepiece. The drop is so small that the frequent collisions with the air particles reduce its average motion to one of constant velocity v_d, proportional to the acting force. Thus,

$$mg = Kv_d \qquad (1\text{-}1)$$

where K is the constant of proportionality.

The force of gravity downward may be counterbalanced by an electrical attraction upward by connecting a battery of proper voltage to the plates. With higher voltages the drop may be caused to move upward with a velocity v_u proportional to the net force acting upon it. If e_n is the total charge on the drop and E the electric field strength between the plates (force on unit charge), then Ee_n is the electrical force on the drop, and

$$Ee_n - mg = Kv_u. \qquad (1\text{-}2)$$

From these two equations

$$e_n = \frac{mg}{Ev_d}(v_d + v_u), \qquad (1\text{-}3)$$

in which g is a known quantity, v_d and v_u may be measured using a calibrated scale in the eyepiece of the microscope and E is given as the potential of the battery divided by the distance d between the plates. The determination of the mass m of the drop will be discussed later.

If x-rays are passed through the condenser or if a radioactive substance is placed near the holes in the top plate, electrically charged particles of sub-microscopic size (ions) will be created in the air through which the drop is moving. The charge on the drop may then change to a new value e_m and the drop will move upward with a different velocity (v_w). Then

$$e_n - e_m = \frac{mg}{Ev_d}(v_u - v_w) \qquad (1\text{--}4)$$

$$\Delta e = C\Delta v, \qquad (1\text{--}5)$$

where $C = mg/Ev_d$, a constant for a given drop and electrical field. Thus the charge Δe gained or lost by the drop is directly proportional to its change of velocity, Δv. When many values of Δv are obtained for a given drop, the important fact is found that they are always integral multiples of a certain small value; i.e., there is found a smallest value of Δv and twice, three times, etc., this amount; never a smaller value and never one and one-half, two and a fraction, etc., times this amount. Since there is a common divisor of Δv, it is obvious from the last equation that the same is true of Δe; i.e., the charge gained or lost is an exact multiple of a unit charge. *This constitutes a proof that electricity is granular* without requiring a measurement of the mass of the drop or of any of the other quantities in C of equation 1-5, but it does not give a numerical measure of this charge. The value of this charge is obtained as follows:

In order to determine the mass of the drop, the density σ of the oil is measured. Then, assuming the drop to be a sphere of radius a and volume $4\pi a^3/3$,

$$m = \frac{4\pi a^3}{3}\sigma. \qquad (1\text{--}6)$$

The radius, which may be of the order of ten times the mean-free-path or one thousand times the size of the air particles, is too small to be measured directly. Recourse is had to Stokes' law for the free fall of spheres of this size through air at ordinary pressures, which states that

$$v_d = \frac{2ga_1^2\sigma}{9\eta}, \qquad (1\text{--}7)$$

where η is the coefficient of viscosity of the air at the existing temperature. Thus the radius of the drop is

$$a_1 = \sqrt{\frac{9\eta v_d}{2g\sigma}}. \qquad (1\text{--}8)$$

When Millikan determined the mass in the manner just described and used its value in equation 1-3, he found that the values of the charge e_n varied with the size of the drop. On the other hand, it was known that the drop gained or lost charges of a definite amount regardless of its size. Since the value of the unit charge is independent of the size of the drop, it was concluded that Stokes' law required a correction. Thus

$$v_d = \frac{2ga^2\sigma}{9\eta}\left(1 + \frac{b}{pa}\right) \tag{1-9}$$

where $b = 0.000617$ and p is the pressure of the air. Since this quadratic equation is of awkward form when solved for a, and since the correction is not too large, one may use a method of successive approximations. In order to do so, the rough value of a, called a_1 of equation 1-8 is calculated and used in the correction term b/pa. Then the corrected form of Stokes' law may easily be solved. Thus

$$a = \left[\frac{9\eta v_d}{2g\sigma(1 + b/pa_1)}\right]^{\frac{1}{2}} \tag{1-10}$$

This is used in equation 1-6 to give an expression for the mass of the drop. Finally,

$$E = \frac{V}{300d} \tag{1-11}$$

where V is the voltage of the battery. The factor 300 is used to convert volts into e.s.u. Then equation 1-3 becomes

$$e_n = \left[400\pi d\sqrt{\frac{(9\eta/2)^3}{g\sigma}}\right]\sqrt{v_d\left(\frac{1}{1 + b/pa_1}\right)^3}\left(\frac{v_d + v_u}{V}\right), \tag{1-12}$$

$$= k_1 k_2 \left(\frac{v_d + v_u}{V}\right) \tag{1-13}$$

The first term k_1, in brackets in equation 1-12, is a constant for a given apparatus and the second square root, k_2, is a constant for a given oil drop, which simplifies the calculations. For convenience in the experimental work described at the end of this chapter, the meaning of the symbols used in this equation will now be repeated;

d is the distance in centimeters between the inside faces of the plates, σ is the density of the oil, η is the coefficient of viscosity of air (0.000183 poises at 23° C.), g is the acceleration of gravity in centimeters per second per second, $b = 0.000617$, p is the barometric pressure of the gas in centimeters of mercury, a_1 is the approximate radius of the drop in centimeters as given by equation 1–8, v_d is the velocity of free fall of the drop in centimeters per second, v_u is the velocity of rise under the opposing forces of the electrical field and gravity and V is the potential difference in volts between the two plates.

The charge gained or lost by a drop (Δe), may be calculated from equation 1–13. Thus

$$\Delta e = k_1 k_2 \frac{\Delta v}{V} \tag{1–14}$$

where Δv is the difference between two upward velocities.

The value of e_n was found by Millikan to be an integral multiple of $e = 4.774 \times 10^{-10}$ e.s.u. A correction was made by Birge[1] in 1929, so that the "oil-drop" value became $e = 4.770 \times 10^{-10}$ e.s.u. (± 0.005) $= 1.590 \times 10^{-19}$ coulombs.

1–4. The Accepted Value of e.—For a number of years, the value $e = 4.770 \times 10^{-10}$ e.s.u. was accepted as the most accurate known. Later, an x-ray method, to be described at the end of this chapter, yielded a value of e differing from the oil-drop value by an amount appreciably greater than the experimental errors in either of the two methods. After many attempts to determine the cause of this discrepancy, it was found that the coefficient of viscosity of the air, used in the oil-drop calculations, was in error. Instead of the value (at 23° C.) of 1822.7×10^{-7}, Kellström[2] found 1834.8×10^{-7}. Additional determinations of η (Birge's average value $= 1832.5 \times 10^{-7}$) and repetitions of the oil-drop experiment have finally brought the two values of e into good agreement. The accepted value is

$$e = (4.803 \pm 0.001) \times 10^{-10} \text{ abs. e.s.u.}$$

$$= (1.602 \pm 0.0003) \times 10^{-20} \text{ abs e.m.u.}$$

$$= (1.602 \pm 0.0003) \times 10^{-19} \text{ coulombs.}$$

1–5. The Thermionic Method.—A hot filament, sealed in a highly evacuated tube, emits negative electricity in amounts which vary slightly around an average value from one moment to the next. The nature of the irregularities in this varying current of electricity will be different if the emission consists of large numbers of discrete charges than if it consists of a continuous flow of electricity. The examination of these irregularities will be discussed in Chapter 5 under the title of "The Shot Effect." The result of a series of careful experiments shows that the electricity is emitted as discrete charges of amount

$$e = 4.76 \times 10^{-10} \text{ e.s.u.}$$

which is in reasonable agreement with the value obtained for the charge of the electron by the oil-drop method, although the accuracy is not so great.

1–6. The Charge of the Alpha Particle.—Certain radioactive substances, radium, for example, spontaneously throw out positively charged bodies called alpha particles. In order to measure the charge on each alpha particle, a determination is made of the total amount of electricity carried by a known number of particles, as described in Chapter 12. The result is

$$2e = 2 \times (4.769 \pm .004) \times 10^{-10} \text{ e.s.u.,}$$

which is twice the charge of the electron as measured by the oil-drop method. However, this charge is positive, not negative.

1–7. The Faraday.—The first experimental evidence for the atomicity of electricity appears in the studies which Faraday made early in the nineteenth century, of the passage of electricity through solutions. He stated, as one of the laws of electrolysis, that the mass of the substance liberated at an electrode is directly proportional to the quantity of electricity sent through the solution. For example, since the International Electromagnetic Unit of electricity (ten coulombs) is defined as that quantity which, in passing through a standard silver solution, will deposit 0.01118 grams of silver, then twice this quantity will deposit 0.02236 grams. From many similar cases, Faraday was able to assert that a certain definite quantity of electricity is always associated in electrolysis with a definite amount of matter.

Faraday's second law states that if the same quantity of electricity is passed through different solutions, the masses liberated are directly proportional to the atomic weights and inversely proportional to the valences of the elements deposited.* For example, if 9649 electromagnetic units of quantity of electricity are passed through water which contains a small amount of acid, 8.000 grams of oxygen (atomic weight = 16.000, valence = 2) and 1.008 grams of hydrogen (atomic weight = 1.008, valence = 1) will be given off at the positive and negative electrodes respectively. In 1874, Stoney advanced the viewpoint that, since this law is true and since the elements are known to be made up of atoms, then electricity must also be granular.

The quantity of electricity needed to deposit a mass, in grams, equal to the atomic weight divided by the valence (one gram-equivalent) is a universal constant called *the faraday*, (F).

$$F = 9649 \text{ e.m.u./gram equivalent.}$$
$$= 2.893 \times 10^{14} \text{ e.s.u./gram equivalent.}$$

From the suggestion of Stoney and for univalent elements, this quantity of electricity may be divided into a large number (N) of equal charges (e), each of which is associated with one atom. N is known as Avogadro's number. If the element has a valence v, the charge on each atom will be ev and the number of atoms deposited by each faraday will be N/v. Then

$$F = \frac{N}{v} \cdot ev, \tag{1-15}$$

or
$$F = Ne. \tag{1-16}$$

Calculations of the product Ne for gaseous ions have been made from a derived relation between this quantity and the measurable mobilities and diffusion rates of ions. The values obtained by these two methods are in reasonable agreement with the measurements in electrolysis. They are not, however, so precise.

---

* This statement applies strictly to reactions in which the free element is liberated or consumed. In other reactions in which the free element is not involved, the words valence-change should be used instead of valence.

Avogadro's number (N) has been determined by kinetic theory methods which chiefly involve the viscosity of a gas. The rough values so obtained lie between 2×10^{23} and 20×10^{23}. N has also been obtained by other methods such as those described in the remaining sections of this chapter.

From the product Ne, which is known with accuracy, and a separate measurement of N or e, the remaining quantity may be calculated. If e is taken as 4.803×10^{-10} e.s.u., then

$$N = 6.02 \times 10^{23} \ (\pm 0.001).$$

1-8. Brownian Movements.—When examined under a high-power microscope, small particles suspended in a fluid, such as smoke particles in air, for example, are found to be moving rapidly in a random fashion. These movements were discovered by Robert Brown in 1827. The particles are composed of clusters of atoms or molecules and their motion, which is one of the best evidences of the vibrations taking place in gases, is due to an unbalanced bombardment of the visible particle by the many invisible molecules of the fluid. Taken over a sufficiently long time interval, the number of gas molecules striking one side of the particle would equal the number striking the opposite side, but during a short time interval the chance bombardment is sometimes greater on one side than on the other. Hence, the particle is knocked back and forth in a tortuous path. This motion is always present; it is the same for various particles of appropriate size but of different nature, and it is not influenced by outside vibrations or currents in the fluid.

Due to Brownian movements, small particles in a suitable suspension may be found supported against the force of gravity. Air particles are prevented from falling to the earth's surface because of the counterbalancing force due to the bombardment of the denser particles below. Just as the density of the air in the earth's atmosphere varies with the distance above the surface, so also the number of particles in a suspension increases toward the bottom. The form of the law is the same in both cases but the apparent mass of the particles in suspension is appreciably less than the true mass because of the buoyant effect of the fluid displaced. The equation, first derived by Laplace, which expresses the number of particles per cubic centimeter at different heights is

$$n = n_o \epsilon^{- \left[\frac{Nmg}{RT}\left(1 - \frac{d}{D}\right)\right]h}, \qquad (1\text{-}17)$$

in which n_o is the number per cubic centimeter at a given distance h below the plane in which n is measured, m is the true mass, D is the density of the particle, while d is the density of the fluid, g is the acceleration of gravity, R is the universal gas constant, T is the absolute temperature and N is the quantity sought, i.e., Avogadro's number. Perrin, after extensive tests with colloidal suspensions, found $N = 6.82 \times 10^{23}$ ($\pm.38$) which is surprisingly close to the accepted value considering the difficulties of the experiments. Substitution in the equation $Ne = 9649$, gives a reasonable, although not an accurate value of e (4.24×10^{-10} e.s.u.).

Einstein has derived an equation for the average-squared-distance $\overline{x^2}$ through which a suspended particle moves in a given direction in a time t. This is

$$\overline{x^2} = \frac{2RTt}{NK}, \qquad (1\text{-}18)$$

in which R is the gas constant per gram-molecule, T is the absolute temperature, N is Avogadro's number and K (which is the same as that in equation 1–1) is the resistance to the motion. Perrin tested this equation with colloidal suspensions and found $N = 6.88 \times 10^{23}$. Together with $Ne = 9649$, this gives gives $e = 4.26 \times 10^{-10}$ e.s.u., again in approximate agreement with the oil-drop value.

1–9. Avogadro's Number from Brownian Movements.[3]— Einstein's Brownian motion equation may be solved for Avogadro's number N. Thus

$$N = \frac{2RTt}{K\overline{x^2}}, \qquad (1\text{-}19)$$

where R is a known constant and the remaining quantities on the right-hand side of the equation may be determined by the use of the oil-drop apparatus in the following manner. The microscope is oriented so that the scale in its eyepiece is horizontal instead of vertical. Oil is sprayed into the condenser and a small drop is selected. If the radius of the drop is sufficiently small, say 10^{-5} cm., the Brownian movements will be readily observed. The drop is balanced by so adjusting the potential of the battery that the downward force of gravity is just counterbalanced by the upward electrical force. The drop will be seen to move back and forth with Brownian motion in a haphazard fashion. The number of centimeters x which it moves in the *horizontal* direction during a given time interval t, of say 30 seconds, is measured many times. One may disregard the sign of the displacements (whether to the left or to the right) since the individual values are to be squared. The average of their squares is $\overline{x^2}$ in equation 1–19.

In order to determine the friction constant K, the corrected form of Stokes' law, as given by equation 1–9, and the mass equation 1–6 are substituted in the force equation 1–1. Thus

$$K = \frac{6\pi\eta a}{1 + b/pa}. \tag{1-20}$$

When substituted in equation 1–19, this leads to

$$N = \frac{2RT}{6\pi\eta} \cdot \frac{t}{\overline{x^2}} \left(\frac{1 + b/pa}{a} \right) \tag{1-21}$$

where $R = 8.32 \times 10^7$ ergs per degree, $T = 273 + {}^\circ C, b = 6.17 \times 10^{-4}$, p is the barometric pressure of the air in centimeters of mercury, t is the time interval in seconds during which a Brownian displacement of x centimeters occurs. The radius of the drop a, in centimeters, to be used in the two places in this equation should be an exact value since the correction term b/pa is large for the small drops used. It may be obtained by solving equation 1–9. Thus

$$a = -\frac{b}{2p} + \sqrt{\left(\frac{b}{2p}\right)^2 + cv_d}. \tag{1-22}$$

Here

$$c = 9\eta/2g\sigma \tag{1-23}$$

where $\eta = 1.83 \times 10^{-4}$, $g = 980$, $\sigma =$ is the density of the oil in grams per cubic centimeter and v_d is the velocity of free fall of the drop in centimeters per second.

In order to determine v_d, the microscope is rotated so that its scale is vertical and the time for the drop to fall a given distance is measured. The drop is drawn back to its starting point by an upward electrical attraction (whose magnitude is immaterial) and allowed to fall again. The individual values of the free fall time will be found to vary appreciably around the average (v_d) because the Brownian movements sometimes increase and sometimes decrease the time required to fall a given distance under the force of gravity alone. In fact, these variations from the average may also be used to determine x in the Einstein equation. (See the work of Fletcher, reference 3.)

1-10. X-ray Method.—The charge of the electron may be measured by an indirect process using x-rays. Briefly, the method consists of: first, a direct measurement of the wave-length of an x-ray; second, a measurement of the "grating constant" of an elementary crystal; third, a calculation of Avogadro's number, and finally, the evaluation of e from the equation $Ne = 9649$.

The wave-length of x-rays was first measured in a direct manner by A. H. Compton and Doan.[4] As seen in figure 1-2,

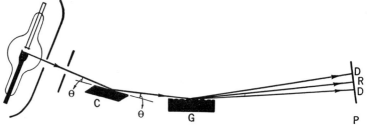

FIG. 1-2.   Measurement of the wave-length of x-rays by the grating method.

a collimated x-ray beam, reflected from a calcite crystal C, is allowed to fall upon the surface of a diffraction grating G at a very small glancing angle (exaggerated in the figure). As with optical gratings, the x-rays, reflected from the polished parts of the ruled surface recombine at the photographic plate P to give a directly reflected beam R and various diffraction orders, D, on either side. From the known distance between the rulings on the grating and the positions of the spectral lines, the wave-length of the x-rays reflected from the calcite crystal is calculated. Bearden,[5] and others, have made a number of accurate x-ray wave-length determinations in this manner. For example, Bearden has found for the copper K_{α_1} line, a wave-length of 1.5405 angstroms.

The angle θ through which an x-ray beam is diffracted from a crystal may be measured and used in the well-known Bragg law

$$n\lambda = 2d \sin \theta *\qquad (1\text{--}24)$$

to compute the grating constant d, provided the wave-length λ of the ray is known. The order of the diffracted beam is n ($=1, 2, 3$, etc.).

Consider a cubic crystal of rock salt as made up of many small elementary cubes with alternate sodium and chlorine atoms at the corners. Let the crystal be one which weighs 58.454 grams (one gram-molecule, M), which is the sum of 22.997 grams of sodium and 35.457 grams of chlorine. From the definition of Avogadro's number, it will then contain N atoms of each or $2N$ atoms in all. Along each edge there will be $\sqrt[3]{2N}$ atoms, each at a distance d centimeters from the next. The length of each edge will then be $d\sqrt[3]{2N}$ and the volume of the crystal will be $d^3 \cdot 2N$ cubic centimeters. By definition, the density ρ of the crystal is its mass divided by its volume, so that

$$N = \frac{M}{2\rho d^3}.\qquad (1\text{--}25)$$

A similar equation may be obtained for calcite ($CaCO_3$), where the elementary space lattice is a rhombohedron or distorted cube. To allow for the distortion, a factor $\phi(\beta)$ is included in the denominator of equation 1–25. For calcite, $M = 100.07$, $\rho = 2.7102$, and $\phi(\beta) = 1.09630$. If, then, the grating space d is known, N may be calculated. Thus

$$N = 6.023 \times 10^{23}$$

molecules per gram-molecule. From this and the known product of N and e, ($F = 9648.8$ e.m.u./gram equivalent),

$$e = 4.802 \times 10^{-10} \text{ e.s.u.}$$

This is an accurate value.

* See Chapter 9 for a derivation of this law. For higher orders and precise wave-length measurements, a small correction must be made to this equation by multiplying the right hand side by $(1 - \delta \sin^2 \theta)$, where δ is the unit decrement of the index of refraction μ, i.e., $\mu = 1 - \delta$. In this manner allowance is made for the slight bending of the x-rays as they enter and leave the crystal surface.

TO MEASURE THE CHARGE OF THE ELECTRON

Apparatus.—The condenser of figure 1–3 consists of two thick metal plates PP which have been carefully faced and are separated by insulator strips B of a definite and uniform thickness. The plates may be two or more inches square and three to five millimeters apart. The condenser is rigidly mounted in a horizontal position. Several small holes in the top plate, under the cover C,

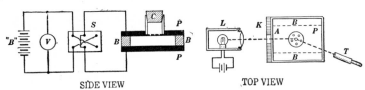

SIDE VIEW   TOP VIEW

FIG. 1–3.   Measurement of the charge on oil drops.

allow drops of oil, sprayed from an atomizer, to fall into the region between the plates. The process of atomizing the oil serves to electrically charge the drops. Glass windows across the front and back sides allow observation of the drops and eliminate air currents. Light from a flash lamp, L, is reflected from a drop and is observed in a long focus microscope T, as in the figure. In the eyepiece of the microscope there is a finely divided scale. The magnification is such that each small division corresponds to about 0.005 cm. A dark background is provided in the corner A, either by means of a cardboard screen K, which has a vertical slit, or by means of L-shaped insulators between the plates. A battery, " B " or other steady source of potential is used to charge the plates. The switch S is used to reverse the polarity of the plates and, in its intermediate position, to short circuit them. Thus, the charged oil drop may be drawn upward or allowed to fall freely under the action of gravity alone.

The source of potential, " B " of figure 1–3, may consist of from two to four radio " B " batteries (90–180 volts), the 110 or 220 volt d.c. line or a B battery eliminator of about the same voltage. A convenient unit for this and other experiments is shown in figure 1–4. Here, T is a step-up transformer, '80 is a

full-wave rectifier tube, the iron core choke coil and the electrolytic
condensers serve to filter out voltage fluctuations, the 25,000 ohm
10 watt "bleeder" resistance serves to regulate the output
voltage and the 0–100,000 ohm variable resistor serves to change
this voltage. The latter is accomplished, in this case, by means
of the variable ir drop of the current to the voltmeter V of figure
1–3. The transformer T may also have one or more low voltage
secondaries which are used to light the flash lamp. The author
has found it advisable to overload the ordinary flash lamps in
order to obtain better illumination, at a cost of shortened life of
the lamps. If the lamp is too large the heat is excessive, an

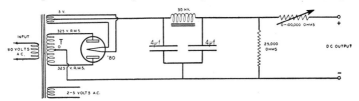

Fig. 1–4. A convenient voltage supply.

absorbing water cell is needed and the apparatus becomes more
complicated. A high resistance voltmeter (0–250 volt, 1000 ohms
per volt) serves nicely to measure V.

Adjustments.—1. Turn the flash lamp to one side and adjust
its position or focus until a bright spot about two millimeters in
diameter is seen on a sheet of paper located at the same distance
as the center of the condenser.

2. Turn the lamp until the beam passes through the condenser,
illuminating the upper and lower plates equally. It should just
barely strike the insulator strip at the corner marked P, in the
top view of figure 1–3, in order to aid in the illumination of the
scale in the eyepiece. If this scattered light is too bright, the oil
drops will not stand out clearly against the background or may
not be seen at all.

3. With zero potential on the plates, insert a small wire vertically in the central hole in the top plate and focus the microscope
on the bright streak of light reflected from its side. The microscope should point toward the dark corner A and the lines of its
scale should be horizontal. The angular position of the microscope is changed until the background of light just permits the

scale divisions to be clearly distinguished. Adjust the focus of the microscope as a whole and also that of its eyepiece until there is no parallax between the streak of light and the scale. Do not change the focus during the remainder of this experiment.

4. Remove the wire before applying the potential V. To avoid a possible short circuit, a splinter of wood or a fine glass tube may be used instead of the wire.

5. With the atomizer six inches or more above and to one side of the condenser, gently spray some oil toward the holes and put the cork C, or the cover of figure 1–3, in place. On looking through the microscope, a diffused light will be seen at first which soon thins out. Then, small individual bright spots, the oil drops, may be seen. In selecting one of the smaller drops, choose one which moves very slowly, both up and down. It will then carry fewer charges and will demonstrate the granular nature of electricity more clearly. Brownian movement may cause the drop to waver back and forth a slight amount. If the drop tends to drift out of focus, move the microscope as a whole, without changing its magnification. If the drifting is excessive, re-level the condenser plates.

Observations.—6. Read the barometric pressure, p, at the beginning and end of the experiment and use the average value.

7. Calibrate the microscope scale by observing a standard 0.1 mm. scale and noting the number of centimeters which correspond to one division of the scale $(=k)$. Be careful not to change the focus of the microscope from now on.

8. Measure the distance d between the inner faces of the condenser plates by means of the calibrated microscope.

9. Record the remaining constants of equation 1–12. The density of Nye's Watch Oil is 0.92 grams per cubic centimeter. The coefficient of viscosity of the air may be taken as that at 23° C. since it does not change rapidly with temperature.

10. Follow a drop as long as possible; for at least one-half hour; recording the time for the drop to move up (down, in the microscope) a given number of divisions. Occasionally, record the voltage V and the time for the drop to fall the same number of divisions. The time to move up in the electrical field will change whenever the drop gains or loses one or more electrons. This process may be augmented by placing a small amount of

radioactive material, such as a radium E tube, for a short time near the holes in the top plate.

Calculations.—11. Average those values of the times of rise of the drop which are of nearly the same value and, from the microscope calibration, compute the average velocities of rise. Also compute the average velocity downward.

12. Calculate the value of the approximate radius of the drop from equation 1–8. Also calculate the apparatus and drop constants k_1 and k_2 from equations 1–12 and 1–13.

13. Calculate the charge gained or lost, using equation 1–14. If the charge did not change during the observations, calculate the total charge on the drop from equation 1–13. The former procedure is preferable since Δe is usually a smaller multiple of the electronic charge than e_n.

14. From a rough inspection of the data of (13), determine the number of electrons gained or lost, or the number on the drop. Then divide the charges Δe, or e_n, by these integers to obtain values of e. Average these values of e. The individual values may fluctuate considerable but their average should be within 2% of the accepted value if the experiment has been performed correctly.

EXPERIMENT 1–2

AVOGADRO'S NUMBER FROM BROWNIAN MOVEMENTS[3]

Apparatus.—The oil-drop apparatus is to be used.

Adjustments.—Adjust the instrument as described in steps 1 to 5 of experiment 1–1. It is very important that the condenser plates be accurately levelled, to avoid drift motion.

Observations.—6. Record the barometric pressure and the temperature at the beginning and end of the experiment and average.

7–8. The same as 7 and 8 in experiment 1–1.

9. Record the constants of equation 1–21.

10. Choose the smallest (slowest falling) drop possible. If the Brownian movements are to be measured easily, the drop must be smaller than those which can be used for the determination of the electron charge. Measure the time for the drop to

fall over a given number of divisions. Remember that the microscope inverts the motion. Repeat no less than twenty-five times. The values of the electric field and of the charge on the drop are immaterial.

11. Adjust the electric field until the drop does not move up or down. If the charge or the voltage changes, re-balance. The voltage and charge do not enter into the calculations. Turn the microscope so that its scale is horizontal, i.e., the graduations are vertical. The drop will be seen to shift horizontally, back and forth. Record its position on the scale at regular intervals of, say 30 seconds $(=t)$, until at least one hundred readings have been taken.

Calculations.—12. Average the times of fall and compute the velocity of fall v_d. Compute the radius of the drop, using equations 1–22 and 1–23. (These equations might also have been used in the determination of the charge of the electron.)

13. Take differences $(=s)$ between the successive scale positions of the drop in (11). Square each value and then average $(=\overline{s^2})$. Multiply by the square of the number of centimeters corresponding to each division of the scale $(=k^2)$. Then, $\overline{x^2} = k^2\overline{s^2}$. These are the average-squared Brownian displacements in the x direction in the time t. If a very large number of individual displacements s have been observed a sufficiently accurate value is given by $\overline{x^2} = \pi(k\overline{s})^2/2$.

14. Calculate N from equation 1–21 and compare with the accepted value.

REFERENCES

1. R. T. Birge, Rev. Mod. Phys. (Phys. Rev. Supp.), 1, 1 (1929).
2. Kellström. Nature, 136, 682 (1935). W. N. Bond, Phil. Mag., 22, 631 (1936). Ishida, Fukushima and Suetsugu, Nature, 140, 29 (1937). W. V. Houston, Phys. Rev., 52, 751 (1937), finds η (at 23° C.) = 1.8292 × 10⁻⁴. With the Millikan oil-drop data this gives e = 4.796 × 10⁻¹⁰ e.s.u.
3. This procedure is the author's modification of the methods used by Fletcher to measure Ne and N. See Phys. Rev., 33, 81 (1911); second series, 4, 440 (1914).
4. A. H. Compton and R. L. Doan, Proc. Nat. Acad. Sci., II, 598 (1925).
5. J. A. Bearden, Phys. Rev., 37, 1210 (1931); 47, 883 (1935).

GENERAL REFERENCES

A.—R. A. Millikan, *Electrons* (+ *and* −). The University of Chicago Press (1935).

B.—J. A. Crowther, *Ions, Electrons and Ionizing Radiations.* Longmans, Green & Co. (1934).

CHAPTER 2

THE MASS OF THE ELECTRON

2–1. Cathode Rays.—Connect the secondary of an induction coil to two metal electrodes sealed in a glass tube, as in figure 2–1, and study the passage of electricity between them as the air is gradually removed. A point will be reached, at pressures around 0.05–0.005 mm. of mercury, where a greenish or bluish fluorescence appears on the walls of the tube and a faint streak of light may be seen coming from the negative electrode. Many interesting phenomena may now be observed. For example, a solid object at X casts a shadow on the walls at B. Since the edges of this shadow are clean cut, the rays which cause the glass to fluoresce must have travelled in straight lines from the cathode. If a concave cathode is used, the rays come to a focus, where they may melt a piece of metal foil. This shows that they leave the cathode perpendicularly and possess great energy. If they strike a light, carefully pivoted paddle wheel, they cause it to rotate, showing that they have inertia or mass.* Then it must be true that they have either great mass or high velocity.

Fig. 2–1. To study cathode rays.

These "cathode rays" can be deflected by an electric or magnetic field. Hence, they consist of electrical charges in motion. From the direction in which the rays are deflected, their charge is found to be negative. This has been verified by catching them inside a small metal cup (a Faraday chamber) which is connected to an electrometer.

If a thin aluminum window is used instead of the glass at B, figure 2–1, cathode rays will be found to emerge into the air. These

---

* This experiment is usually performed in a tube containing a moderate amount of gas. The paddle wheel is then set into rotation by the heat caused by the bombarding rays, as in Crookes' radiometer, and the effect discussed is masked. A high degree of evacuation should be used.

will travel for a distance of several centimeters. They are then called Lenard rays,[1] after their discoverer, and are produced in large quantities by the Coolidge cathode-ray tubes.[2]

The motion of cathode rays may be studied by the fluorescence they produce when they strike glass or a luminescent screen such as calcium tungstate, by the streak of light which they produce in a gas through which they are passing, by metal collectors leading to an electrometer, and by the blackening which they can produce on a photographic plate.

Electrons emitted from a hot filament in a vacuum exhibit these same properties. This indicates that cathode rays consist of electrons. They can be produced in a vacuum tube regardless of the gas used or the cathode material, so that they are a common constituent of all matter. It is also interesting to note that, since they can pass through thin aluminum foil, they must be comparatively small and the inter-atomic spaces of matter must be comparatively large.

When cathode rays are suddenly stopped by a solid body, they set up x-rays much as the bullets of a machine gun striking a target produce sound waves.

As the following experiments will show, the velocity of these electrons is great and their mass is very small. A direct measurement of their mass has never been made. Instead, the ratio of their charge to their mass, e/m, is measured and then, from the known charge e, the mass may be calculated.

2-2. The Method of J. J. Thomson to Measure e/m.—In 1897, J. J. Thomson[3] first measured the ratio of charge to mass (e/m) and the velocity (v) of cathode rays by bending them in a combined electric and magnetic field. As shown in figure 2-2, a hot filament F is located in a glass tube which has been well evacuated. It emits electrons, each of which has a mass of m grams and carries a charge of e electromagnetic units. These are accelerated toward a positively charged metal plate P and some pass through a small hole with a velocity of v centimeters per second. Ordinarily they pass straight ahead to form a point of light on the screen at S. This screen consists of a glass plate coated with a fluorescent material, such as willemite, luminescent calcium tungstate or zinc sulphide. If a uniform magnetic field of strength H oersteds is applied perpendicularily across the

region BC, as indicated by the dots, the spot of light is deflected
to S'. Thus the rays are bent into a circular path of radius r
centimeters while moving through the field BC and thereafter
travel in a straight line.

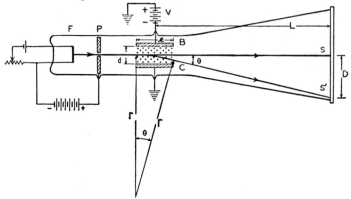

Fig. 2–2.   J. J. Thomson's method of measuring e/m and v.

Consider a space one centimeter in cross-section and v centimeters long which contains n electrons per cubic centimeter, each
of charge e. Then ne is the charge per cubic centimeter. If v is
the velocity with which the electrons are moving, $(ne)v$ is the total
quantity of electricity which will pass a given point in one second.
Thus a stream of electrons is equivalent to a current $i = nev$.
Now, by definition of the electromagnetic unit of current, the
magnetic force on the current is Hi and hence on each electron is
Hev. This inward or centripetal force is counterbalanced by the
outward centrifugal force mv^2/r, so that the electron travels in a
circular path of radius r as long as it remains in the magnetic
field. Thus we may write

$$Hev = mv^2/r, \quad \text{or} \quad e/m = v/Hr. \tag{2-1}$$

The magnetic field intensity H can be calculated from the magnitude of the current used to produce it and the dimensions of the
coil, or it may be measured directly with a flux-meter. The
radius r may be calculated from the dimensions of the apparatus
and the deflection D (see figure 2–2). Thus

$$\sin \theta = l/r = D/\sqrt{D^2 + L^2}, \quad \text{or} \quad r = l\sqrt{1 + L^2/D^2}. \tag{2-2}$$

If one of the quantities, v or e/m in equation 2–1, can be determined the other can then be evaluated.

In order to determine the velocity v of the electrons, Thomson applied an electrostatic potential to the metal plates BC in such a direction that the upper plate was positive and the lower was negative, and of such an amount that the electrons were brought back to the point S. If, then, E is the electric field intensity or force on unit charge in the condenser BC, then Ee is the electrical force on each electron. When the combined electric and magnetic forces are equal

$$Ee = Hev \quad \text{or} \quad v = E/H. \tag{2–3}$$

The electric field, E, is equal to the potential difference between the condenser plates divided by the distance, d, between their inner faces. Thus, if the potential difference, V_m, is measured in electromagnetic units, $E = V_m/d$ and if measured in volts V, $E = 10^8 V/d$. Then

$$v = \frac{V_m}{Hd} = \frac{10^8 V}{Hd} \text{ cm./sec.} \tag{2–4}$$

The velocities found were surprisingly high, of the order of one-third the velocity of light.

Substitution of equation 2–4 in equation 2–1 gives

$$e/m = \frac{10^8 V}{H^2 rd} \text{ e.m.u./g.} \tag{2–5}$$

In this pioneering work, Thomson obtained a value for e/m of 7.7×10^6 e.m.u./g. which was of the order of magnitude of the now accepted value, $(1.76 \times 10^7$ e.m.u./g.$)$. He used a cold discharge tube as a source of electrons instead of the hot filament described here and found that the cathode rays had the same ratio of charge to mass regardless of the gas used in the tube or the metals of the electrodes, thus demonstrating that electrons are to be found widespread through Nature and that they can be obtained from matter which is ordinarily electrically neutral. Since matter is made up of atoms, this implies that electrons exist in atoms. In other words, ordinary neutral matter is made up of electrical constituents.

2–3.—The Method of Lenard.—As in figure 2–3, electrons from a suitable source such as the hot filament F, in a vacuum, are accelerated toward a positively charged metal plate P, by means of a known potential. Let the accelerating potential be V_m electromagnetic units. Then V_m is the number of ergs of work done upon one electro-magnetic unit of charge in moving it from the filament to the plate * and $V_m e$ is the corresponding work done upon each electron. This appears in the form of kinetic energy, so that the electrons which pass through a hole in the plate have a velocity v and an energy $mv^2/2$. Thus

$$V_m e = 10^8 V e = \tfrac{1}{2} m v^2, \qquad (2\text{–}6)$$

where V is the accelerating potential in volts and e is measured in e.m.u. The electrons, which would normally travel straight ahead to produce a spot of light at S on a fluorescent screen, are bent by a magnetic field into a circular path of radius r and reach the screen at S'. Lenard applied the field over the entire path of the electrons. In figure 2–3, the lines of force (H per square centimeter) are at right angles to the paper and cover the entire region indicated by the large circle. As in the Thomson method, the magnetic and centrifugal forces are equal, so that, again

$$Hev = mv^2/r. \qquad (2\text{–}1)$$

Together with equation (2–6), this gives

$$v = \frac{2V10^8}{Hr} \text{ cm./sec.} \qquad (2\text{–}7)$$

and

$$e/m = \frac{2V10^8}{H^2r^2} \text{ e.m.u./g.} \qquad (2\text{–}8)$$

in which V is in volts, H is in oersteds and r is in centimeters. In order to determine r from the observed deflection of the spot of light, we note, in figure 2–3 that $r^2 = L^2 + (r - D)^2$, or

$$r = (L^2 + D^2)/2D. \qquad (2\text{–}9)$$

---

* This assumes that every point on the filament is at the same potential and that the electrons have zero velocity as they leave the filament. Corrections for departures from the ideal conditions assumed need not be made except for precise work or when the accelerating potential, V, is comparatively small.

Instead of measuring the velocity and the charge-to-mass ratio of electrons emitted by a hot filament, Lenard[4] made his observations on photo-electrons emitted from a cold metal plate irradiated with light. Since his value of e/m was in rough agreement with that of Thomson he concluded, correctly, that these charged particles were the same as cathode rays. More recent

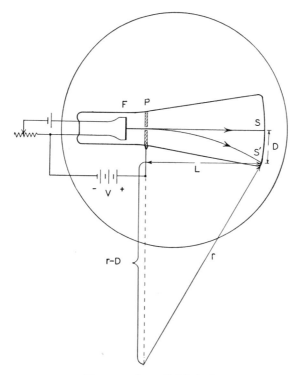

Fig. 2–3. Lenard's Method

measurements of greater accuracy have shown that all photo-electrons have the same ratio of charge to mass, whether they come from one metal or another, again showing that electrons are to be found widespread throughout the bodies in the world around us and that they exist in the atoms of which the matter is built up. In other words, ordinary neutral matter contains electrical constituents.

2–4. Kirchner's Modification of the Wiechert Method.—As shown in figure 2–4, a collimated beam of electrons passes directly to the fluorescent screen S, unless deflected by electric fields at C_1 or C_2. A vacuum tube oscillator O produces alternating potentials of very high frequency (say 10^7 cycles per second) simultaneously across the two sets of deflecting plates. As the electrons pass through C_1 they are deflected back and forth rapidly in the plane of the paper so that only those which had passed through C_1 at the instant when its potential was zero will be able to go through the central hole in the diaphragm D and enter the second condenser C_2. Thus, spurts of electrons will enter C_2, one each half cycle of the oscillator. If, now, during the time t

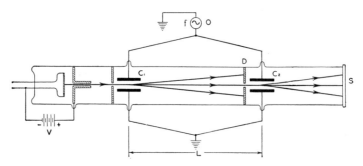

Fig. 2–4. The Kirchner-Wiechert method.

required for the electrons to travel from C_1 to C_2, a distance L, the potential on the second condenser has again returned to zero, the electrons will continue to travel straight ahead to produce a single spot of light at the center of the screen. If the time for the electrons to travel this distance is less than one half cycle (or any multiple thereof), a potential difference will exist across the second plates and the electrons will be deflected to form two distinct spots on the screen. This may be seen from figure 2–5. Thus, electrons which pass through C_1 at 1, are deflected by a potential across C_2 shown by the arrow 1 in the lower half of the figure, whereas those which were undeflected at time 2, reach C_2 to be deflected in the opposite direction. The period T of the oscillator, or the velocity v of the electrons, is varied until the phase of the potential on C_2 is zero just at the instant each half cycle group of electrons arrives.

As this condition is approached the two spots become closer and closer together until finally only one spot is observed. Then

$$v = \frac{L}{T/2} = 2fL, \qquad (2\text{–}10)$$

where f, the frequency of the oscillator, may be measured in terms of its wave-length $\lambda \ (=c/f, \ c = 3 \times 10^{10})$ by means of Lecher

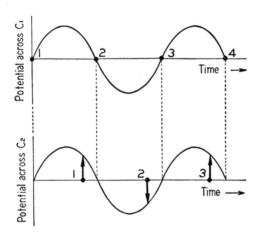

FIG. 2–5.   Deflecting forces.

wires. Thus, a direct measurement of the velocity of the electrons may be made and used in the equation

$$10^8 Ve = \tfrac{1}{2}mv^2 \qquad (2\text{–}6)$$

to give

$$e/m = \frac{2f^2L^2}{10^8 V} \ \text{e.m.u./gr.} \qquad (2\text{–}11)$$

In this, f is in cycles per second, L is in centimeters and V is in volts.

This principle was first used by Wiechert [5] in 1899. However, he used magnetic instead of electric deflecting forces and a cold discharge tube instead of a hot filament as a source of electrons.

In the hands of Kirchner,[6] and also Perry and Chaffee,[7] precision results have been obtained. Thus

$$e/m = 1.760 \times 10^7 \text{ e.m.u./g.,}$$

to within $\pm 0.0025 \times 10^7$.

2–5. Units of Energy, Velocity and Momentum.—The energy of a moving charged particle may be expressed in a variety of ways. As is well known, the kinetic energy of a particle of mass m (grams) and velocity v (centimeters per second) is $mv^2/2$ *ergs*. Instead of expressing the energy in ergs, it is common practice today to state its value in electron-volts (abbreviated e.v.).

One electron-volt is the energy which an electron acquires when accelerated by a potential difference of one volt.

The conversion from ergs, $\mathscr{E}$, to electron-volts, V, or vice versa, is made by means of the equation

$$\mathscr{E} = \tfrac{1}{2}mv^2 = 10^8 V e_m = \frac{V e_s}{300} \qquad (2\text{–}12)$$

where e_m is the charge of the particle in electro-magnetic units and e_s is the charge in electro-static units. The factors 10^8 and 300 are used to convert from volts to e.m.u. and e.s.u., respectively. As an example, an electron, accelerated from rest by a positively charged metal plate whose potential is one hundred volts ($V = 100$), will have an energy $\mathscr{E}$ of 1.602×10^{-10} ergs or 100 e.v. when it reaches the plate. Thus, one electron-volt is equivalent to 1.602×10^{-12} ergs.

It is also common practice today to refer to the velocity of a charged particle in terms of the accelerating voltage needed to give it its velocity. It is understood, of course, that this is only a matter of convenience. Instead of solving equation 2–12 for the velocity v of the particle, one merely states the voltage V. From the known charge and mass values, it may be shown that one electron-volt will give an electron a velocity of 5.95×10^7 centimeters per second, a proton a velocity of 1.38×10^6 centimeters per second and an alpha particle a velocity of 6.97×10^5 centimeters per second.

Relativistic corrections are necessary for higher velocity particles for computing the velocity and Hr. Now turn to table 9 at the end of this book.

The quantity Hr occurs frequently in work with charged particles. It is a measure of the ease with which the particles may be deflected by a magnetic field. Equation 2–1 shows that

$$Hr = \frac{mv}{e}.\qquad\qquad(2\text{–}13)$$

Thus Hr is proportional to the momentum mv of a given particle. If m is in grams, e in electro-magnetic units and v in centimeters per second, then Hr will be in gauss-centimeters.

2–6. There Are Many Other e/m Methods.—In the experiments of Thomson, Lenard and Wiechert, as just described, there appear four basic equations which relate, (1), the centrifugal to the magnetic deflecting force, (2), the magnetic to the electric deflecting force, (3), the velocity of the electrons to their accelerating potential and (4), the velocity to the frequency of an oscillator. No less than forty-three modifications involving these relationships have been devised. These include the following methods.*

2–7.—The Dunnington Method.—As shown in figure 2–6, electrons from a hot filament, F, in a high vacuum, are accelerated to an anode, A, every alternate half cycle of the high frequency oscillator O. The slower electrons which then emerge through a hole in the anode are readily bent by a magnetic field which is perpendicular to the paper, the faster ones are only deviated a small amount, while those of proper velocity travel in a circle of radius r, succeed in passing through the slits SSS and are caught in a Faraday chamber C, to be registered in the galvanometer G unless prevented from doing so by a retarding potential on the grid B.

They will not enter C if the time they require to rotate through the angle θ is equal to the period T of the oscillator, or any multiple, n, thereof, since B is also connected to the same oscillator and will

---

* *A. E. Shaw* (Phys. Rev., **51**, 887 (1937), has given a precision value of e/m = 1.7571×10^7 e.m.u./g. The electrons were deflected through an angle of 127° in a curved condenser by crossed electric and magnetic fields. See references 9 and 10 of chapter 10. Great care was taken to eliminate errors due to contact potential differences and surface charges, which were sometimes as great as 25 volts. See also, Phys. Rev. **54**, 193 (1938).

then draw them back from C. Their velocity v is then equal to the distance $l\,(=r\theta,$ where θ is in radians) divided by nT, or

$$v = \frac{r\theta}{nT} = \frac{r\theta f}{n},\qquad (2\text{--}14)$$

where f is the frequency of the oscillator. Together with equation 2–1, this leads to the relation

$$e/m = \frac{\theta f}{nH}.\qquad (2\text{--}15)$$

One may vary the magnetic field strength instead of the frequency of the oscillator and observe the critical value of H for which the galvanometer current dips sharply to zero. This is a precision method and has given the value [8]

$$e/m = 1.7597 \times 10^7 \text{ e.m.u./g.}$$

The accuracy in this method $(\pm 0.0004 \times 10^7)$ depends almost solely on the measurement of H, the field strength, since f, the frequency, is known to at least one part in a million (crystal controlled oscillators are used), n is an integer and θ is an angle which can be determined very accurately from measurements on the apparatus with built-in microscopes. It is to be noted that the radius r does not enter into the final equation, 2–15.

2–8. The Magnetron of Hull.—A two-electrode vacuum tube, which consists of a hot filament stretched along the axis of a cylindrical anode, is placed in a solenoid or between the poles of an electromagnet in such a manner that the magnetic lines of force are parallel to the filament. The flow of electrons from the filament to the anode constitutes an electric current which may be measured by means of a milliammeter connected in series with the anode battery. This current remains constant as the magnetic field strength is increased from zero, until a critical point is reached, when it suddenly drops to zero. This assumes, of course, that the anode potential and the filament temperature remain constant. If the filament, field and cylinder are not accurately in line with one another (a condition difficult to obtain in practice), the current does not drop sharply to zero at the critical field strength but gradually decreases. Let H_c be the strength of the field, in oersteds, when the anode current has dropped to one-half its zero field value.

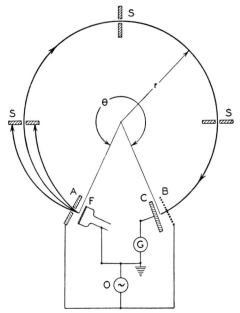

Fig. 2-6. The Dunnington method.

The electrons, after leaving the filament, acquire a velocity v, centimeters per second, given by

$$10^8 Ve = \tfrac{1}{2}mv^2, \tag{2-6}$$

within a fraction of a millimeter of the filament, since it is here that the majority of the potential drops takes place in a tube of this configuration. Consequently, as they continue their motion toward the anode, they are bent by the magnetic field in curved paths, called cardiods, whose shape is nearly that of a circle. When the critical field H_c is applied, they travel in approximate circles whose diameters are equal to the radius R (centimeters) of the cylinder. Then

$$H_c ev = \frac{mv^2}{R/2}. \tag{2-16}$$

With the preceding equation, this gives

$$e/m = \frac{8V10^8}{H_c^2 R^2} \text{ e.m.u./g.} \qquad (2\text{--}17)$$

V is the anode potential in volts.   If the filament is of appreciable size in comparison with the anode, a correction is needed.   Then

$$e/m = \frac{8V10^8}{H_c^2 R} \left(1 - \frac{r^2}{R^2}\right)^{-2} \qquad (2\text{--}18)$$

where r is the radius of the filament in centimeters.   This method, though simple, does not yield precision results [9] because of the lack of sharpness in the cut-off of the current.

It is interesting to note that when the magnetron has been adjusted to the critical region, the circling electrons act as simple harmonic oscillators to produce radio waves whose period is approximately equal to twice the running time of the electrons from filament to anode. The wave-length of the radio waves in centimeters is approximately given by [10]

$$\lambda H_c = 13,100. \qquad (2\text{--}19)$$

Undamped radio waves whose wave-length is only 0.49 centimeters have been generated by this method.[11]

2-9.   The Helical Method.[12]—Electrons from the hot filament F, in the vacuum tube of figure 2–7, are accelerated and collimated

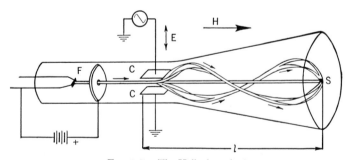

Fig. 2–7.   The Helical method.

so as to focus at the center of the screen S.   The time t which they require to travel the distance l is equal to l/v, where v is their

velocity along the axis. The latter may be expressed in terms of
the accelerating voltage V by equation 2–12. Then

$$t = \frac{l}{\sqrt{(2Ve/m)10^8}} \text{ sec.} \qquad (2\text{–}20)$$

An alternating potential is applied across the condenser plates C
and serves to sweep the electron beam back and forth. A line
instead of a spot is then observed on the fluorescent screen. The
electrons travel in parabolic paths, with increasing transverse
velocity, as they pass through the condenser, after which they
travel in a straight line to the screen. Finally, a magnetic field
of strength H, oersteds, is applied
in such a manner that the lines
of force are parallel to the axis
of the tube. This field does not
affect the forward motion of the
electrons but does act upon the
transverse motion. From the elementary motor rule, one may see
that the electrons will be deflected into circular paths in
planes at right angles to the tube
axis at the same time that they

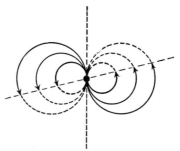

FIG. 2–8. Projection of electron paths
on the screen.

move down the tube. The resultant of the combined uniform
circular and uniform linear motions is such that the electrons
travel in helical paths down the tube.

If it were possible to see the electrons as they moved down the
vacuum tube, and the observer stood at the screen end, it would be
found that the circular paths of the various electrons are all
tangent to the axis of the tube, as indicated in figure 2–8 where
the black dot represents the intersection of the axis with the screen.
The circles have larger radii, r, when the electrostatic deflecting
potential is larger. For a given deflecting force, the electrons
travel in circles whose radii are small at the left or entering edge
of the plates C, larger at the right or emergent edge and of constant magnitude from there to the screen. The velocity of an
electron in one of the circles is equal to the transverse velocity, v_t.
This velocity is small when the radius is small and vice versa.

Now, equation 2-1 may be written in the form $Hev_t = mv_t^2/r$ or $v_t/r = He/m$. But v_t/r is equal to the angular velocity ω of the electrons in the circles. Then, if T is the time for an electron to make one complete rotation,

$$\omega = \frac{2\pi}{T} = He/m \quad \text{or} \quad T = \frac{2\pi}{He/m}. \tag{2-21}$$

It is to be noted that the angular velocity ω is independent of the radii of the circles. Thus the electrons travel faster in the larger and slower in the smaller circles. All electrons require the same time T to complete one revolution, regardless of the size of the circle.

When, for a given accelerating voltage, the magnetic field is varied until the time T for the electrons to make one rotation is equal to the time t for them to travel forward from the condenser plates to the screen, a distance l, all electrons will again be on the axis. This condition may be detected by observing the line of light on the screen. As the magnetic field is increased from zero, the line shortens and rotates until, at a critical field strength H_c, it is reduced to a small spot on the screen. With stronger fields than H_c, the electrons make more than one complete revolution while travelling down the tube. For one revolution, equating equations 2-20 and 2-21 to each other gives

$$e/m = \frac{8\pi^2 V 10^8}{H_c^2 l^2} \text{ e.m.u./g.} \tag{2-22}$$

Here, V is the accelerating potential in volts, H_c is the critical magnetic field strength in oersteds and l is the distance in centimeters indicated in figure 2-7.

This method is an extension of that used by Busch.[13] Instead of *adding* a transverse motion to the forward motion of the electrons down the tube, however, his longitudinal magnetic field acted upon the perpendicular *component* of the motion of a hollow cone of electrons diverging from a cold discharge tube. When the electrons are focussed in the Busch method, the electron charge-to-mass ratio is given by

$$e/m = \frac{8\pi^2 V 10^8}{H_c^2 l^2} \cos^2 \beta \tag{2-23}$$

where β is the angle of divergence of the electron beam from the axis of the tube. His method, therefore, requires the additional measurement of the angle β. Wolf [14] has used the Busch method and found $e/m = 1.769 \times 10^7$ e.m.u./g., a value slightly higher than the accepted value.

2-10. Spectroscopic Determinations of e/m.—When a strong magnetic field, H, is placed around a source of light it is found that each spectrum line is split into several lines. In the simplest case, a single line will become two lines equally separated from the original by the frequency $\Delta\nu$. It can be shown that for this " normal " Zeeman pattern,

$$e/m = \frac{4\pi\Delta\nu}{H}. \tag{2-24}$$

From simple cases of this type and from more elaborate patterns, a very precise value of e/m has been determined; [15] namely,

$$e/m = 1.758 \times 10^7 \text{ e.m.u./g.}$$

Precise measurements of the wave-lengths of corresponding lines in the emission spectra of hydrogen and ionized helium, and also of hydrogen and its isotope, deuterium, have permitted the calculation of a value of e/m of great accuracy.[16] Thus

$$e/m = 1.7579 \times 10^7 \text{ e.m.u./g.}$$

2-11. The Mass of the Electron.—In the thermionic or shot-effect method of measuring the charges emitted by a hot filament, mentioned in chapter 1 and discussed in chapter 5, it is established that these are electrons of charge $e = 4.80 \times 10^{-10}$ e.s.u. The experiments above have shown that $e/m = 1.759 \times 10^7$ e.m.u./g. It follows that the mass of the electron is

$$m = 9.11 \times 10^{-28} \text{ grams.}$$

One electromagnetic unit of electricity (ten ab-couls) passing through a standard silver solution will deposit 0.0111807 gram of silver. The ratio of charge to mass, E/M_1, of silver is then $1/0.0111807 = 89.45$ e.m.u/g., where E is the quantity of electricity associated with M_1 grams of the substance. If this electricity is distributed in equal amounts e on each of N atoms of silver, each of mass M, then $e/M = 89.45$. In the case of hydrogen, the lightest known element, electrolysis has shown that the ratio of charge to mass of the atom is 9574.2 e.m.u./g. The lighter the particle, the larger is its charge-to-mass ratio. The charge e is that of the electron, as originally defined by Stoney. Inasmuch as the ratio of charge-to-mass of the electron is greater than that for the hydrogen atom and the charge is the same, the electron must have a mass less than that of the lightest atom. The hydrogen atom is thus found to have a mass 1837 times that of the electron or 1.6734×10^{-24} grams. If the mass of one electron is subtracted from this, it is seen that the mass of the proton or nucleus of the hydrogen atom is 1.6725×10^{-24} grams.

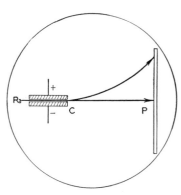

FIG. 2–9. A velocity filter method.

Several experimenters,[17] who worked during the years from 1902 to 1916, measured the ratio of charge-to-mass of the negatively charged or beta particles emitted by radioactive substances. Thus, in figure 2–9, the particles are emitted from the source Ra in an evacuated chamber and pass through a very narrow slit formed by the plates of the condenser C. Simultaneously they are acted upon by a magnetic field perpendicular to the plane of the paper and extending over the entire apparatus. As may be seen from equation 2–3 ($v = E/H$), particles of only one velocity can emerge from the condenser and continue on to the photographic plate P. The velocity and charge-to-mass ratio of these particles may then be measured as in the Thomson method. If the electric field E between the plates is altered, particles of a different velocity may be selected for study. It was found that the particles of greater velocity had a smaller e/m ratio For example, those of velocity equal to 32 per cent of the velocity of light had a value of 1.66×10^7 e.m.u./g., while those with velocities equal to 69 per cent of that of light had a value of 1.28×10^7. Extrapolation to zero velocity gave the value 1.76×10^7, thus identifying the beta particles as electrons.

It is obvious that either m or e changes with the velocity of the particle. There is a theory, developed independently from this type of experiment, that indicates that the mass of a moving body should increase by a small amount as its velocity increases. There is no evidence, nor any theory, to indicate a change of charge. Hence, it is most likely a change of mass which is observed in these experiments. Since the value of e/m of the electrons is found to decrease at the higher velocities, the mass must increase. The mass of an electron accelerated by 4000 volts has been found to be 1.007 times that of an electron accelerated by 1000 volts. An equation, first used by Lorentz and later included in the special theory of relativity, expresses this variation of mass with velocity. It is

$$m = \frac{m_0}{\sqrt{1 - v^2/c^2}} \qquad (2\text{-}25)$$

where m is the mass of the particle travelling with velocity v, m_0 is the rest mass, or mass at zero velocity and c is the velocity of light (3×10^{10} cm./sec.). From this equation, the ratio of masses of electrons accelerated by 4000 and 1000 volts is computed to be 1.006, in essential agreement with the experimental value.

The special theory of relativity states that the kinetic energy of a particle is expressed by the equation

$$\mathscr{E} = m_0 c^2 \left(\frac{1}{\sqrt{1 - v^2/c^2}} - 1 \right). \qquad (2\text{-}26)$$

When the term in the parenthesis is expanded by the binomial theorem, it is found that $\mathscr{E} = \frac{1}{2} m_0 v^2 \left(1 + \frac{3}{4} \frac{v^2}{c^2} + \ldots \right)$. The first term is the familiar expression $mv^2/2$ for the kinetic energy of a body as used in the usual mechanics. The succeeding terms are negligible for all of the velocities of the large bodies which one encounters in daily life and need only be taken into account for objects of exceedingly high velocity.

The relativity theory gives

$$Hr = \frac{m_0 v}{e} \frac{1}{\sqrt{1 - v^2/c^2}} \qquad (2\text{-}26a)$$

The relativity theory also states that mass and energy are theoretically interchangeable. Thus the energy change $\mathscr{E}$, in ergs, equivalent to a mass change of m grams is given by the expression

$$\mathscr{E} = mc^2 \qquad (2\text{–}27)$$

where c is the velocity of light. From this, the mass of an electron at rest is the equivalent of 0.813 micro-ergs, the mass of 0.001 units of atomic weight is the equivalent of 1.484 micro-ergs or, approximately, one million electron-volts ($=1$ M.e.v.). More accurately 1.000 M.e.v. $= 0.001074$ mass units and 1.000 mass units $=$ 931 M.e.v. The quantity mc^2 is called the *self-energy* of the particle whose mass is m.

EXPERIMENT 2–1

MEASUREMENT OF e/m BY THE HELICAL METHOD [12]

Apparatus.—The vacuum tube, solenoid and associated circuits are shown in figures 2–10 and 2–11. In figure 2–10, the electron gun consists of an indirectly heated ($2\frac{1}{2}$ volt a.c.) cathode, K, a control grid G (0–40 volts negative with respect to K) which serves to vary the number of electrons emitted by the gun and

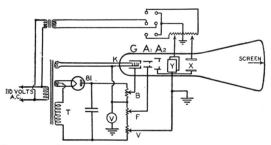

FIG. 2–10.   Vacuum tube and circuit for the helical method

hence the brightness of the spot on the screen, a positively charged anode A_1 (about 250 volts above the cathode potential) and a positively charged anode A_2 (about 1000 volts above K). The voltages are supplied by means of a transformer, T, a rectifier tube, 81, a filter condenser (2 microfarads) and a series of resistor units. A change of the potentiometer B alters the brightness of the spot on the screen. The focussing action of the electron gun (see section 6–12, Electron Optics) depends on the relative voltages on the two anodes. For a fixed voltage V, the potentiometer, F, serves to control the size of the spot.

It is necessary that the electrons leave the gun in an essentially parallel beam. Otherwise, the magnetic field of the solenoid will start their rotation at an indefinite distance from the screen. The electrons must not converge or diverge from the axis until the deflecting electro-static field is applied to the x or y condenser plates. This condition may be determined by adjusting the diameter of the spot on the screen until it is equal to that of the " crossover " image of the cathode. In a special commercial tube of the RCA 906 type, but constructed throughout of non-magnetic materials, this spot diameter is about one-half millimeter.

The voltmeter V, of figure 2–10, may be one of the type which has 1000 ohms-per-volt. With a 0–750 volt voltmeter of this type, a multiplier whose resistance was 750,000 ohms has been used to double the readings. The resistances in the multiplier must be large enough that they do not overheat and change in value.

The a.c. deflecting potential (0–100 volts) is applied either across the x or the y plates, of figure 2–10. Its value may be altered by means of a high resistance potentiometer and is not of importance. Since the 110-volt line is usually grounded on one side, it is advisable to introduce a one-to-one line transformer in the circuit, as in the upper left-hand corner of figure 2–10.

In order to produce the uniform longitudinal magnetic field, a large solenoid is used as in figure 2–11. The field H at the center in oersteds, is given by the equation

$$H = \frac{4\pi NI}{10L} \cos \theta, \qquad (2-28)$$

where N is the total number of turns of wire, I is the current in amperes, L is the total length of the windings in centimeters and θ is the angle indicated in the figure. The field strength is 40–50 oersteds.

With a coil of about 60 cm. length and 16 cm. diameter, H will decrease by about one-third of one per cent 5 centimeters from the center. The current through the solenoid is controlled by means of a coarse and a fine rheostat, since the focussing action is very sharp. A reversing switch is used to correct for extraneous magnetic fields, such as that of the earth. The solenoid is wound on a metal tube which is to be grounded in order to avoid erratic electro-static effects.

Procedure.—1. Measure and record the constants of the solenoid.

2. Mount the tube in front of a cathetometer and measure the distances from the outside of the glass, at the screen end, at the

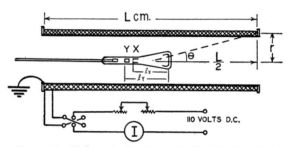

Fig. 2–11.   Tube and solenoid used in the helical method.

center of the screen, to the edges of the condenser plates nearest the cathode. Subtract the thickness of the glass from these distances to obtain l_x and l_y of figure 2–11. In one tube, the thickness of the glass was 0.25 cm., as determined with a microscope. The microscope is focussed on top of the glass, then on the screen material. The distance which it is moved, multiplied by the index of refraction of the glass (about 1.5), is the thickness of the glass. (The distances, l_x and l_y, are measured to the edges and not the center of the condenser plates, since electrons start their deflection from the axis, and their rotation, as they enter the plates.

3. Place the axis of the solenoid in the east-west line and ground its metal tube. Mount the vacuum tube in the solenoid. A variation of one or two centimeters from the center, along the axis, is permissible. The power supply rheostats and meters must not be closer than one and one-half feet from the coil; otherwise their stray magnetic fields will invalidate the calculated value of H. Screw-drivers, keys and other magnetic objects must be kept away from the coil for the same reason.

4. Turn on the electron gun and set V at one of its higher values, say 1200 volts. Adjust B and F, of figure 2–10, until a small spot appears on the screen. It is important that this spot be very small (about $\frac{1}{2}$ mm. in diameter and not very bright). If the spot is too large, values of e/m will be found to be too large because the electrons then diverge from the axis at some point in the gun and the values of l_x and l_y, measured as above, will be too small; and vice versa. Various sized spots may be used and an average value of e/m obtained.

5. Apply the electro-static deflecting potential to one set of plates. The exact length of the line is not of great importance (1–3 cm.).

6. Turn on the solenoid circuit and increase the current until the line is reduced to a small point for the first time. This adjustment will be found to be exceedingly sharp. Reverse the solenoid current and re-adjust to a fine point. The average of these two currents in amperes is I_c.

Observations.—7. Simultaneous values of I_c and V are to be taken several times while using the x and again while using the y deflecting plates.

8. Repeat (7), with at least two other voltages, V. It will be necessary to re-focus the tube at each voltage. The data may conveniently be recorded in a table with headings marked, plate (x or y), volts, amperes, average voltage, average amperes and e/m.

Calculations.—9. Substitution of equation 2–28 in 2–22 leads to

$$e/m = \left[5 \times 10^9 \left(\frac{L}{Nl \cos \theta} \right)^2 \right] \frac{V}{I_c^2} = K \frac{V}{I_c^2} \text{ e.m.u./g.,} \quad (2\text{–}29)$$

where K is a constant for a given solenoid and set of condenser plates, $l \equiv l_x$ for x, and $l \equiv l_y$ for y plates. Compare the average of your computed values with the accepted value of 1.76×10^7 e.m.u. per gram.

10. Compute the mass of the electron from the values of e and e/m.

11. Compute the velocities of the electrons by means of equation 2–12, using your value of e/m and the correct value. State, approximately, the error introduced by neglecting higher order terms of the relativistic energy equation.

MEASUREMENT OF e/m BY A MODIFIED LENARD METHOD

Apparatus.—In figure 2–12, the electrons are produced by the filament F. This may be heated by means of a storage battery or by the use of a step-down transformer. (Bell-ringing or toy transformers have been used satisfactorily.) The control rheostat B is preferably located in the primary circuit since the secondary is connected to the high voltage used to accelerate the electrons.

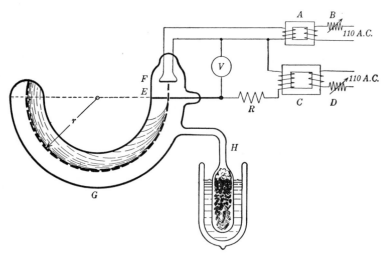

FIG. 2–12. Apparatus for determining e/m and v.

The accelerating potential is supplied by the step-up transformer C, whose secondary voltage may be varied from 200 to 600 volts by means of the rheostat D. This potential is measured by the high resistance a.c. voltmeter V (say of the Kelvin electro-static type). To prevent excessive current flow between the filament F and the anode E, with consequent destruction of the filament, the resistance R is placed in the circuit as shown. This may consist of half a dozen electric light bulbs connected in series.

The vacuum tube G may be a glass tube, about 3 cm. in diameter, bent into a circle of radius 6 cm. A ground joint sealed with wax may be used for the filament to allow replacements. This joint should be about 10 cm. from the filament to avoid melting its wax by the heat from the filament.   The filament should be of the dull emitter type, otherwise, the light from the electron beam will be masked by the light from the filament.   The slit in the anode may be about 1 mm. wide and 5 mm. long, placed vertically to the plane of the paper in figure 2–12.   The tube is exhausted to about 0.005 mm. pressure or until the electron beam is clearly defined as it passes through the anode.   If the pressure is too high, the beam will be diffuse and accurate measurements can not be made. If the pressure is too low, the beam will not be visible.*   By the use of a charcoal trap H which has been baked out during the evacuation, and liquid air or carbon dioxide snow (" dry ice "), the pressure may be adjusted quite satisfactorily.

A second diaphragm with a comparatively wide slit, mounted about 5 millimeters beyond the anode E and electrically connected thereto, may be used to cut off the slower electrons and sharpen the definition of the electron beam.   It has also been found advisable to silver the inner walls of the tube, except in the region of the filament and a narrow observation slit of radius r.   The anode touches this silvered surface and prevents the accumulation of electro-static charges on the inner walls.

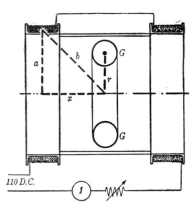

Fig. 2–13.   The field coils.

The electron beam is bent into a circular path by means of a magnetic field whose lines of force are perpendicular to the plane of the paper (figure 2–12).   This field may be produced by the double coil shown in figure 2–13.   This is constructed after the

* Good results may be obtained by exhausting the tube as highly as possible and observing the path of the electrons by a series of wire gauzes coated with luminescent material.   The luminescent material is sprinkled onto a thin layer of water glass on the gauze.   (Be sure to leave the holes clear.)   The series of gauzes, each of which is perpendicular to the electron beam, is supported by a small metal band fastened at its end to the anode.   This also serves to prevent the accumulation of electrical charges on the walls of the glass tube.

fashion of the Helmholtz–Gaugain galvanometer coils so as to insure uniform field strength over the region where the vacuum tube G is located. Each coil may be about 13 cm. in diameter, 2.5 cm. wide, of 60 turns of No. 16 D.C.C. copper wire. For simplicity of calculation of the field strength, the distance between the centers of the coils should equal their radius, i.e., $2x = a$. They are connected in series aiding. The current (1 to 5 amperes) is controlled by a rheostat and measured with the ammeter I.

Since the accelerating potential is alternating, electrons pass through the anode only half the time, i.e., when it is positive. They emerge with all velocities from zero to a maximum obtained under the maximum voltage V. Those with greatest velocity will be bent the least and vice versa, as indicated by the dotted curves in figure 2–12. The outer edge of this beam will be found

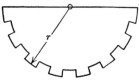

Fig. 2–14. For measurement of the radius of the electron beam.

to be clearly defined and should be used in measuring the radius r. Since this corresponds to electrons of maximum velocity, all voltmeter readings (effective values) should be multiplied by $\sqrt{2}$. Obviously, a more elaborate electron gun and a source of direct potential may be used instead of the simple apparatus used here. With d.c., the factor, $\sqrt{2}$, should be omitted from the equations.

The accuracy of the experiment is largely determined by the measurement of the radius r. A notched cardboard semicircle, figure 2–14, is placed about two centimeters above a similar semicircle. These are cut to a carefully determined radius and placed over the tube G. Two semicircles are used to avoid parallax. The electron beam may be seen between the notches. The accelerating potential and the current through the field coils are varied until the beam just fits the cardboard circles. Its radius is then known.

Procedure.—1. The filament is heated *dull* red. If electrons do not come off immediately it may be necessary to heat the filament to a yellow color for a short time.

2. The accelerating potential V (volts) and the field current I (amperes) are varied until the beam fits the circle of known radius r (cm.)

3. The values of V and I are then recorded.

4. This is repeated from four to nine times with various values of V and I.

Calculations.—1. The field strength H is calculated from the equation

$$H = \frac{2\pi n a^2 I}{10 b^3} \left[1 + \frac{3}{4} \frac{r^2}{b^4} (a^2 - 4x^2) + \ldots \right] \text{ oersteds} \qquad (2\text{-}30)$$

where n is the total number of turns on both coils, I is the current in amperes, a, b, x, and r are the distances in centimeters indicated in figure 2-13.

2. The ratio of charge to mass is calculated from the equation

$$\frac{e}{m} = \frac{2\sqrt{2V} \times 10^8}{H^2 r^2} \text{ e.m.u./g.} \qquad (2\text{-}31)$$

3. The velocity of the electrons is calculated from the equation

$$v = \frac{2\sqrt{2V} \times 10^8}{Hr} \text{ cm./sec.} \qquad (2\text{-}32)$$

EXPERIMENT 2-3

ALTERNATIVE METHOD OF MEASURING e/m

A. *Modified Lenard Method II*: A large solenoid wound on a barrel is used to produce the magnetic field instead of the Helmholtz coils of experiment 2-2. The field strength may be measured by means of a tangent galvanometer.

B. *Cathode Ray Tube and the Earth's Magnetic Field:* The tube is mounted at right angles to the earth's magnetic field and the position of the spot on the screen noted. The tube is then inverted, i.e., turned through 180°, and the new position of the spot noted. With low voltage tubes the total deflection of the spot will amount to $\frac{1}{2}$–1 cm. From this deflection and the length of the electron path beyond the gun, the radius of curvature of the beam is computed. The total intensity of the earth's field is measured, as well as the accelerating voltage. Equation 2–8 of the Lenard method is used to compute e/m.

C. *Cathode Ray Tube and Two Solenoids:* Deflection of an electron beam in a tube whose axis is vertical is accomplished by two long and narrow solenoids mounted horizontally on opposite sides of the tube, near the deflecting plates. Deflections are noted for a reversal of the current in the solenoids and for various distances between their ends. Extrapolation is then made to the condition which would exist if the coils could be placed end to end,

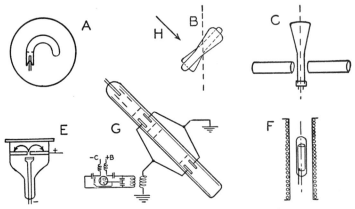

FIG. 2–15.   Alternate methods of measuring e/m

without the gap occupied by the tube. The extrapolated deflection is used to compute r in equation 2–8 of the Lenard method.

Solenoids of sufficient diameter to produce a nearly uniform field over the entire tube have been used in a similar fashion.

D. *Thomson Method with a Cathode Ray Tube:* The principle is discussed in section 2–2. Two transverse coils, as in *C* above, are used.

E. *Classen Method:* Electrons from a hot filament are accelerated through a hole in the anode and are deflected by a strong magnetic field into a small circle (2 or 3 cm. radius). They are observed on a luminescent surface lying in the plane of the anode. The field is reversed, deflecting the electrons to the opposite side of the hole, where they are observed on the screen. The distance between the two spots of light is equal to four times the radius of the electron circle. The filament must be very close to the anode. The Lenard equation (2–8) is used. One can now buy this apparatus.

F. *Magnetron Method:* See section 2–8. A commercial magnetron or, for cruder work, a radio tube with cylindrical symmetry may be used. Use comparatively high anode potentials to reduce the effects of space charge and reverse the current through the solenoid to correct for stray fields, such as that of the earth. The radius of the anode may be measured, approximately, with a cathetometer. Equation 2–18 is applied. Take values of H and V when the anode current is about half way down the break.

G. *Kirchner's Modification of the Wiechert Method:* See section 2–4. The principle of this method is outstandingly simple. The author has used an accelerating potential of 250–350 volts, a distance of 25 centimeters between deflecting plates and a 15 meter wave generated by a type 45 tube in a Colpitt's circuit. See also, Harnwell and Livingood, " Experimental Atomic Physics," page 130, for a higher voltage arrangement with a magnetron oscillator.

REFERENCES

1. Lenard, Ann. der Physik., **51**, 225 (1894).
2. W. D. Coolidge, Jr. Frank. Inst., **202**, 693, 721 (1926).
3. J. J. Thomson, Phil. Mag., **44**, 293, 310, 318 (1897).
4. Lenard, Wied. Ann., **64**, 279 (1898).   Ann. der Physik., **2**, 359 (1900).
5. Wiechert, Ann. der Physik., **69**, 739 (1899).
6. Kirchner, Ann. der Physik., **8**, 975 (1931).
7. Perry and Chaffee, Phys. Rev., **36**, 904 (1930).
8. Dunnington, Phys. Rev., **52**, 475 (1937).
9. A. W. Hull, Phys. Rev., **18**, 31 (1921).
10. See J. B. Hoag, Proc. Inst. Radio Engs., **21**, 1132 (1933).
11. Cleeton and Williams, Phys. Rev., **50**, 1091 (1936).
    H. Richter, Hoch. Tech., **51**, 10 (1938).
12. This method is published here for the first time.
13. Busch, Phys. Zeit., **23**, 438 (1922).
14. Wolf, Ann. der Physik., **83**, 849 (1927).
15. Campbell and Houston, Phys. Rev., **39**, 601 (1932).
16. Shane and Spedding, Phys. Rev., **47**, 33 (1935).
17. Bestlemeyer, Ann. der Physik., **22**, 429 (1907).
    Bucherer, Ann. der Physik., **28**, 513 (1909).
    See also Zahn and Spees, Phys. Rev., **53**, 357, 365 (1938).
18. Bearden, Phys. Rev., **54**, 698 (1938); **55**, 584 (1939).

GENERAL REFERENCES

A.—J. J. Thomson, *Conduction of Electricity Through Gases.* Cambridge University Press (1928).

B.—J. A. Crowther, *Ions, Electrons and Ionizing Radiations.* Longmans, Green & Co. Sixth Edition (1934).

C.—Geiger and Scheel, *Handbuch der Physik.* Vol. XXII/1, Springer (1931).

D.—J. S. Townsend, *Electricity in Gases.* Oxford, Clarendon Press (1915).

E.—H. A. Lorentz, *Theory of Electrons.* Chapter I. Steckert & Co. (1916).

F.—J. D. Stranahan, *The Particles of Modern Physics.* The Blakiston Co. (1942).

CHAPTER 3

THE WAVE-LENGTH OF THE ELECTRON

3-1. Introduction.—In addition to the properties of inertia and charge, the electron also has a wave nature. The length of the wave associated with an electron decreases as the electron gains speed. For example, an electron travelling 7.2×10^8 centimeters per second has a wave-length of 10^{-8} centimeters (1 angstrom), whereas one which is travelling 1.24×10^{10} centimeters per second has a wave-length of only 0.05 angstroms. These velocities may be acquired by accelerating the electron with 150 and 50,000 volts, respectively.

"The evidence that electrons are waves is similar to the evidence that light and x-rays are waves."[1] Certain experiments are best explained by considering the electron as a corpuscle, whereas others require the wave viewpoint. The dualistic character of the electron will be discussed in a later section of this chapter.

For many years the concept of a corpuscular electron was considered sufficient to explain all observed phenomena. However, in 1924, L. de Broglie[2] predicted that an electron should also have a wave nature. In 1927, Davisson and Germer[3] discovered this property and measured the wave-length of the electron. Their work was soon confirmed by G. P. Thomson[4] by a different experimental method.

3-2. De Broglie's Equation.—It is possible to state a relationship between matter and waves in mathematical form, as was first demonstrated by L. de Broglie in 1924. His work was soon followed by the "wave-mechanics" of Schrödinger, an equivalent of the matrix mechanics of Heisenberg, from which many new discoveries in Physics have been made. We shall now reverse the process and derive de Broglie's equation for the wave-length of an electron from the *wave-equation* which Schrödinger[5] discovered in

1926.   In simplified, non-relativistic form, for a particle of mass m_o, moving in the x direction, this equation is

$$\frac{d^2\psi}{dx^2} + \frac{8\pi^2 m_o(\mathscr{E} - U)}{h^2}\psi = 0, \tag{3-1}$$

where h is Planck's constant, $\mathscr{E}$ is the total and U is the potential energy of the particle.   The square of the absolute value of the " wave-amplitude," $|\psi|^2$, is equal to the probability per unit length of finding the particle at a given point.

For a free particle travelling with a velocity v in the x direction, the potential energy, U, is a constant and may be set equal to zero and $\mathscr{E}$ is equal to the kinetic energy $m_o v^2/2$.   Equation 3–1 then becomes

$$\frac{d^2\psi}{dx^2} + \left(\frac{2\pi m_o v}{h}\right)^2 \psi = 0, \tag{3-2}$$

which has a solution of the form

$$\psi = A \sin\frac{2\pi x}{\lambda}, \tag{3-3}$$

provided the wave-length λ is given by

$$\lambda = \frac{h}{m_o v}, \tag{3-4}$$

as may be seen by twice differentiating (3–3) and substituting in (3-2).   This equation, (3–4), is the non-relativistic form of de Broglie's equation.   Here, λ is the wave-length of the electron in centimeters, $h = 6.54 \times 10^{-27}$ erg-seconds, $m_o = 9.03 \times 10^{-28}$ grams (the rest mass of the electron), and v is the velocity of the electron in centimeters per second.   This equation applies with good accuracy to free electrons accelerated by not more than a few thousand volts.   The accelerating voltage, V, times the electronic charge, is equal to the kinetic energy of the electron.   Then

$$\lambda^2 V = 150, \tag{3-5}$$

where λ is in angstroms and V is in volts.

For faster electrons, de Broglie's equation states that

$$\lambda = \frac{h}{mv} \tag{3–6}$$

or the wave-length λ of an electron, multiplied by its momentum (mv), is equal to Planck's constant. In this relativistic form, the mass of the electron, in grams, is given by $m = m_o/\sqrt{1 - v^2/c^2}$, where c is the velocity of light (3×10^{10} cm./sec.).

3–3. The Reflection of Slow Electrons from Single Crystals.— Davisson and Germer, in 1927, were the first to observe the wave nature and to measure the wave-length of the electron. Their apparatus consisted essentially of a highly evacuated chamber containing three things: an electron "gun," a single, comparatively large crystal of nickel and a Faraday chamber. A beam of electrons, accelerated in the "gun" by a known potential, was directed at an angle against the surface of the crystal. Electrons were found to leave the crystal in various directions. They were caught in the chamber and recorded with an electrometer. Studies were made of the number and energy of the electrons which left the crystal at various angles β' for different accelerating potentials in the "gun" and for different angles of incidence β. The lengths of the lightly drawn arrows in figure 3–1 represent the total number

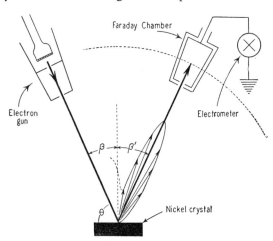

FIG. 3–1. The Davisson-Germer experiment.

of electrons (in a small increment of angle) which left a nickel crystal each second at different angles when the primary electrons were accelerated by 54 volts and were incident on the crystal at an angle of 25 degrees.

In order to measure the energy of the electrons as they left the crystal, an auxiliary chamber was mounted around the Faraday cup. This shielding chamber had a narrow slit on the side facing the crystal so that electrons could pass through into the Faraday chamber and be recorded. As the shield was made increasingly negative, the number of electrons which entered the chamber was found to decrease. When the potential of the shield was numerically equal to or greater than that used in the acceleration of the incident electrons, the electrometer deflection was found to be zero. These facts became intelligible when it was realized that, although the incident electrons all had the same velocity, some of the electrons which left the crystal had low velocities while others had high velocities. When the retarding potential of the shield was small, only the slower electrons were kept out of the chamber, but when the potential was large, even the faster electrons were stopped. It was found that the electrons from the crystal had velocities from zero up to the full value of the incident electrons. The slower electrons consisted of (1) incident electrons which had lost energy in their reflection from the crystal and (2) secondary electrons which had been ejected from the crystal itself by the impact of an occasional primary electron.

By keeping the value of the retarding potential of the shield equal to (or, in practice, slightly less than) that used to accelerate the electrons in the gun, attention was focussed upon those electrons which had the same (or nearly the same) energy as the incident electrons. These were called the *full-speed* electrons and were identified as the original electrons sent out from the gun and reflected elastically from the crystal.

The number of full-speed electrons was measured, in one of the many experiments of Davisson and Germer, when the accelerating potential, i.e., the speed of the incident electrons, was varied. The angles of incidence (β) and reflection (β') were made equal to each other and kept fixed and the crystal was kept fixed. Then, as the voltage was increased, the number of full-speed electrons was found to increase to a maximum, then decrease to a small value, rise again, etc., as in the upper curve of figure 3–2.   Thus it was demonstrated that electrons are more readily reflected when they approach the crystal at certain speeds than at others.   This selective reflection of electrons is analogous to the selective reflection of x-rays by crystals, as shown in the lower curve of the same figure.

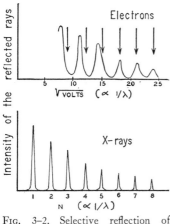

FIG.   3–2.   Selective   reflection   of electrons and x-rays.

3–4.   The Diffraction of Light and X-rays.—The diffraction of light waves by means of a one-dimensional grating is a familiar phenomenon.   The distance between the reflecting or transmitting lines is necessarily of the same order of magnitude as the wavelength of the light waves.   The larger the number of lines, the more will the diffracted light be concentrated, i.e., the sharper will be the spectral lines, the greater the resolving power between adjacent lines.   The usual equation for the diffraction grating is

$$n\lambda = d'(\sin \beta' - \sin \beta), \qquad (3\text{–}7)$$

when n is the order, λ is the wave-length, d' is the surface grating constant, β' and β are the diffraction and incidence angles, respectively.   Two gratings have been ruled on the same surface, with their lines at an angle to each other (sometimes 90°) and with the same or with different constants.   The diffraction patterns are then given by two simultaneous equations like 3–7, each with its appropriate values of d', β and β'.   A three-dimensional grating may be conceived which would diffract those waves which are capable of penetrating through it and whose length is of the same order of magnitude as the perpendicular distance (d = space grating constant) between reflecting planes.

By the use of x-rays it has been demonstrated that a single crystal, such as that used in the Davisson and Germer experiment, consists of large numbers of very small *unit cells*, all alike and extending side by side in three dimensions to form the *space lattice* of the comparatively large crystal.   Each unit cell, in turn, is made up of atoms arranged in some geometrical pattern, such as a cube or a distorted parallelepiped.   Standing at the side of an orchard, one can see rows of trees extending in various directions, at various angles.   Similarly, if the crystal could be sufficiently enlarged, one would see rows of atoms on its surface, forming the lines of a two-dimensional grating and also, inside, one would see various *lattice planes*, populated by atoms, in a three-dimensional array. In certain directions the perpendicular distance between the planes would be comparatively large and in others it would be small.   In some of the planes the atoms would be close to one another and in other planes the atomic population would be small.

There is a particular angle at which x-rays of a given wave-length will be reflected in appreciable intensity from the lattice planes in a given surface of a given crystal.   This angle,* θ, is such that the x-ray waves which are reflected from the various lattice planes have path-differences equal to an integral multiple (n) of the wave-length λ.   Then, the various reflected waves combine, crest for crest, to reinforce each other.   At other angles, destructive interference occurs and the intensity of the x-ray beam is reduced to zero.   Bragg has expressed this phenomenon of *selective reflection* by the equation†

$$n\lambda = 2d \sin \theta. \qquad (3\text{--}8)$$

From this it may be seen that the abscissae (n) in the lower curve of figure 3–2, are proportional to the reciprocal of the wave-length of the x-rays.

3–5. The Diffraction of Electrons.—There is no a priori reason to suspect that electrons, when treated as charged particles, should be readily reflected from the electrically charged constituents of the atoms in lattice planes when travelling at a *particular velocity* and not at another velocity.   Yet this phenomenon was established by the experimental work of Davisson and Germer, as illustrated in figure 3–2.   On the other hand, if the electrons are thought of as waves whose length is comparable to the spacing between the lattice planes and which varies with their speed, then selective reflection should be expected.   The de Broglie equation,

---

* $\theta + \beta = 90°$.

† This equation is derived in the x-ray chapter.

in the form $\lambda^2 V = 150$, shows that the abscissae $(\sqrt{V})$ of the upper curve of figure 3–2 are inversely proportional to the wavelength of the electrons. The analogous action of electrons and x-rays is thus shown in this figure. Large electrometer readings, the ordinates of figure 3–2, will be obtained when the electron waves, reflected from the lattice planes of the crystal, are of the appropriate length to cause constructive interference with each other. In other words, variation of the accelerating voltage, and hence of the speed of the incident electrons, alters their wavelength until the proper value is reached for selective reflection to take place at the Bragg angle.

The wave-length of the electrons reflected from a single crystal in the Davisson and Germer experiment was computed from the simple grating formula (3–7), using the known surface constant d' for nickel and the observed angles of incidence and diffraction, β and β'. Also, the wave-length of the incident electrons was computed from the de Broglie equation. The two values were found to be in excellent agreement. In addition, the wave-length of the electrons which were reflected from the lattice planes in a thin surface layer was computed from the simple Bragg formula (3–8), using the known space constant d for nickel and the observed angle of diffraction θ. When compared with the wave-length of the incident electrons, as computed from the de Broglie equation, the two values were found to be in excellent agreement for the faster electrons but to differ somewhat for the slower electrons. The extent of the agreement is shown by the degree to which the arrows fall at the peaks of the curve in figure 3–2.

3–6. The Index of Refraction of Metals for Electron Waves.

—The apparent discrepancy between the wave-lengths for the slower electrons in the Davisson and Germer experiment, as computed from the simple Bragg law and from the de Broglie equation, is due to a small change in the wave-length of the electrons as they enter the crystal. The index of refraction, μ, of the crystal for electrons is greater than unity. Bragg's law, when altered to account for the bending of the electron ray as it enters and leaves the crystal, may be expressed in the form

$$n\lambda = 2d \sqrt{\mu^2 - \sin^2 \beta}, \tag{3–9}$$

where $\sin \beta = \cos \theta$. Since the experiments on the reflection of electrons from the surface atoms of the crystal has shown that the relation $\lambda = h/mv$ may be used with accuracy in the calculation of the electron wave-length, equation 3–9 may be used to obtain values of μ. In this manner the index of refraction of a nickel crystal has been found to range from 1.00 to 1.12 for electrons accelerated by potentials from 460 to 67 volts.

3–7. Surface Energy.—As is known from other studies, the nature of conductors is such that electrons do not fly off readily into the surrounding space. There is some form of attraction for electrons at the surface of metals. Thus, when an electron approaches sufficiently close to a metal, surface forces act upon it to draw it inside and increase its energy by an amount $\mathscr{E}_p$, called the *surface energy*. Similarly, when leaving the metal, an electron must have an energy sufficient to overcome this *potential barrier* $\mathscr{E}_p$.* When the value of this energy is used as the potential energy in Schrödinger's wave-equation (3–1), the wave-length of the electron in the metal is found to be

$$\lambda_2 = \frac{h}{\sqrt{2m(\mathscr{E} + \mathscr{E}_p)}}. \qquad (3\text{–}10)$$

The wave-length of the electron outside the metal is given, as before, by $\lambda_1 = h/mv$, which is equal to $h/\sqrt{2m\mathscr{E}}$ since $\mathscr{E} = mv^2/2$. Hence

$$\mu = \frac{\lambda_1}{\lambda_2} = \sqrt{\frac{\mathscr{E} + \mathscr{E}_p}{\mathscr{E}}}. \qquad (3\text{–}11)$$

From this equation and the values of the index of refraction μ, calculated as above, $\mathscr{E}_p$ may be evaluated. Thus, the surface energy has been found to be about 16 volts for nickel, about 13.5 for copper, about 14 for iron, about 12 volts for tungsten, etc. Experimental difficulties make these values uncertain by one or two volts.

3–8. The Diffraction of Fast Electrons by Thin Films.—G. P. Thomson sent a narrow bundle of high-speed cathode rays through

---

* In the chapters on photoelectric and thermionic phenomena, it will be shown that electrons, when inside a metal, possess energies of such amounts that they cannot escape from the metal without the addition of light or heat energy from some outside source. The additional energy required to remove the most energetic electrons from the metal is called the " work function " of the surface. In this chapter, the total energy $\mathscr{E}_p$ of the surface forces is considered.

an extremely thin foil to a photographic plate. With foils of gold, aluminum, colloidion or platinum he obtained diffraction patterns on the plate which were similar to those produced by x-rays in the Debye-Sherrer, powdered crystal method. The arrangement of his apparatus is shown in figure 3–3. A potential of from 10,000 to 60,000 volts is applied between electrodes *A* and *B* in such a

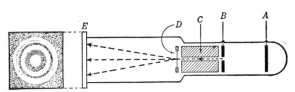

FIG. 3–3.   The G. P. Thomson experiment.

manner that *B* is the anode or positive terminal. Electrons are then accelerated toward *B*, pass through its small hole and are collimated by the capillary hole in the metal block *C*. The thin foil *D* then diffracts the electrons to the photographic plate or luminescent screen at *E*.

There would have been a general illumination of the screen or a blackening of the plate if the foil had scattered the electrons in all directions.   Instead, several rings of light appear whenever the foil is made up of minute crystals oriented in a *random* fashion, as in gold.   Spots or arcs of circles appear on the screen for such foil materials as aluminum, nickel or copper, in which the small crystals have preferred directions of alignment.   Spots, located at the corners of equilateral triangles, are observed when thin mica films are used.   Thus the foil material determines the kind of pattern observed.   The size of the pattern, i.e., the radii of the rings, etc., decreases as the accelerating potential is increased.   This is evidence that the wave-length of the electrons depends on their velocity.   Also, since the pattern is caused by charged particles in motion, it may be shifted around on the screen, as a unit, by means of a magnetic field.

A microscope will show that the foil material contains many small crystals.   Each of these acts upon the electrons in the manner described in section 3–5.   It is obvious that in a foil containing numerous crystals oriented at random, some of the crystals will be tilted at the appropriate Bragg angle to produce constructive interference for electrons of a given wave-length.   This is illustrated in figure 3–4.

Among the multitude of small crystals in the foil, other groups will exist which are so oriented as to give selective reflection at the same angle (ϕ, in figure 3–4), but rotated about the axis of the incident electrons.   As a result, a complete ring appears on the screen.

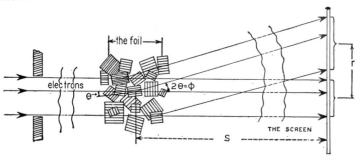

Fig. 3–4.   The diffraction of electrons.

If the crystals could be examined from various directions, other sets of planes would be seen whose atomic population and spacing differ from that of the planes which formed the ring discussed above.   Thus other rings of different intensity and radii (r) are formed on the screen.   Each ring is due to the selective reflection of the electron waves from the planes of crystals having the same grating space and tilted at the same angle with respect to the incident beam.

The patterns are complicated by the fact that solid atomic reflectors do not exist in the crystals.   Each reflecting " point " consists of the nucleus of an atom surrounded by electrons which, in their motion, fill much of the intermediate space.   The intensity of the diffracted beam depends upon the distribution of electrons in the unit cells.   In some cases the patterns of certain orders of reflection are missing.

The wave-length λ of the electrons may be computed from a modified form of the Bragg formula, as used in x-ray crystal structure work.   Thus, for cubic crystals, such as gold, aluminum or platinum

$$\lambda \sqrt{H^2 + K^2 + L^2} = 2a \sin \theta. \qquad (3\text{–}12)$$

Since the angles are small in practice, $\sin \theta = \theta$. From figure 3-4 it may be seen that $\tan 2\theta = r/S$ or, with sufficient accuracy, $2\theta = r/S$. Then

$$\lambda = \frac{ar}{S} \frac{1}{\sqrt{H^2 + K^2 + L^2}}. \tag{3-13}$$

From x-ray measurements, a is 4.07×10^{-8} cm. for gold, 4.04×10^{-8} cm. for aluminum, and 3.91×10^{-8} cm. for platinum. The radical, $\sqrt{H^2 + K^2 + L^2}$ is a constant for a given foil material and a given ring on the screen. For gold it is equal to 1.732 for the smallest ring and 2.000, 2.828, 3.354, 4.000, 4.416, 4.899, 5.196 and 5.950 for the progressively larger rings. The indices H, K and L depend on the geometry of the crystal lattice. Their values, as well as the modifications necessary for crystals which do not have a cubic structure, may be found in texts on the subject of crystal analysis.[B] See also the discussion of Laue Spots and Crystal Analysis in section 9-11, in the chapter on x-rays.

3-9. The Dualistic Nature of the Electron.—The electron was treated as a particle in the deflection experiments of chapter 2 and as a wave in the reflection and diffraction experiments of this chapter. No model of the electron has yet been made which reconciles these two apparently discordant viewpoints. However, a purely illustrative connection between the electron-particle and the electron-wave may be made in the following manner.

First, consider two infinitely long-wave trains. Let them travel in the same direction and at the same velocity (w); but let the wavelength of one be slightly longer than that of the other. When the two waves are added together, the amplitude of the resultant wave, at any instant, will be greater at certain points along their path, where they aid each other, and less at intermediate points where they are out of phase. As time goes on, these maxima and minima will move in succession past a given point. Their velocity will be the same as that of the individual waves (w). As they travel past a fixed observer, they produce the familiar phenomenon of beats.

Next, imagine that not only the wave-lengths of the individual waves but also their velocities differ slightly, one from the other. This would occur if the waves of different frequency were passing through a dispersive medium. Then it would be found that the maxima and minima no longer travel with the same velocity (the average velocity, w) of the individual wave trains, but at some other velocity v which is greater or less than w, according to the nature of the dispersive medium.

Finally, consider a large number of wave trains, each of infinite length, but differing slightly from one another in wave-length and velocity. It has been found possible to find an appropriate combination of these infinitely long waves, as in figure 3–5, such that they nullify each other except over a comparatively restricted portion of their path. In this region, however, they combine to form

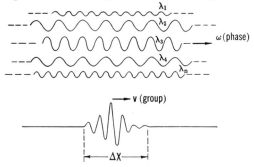

Fig. 3–5.   The formation of a wave-packet.

a *wave-packet*, as in the lower curve of the figure. This figure shows the waves at a given instant. As the waves progress, the packet also moves forward; not, however, at the same velocity as the average, w, of the individual trains. The velocity v of the wave-packet is called the *group velocity** and the velocity w of the individual waves is variously referred to as the phantom, virtual or *phase velocity*. It might be added that the velocity of light, as measured by Michelson, is a group velocity, whereas that which appears in the denominator of the expression for the index of refraction of a medium ($\mu = c/v$) is a phase velocity. In free space, the phase and group velocities of light are equal to each other ($= 3 \times 10^{10}$ cm./sec.).

In the case of the electron, the individual or de Broglie waves

---

* As the wave-packet moves forward it becomes flatter and longer. The extent to which this occurs is small for light waves. Hence, it is very nearly true that the energy of a light beam is transferred at the group velocity, v. However the dissipation of the packet is not negligible for electrons.

serve as a guide for the electron particle. The individual or phase waves travel at an average velocity w and have an average wavelength $\lambda = h/mv$. Their resultant travels at the group velocity v. The probability (per unit length) of observing an electron particle along the path of the electron waves is proportional to the square of the amplitude of the resultant wave. Since this amplitude is practically zero except in the wave-packet, it is here that one may expect to find the electron particle at a given instant. In other words, the likelihood that the particle is somewhere on the x-axis is greatest at the center of the packet and recedes rapidly on either side. Thus the particle travels at the group velocity v.

3-10. The Uncertainty Principle.—In the previous section, the formation of a wave-packet of finite length Δx by the combination of an appropriate set of infinitely long wave trains was discussed. This principle has been known for many years. Let the wave-lengths of the individual waves be $\lambda_1, \lambda_2, \ldots \lambda_n$ and their reciprocals (the wave-numbers) be $1/\lambda_1, \ldots 1/\lambda_n$. Let $\Delta(1/\lambda)$ be used to represent the extreme difference between their wave-numbers, i.e., $1/\lambda_1 - 1/\lambda_n$. Then Rayleigh has shown that $\Delta x \cdot \Delta(1/\lambda) \approx 1$. In other words, the "length" of the wave-packet (Δx of figure 3–5) is inversely proportional to the maximum difference in the number of waves per centimeter, $\Delta(1/\lambda)$, of the individual waves.

Differentiation of the de Broglie equation $\lambda = h/mv = h/p$, (p = momentum) gives $\Delta(1/\lambda) = \Delta p/h$. Substitution in the Rayleigh equation shows that

$$\Delta x \cdot \Delta p \approx h. \qquad (3-14)$$

Thus, the product of the uncertainty in the location of an electron-particle and the uncertainty in the determination of its momentum is of the order of magnitude of Planck's constant. This is known as the Heisenberg Uncertainty Principle.[6] It states that great precision in the location of an electron can only be obtained at a sacrifice in the accuracy with which its momentum can be determined, and vice versa. From equation 3–14 it follows that it is not always possible to measure any two quantities *simultaneously* with extreme accuracy.

To illustrate this principle, consider an electron of mass 9×10^{-28} gram travelling in a straight line with constant velocity due to an acceleration by 1000 volts. If we are content to know the position of the electron at a given instant to within one milli-meter only (Δx = 0.1 cm.), then we may, if our tools are sufficiently refined, measure the velocity to within about 728 centimeters per second (Δv = 728). Thus the velocity of the electron, 1.88 . . . $\times$ 10^9 centimeters per second, may be determined with excellent accuracy, at the expense of the accuracy in position deter-mination. If, however, we wish to know to within one angstrom where to find the electron at a given moment, then, from equation 3–14, it is impossible to state the velocity with which the electron is travelling, since the uncertainty in its value is greater than the quantity itself. Conversely, if a given experiment requires that the velocity be measurable to within a certain degree of accuracy, then the position of the electron can never be computed more accurately than the limit set by equation 3–14.

3–11. The Wave Nature of Heavier Particles.—Hydrogen molecules, helium and hydrogen atoms,[7] as well as protons [8] (the nuclei of hydrogen atoms), have been diffracted from crystals in a manner similar to that for electrons, demonstrating their wave nature. For example, a narrow beam of hydrogen atoms has been directed upon a lithium fluoride crystal. The reflected atoms were detected by their action upon a molybdenum trioxide sur-face. The colored streaks produced upon this detecting material after suitable exposure to the atoms were shown to be the diffrac-tion pattern produced by the two dimensional grating formed by the rows of lithium and fluorine atoms on the surface of the crystal. From the pattern and the known separation of the atoms of the crystal (x-ray analysis), the wave-lengths of the atoms were com-puted and found to agree with the de Broglie wave-lengths, λ = h/mv, for particles of mass equal to that of the hydrogen atom and travelling at the velocity of the atoms in the incident beam. The velocities were those of thermal motion as given by the kinetic theory for the temperature of the source and were dis-tributed about a most probable value according to the usual Max-wellian law.

The wave-lengths of hydrogen atoms at room temperature range from 0.3 to 1.8 angstroms. Protons, accelerated by 15,000 and by 40,000 volts, have wave-lengths of 0.0023 and 0.0014 ang-stroms, respectively. The wave-length of a one-gram mass moving

300 meters per second (670 miles per hour) would be 2.18×10^{-31} centimeters, a quantity too small to be measured.

EXPERIMENT 3-1

THE DIFFRACTION OF ELECTRONS

Apparatus: The apparatus consists essentially of three parts: first, a source of electrons; second, a device for collimating the electrons and an adjustable crystal holder, and, third, an observation chamber. One form of the apparatus is shown in figure 3–6.

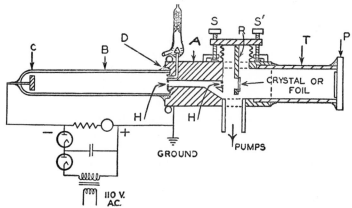

FIG. 3–6.   An electron diffraction apparatus.

The source of electrons may consist of a cold discharge tube, as in the figure.   Here, C is the cathode, an aluminum disc supported by a heavy tungsten wire, and B is a pyrex tube 50–100 cm. long and 3.5–4.5 cm. in diameter.   This is waxed at D into a circular groove in the end of the anode A.   The corners of the metal at the groove must be carefully rounded to prevent breakdown of the glass in the high electric field.   If necessary, a blast of air may be used to prevent the wax from melting or a single turn of copper tubing (O) soldered around A, near D, may be used as a water-cooling system.   Protection from x-rays produced at the anode may be obtained by means of a metal tube around the end of A, extending say 10 centimeters to the left over the discharge tube.

A hot filament may be used to produce electrons instead of the cold discharge.   A spiral of nickel strip, with one edge toward the anode, is coated with barium and strontium oxides and mounted with its center on the axis about 10 centimeters from the anode. Due to the heat from the filament, cooling of the waxed joint at D must be provided and any ground joint, for filament replacements, should be well back from the filament.   Also, with a filament, the gas leak shown in the figure is not needed.   A branch pumping line near the filament is used to keep the pressure in the source chamber as low as possible.

The central section, A, consists of an iron rod about 15 centimeters long and about 7 centimeters in diameter through which various holes are drilled as shown.   The axial hole, between H and H, is 2–3 centimeters in diameter and about 10 centimeters long. It is closed by brass discs pierced with 1 millimeter holes and covered with thin copper.   Small holes, HH, 0.2 to 0.3 millimeters in diameter, are drilled in this thin copper.   Great care must be taken that both of these holes are on the axis of the tube.   As an alternative for ease of replacement and adjustment, the discs and thin copper may be mounted in the ends of a brass tube which is slipped into the axial hole in the iron.   Air from a drying tube is admitted to the discharge tube through the lavite cone leak. Mercury is raised or lowered around this cone to vary the rate at which air is admitted.   Rapid pumping is used to keep the right side of the apparatus at as low a pressure as possible.   The pumping tube should be as large as possible, say 2 to 4 centimeters.

The crystal or foil material is mounted with clips over a hole in the end of the rod R.   A sylphon bellows 2 to 3 centimeters in diameter is used as a flexible seal.   The crystal position is altered by three screws SSS (only two are shown) and is observed through a side window.   New crystals are inserted from the observation end P by removal of the metal tube T.   For transmission experiments, of the type of G. P. Thomson, the foil thickness should be 10^{-5} to 10^{-6} centimeter.   The foils may be prepared by mounting commercial gold foil on a platinum grid and reducing the thickness of the gold with acid.   Another process is to sputter or evaporate a thin layer of gold on glass, coat with lacquer, dry, strip off the lacquer and gold from the glass, place over a platinum grid in a shallow dish with the gold side on the platinum, carefully add amyl acetate, wait until the lacquer is dissolved, wash in the solvent several times and finally withdraw with care. It need hardly be stated that the preparation of the thin foil is one of the most difficult parts of the experiment and that several attempts may be made before a successful foil is obtained.

The observation chamber has a brass tube, T, 12 to 15 centimeters long and about 6 centimeters in diameter. A glass plate, P, not less than 3 or 4 millimeters thick is sealed on the end with wax, or with a rubber gasket and stop-cock grease. There is a coating of luminescent material on the inner surface of P. To form this " screen," the glass is placed horizontally, moistened with saliva and sprinkled with a mixture of finely powdered phosphorescent zinc sulphide (20%) and calcium tungstate (80%). If desired, photographic records of the diffraction patterns may be obtained. Descriptions of various cameras for this purpose will be found in the references [9] or may be designed by the student.

The potential may be supplied by a large induction coil and condenser, a large static machine or a transformer-rectifier-condenser unit. An x-ray power supply serves nicely. Potentials from 10,000 to 60,000 volts will be found satisfactory, although considerable heating will be encountered at the higher potentials. The wave-length of the electrons and hence the radii of the diffraction rings depend on the applied potential. Sharper rings are, therefore, obtained when the potential is maintained at a constant value. Good filtering equipment is needed when a hot filament is used as the electron source. With the cold discharge tube, however, the potential drop across the tube depends to a large extent on the residual gas pressure, as regulated by the leak, and to a lesser extent on the current passing through the tube. A suitable voltage supply may therefore be made up of a transformer, half-wave rectifier tube, an 0.01 microfarad condenser and a series diode operating under saturation conditions to maintain constant current to the discharge tube.

The potential may be measured by means of a sphere gap, by means of a milliammeter in series with a high resistance or with an electrostatic voltmeter across a portion of a high resistance. See chapter 19.

Precautions: The anode A must be grounded.

Keep away from the cathode C at all times as the high potentials are exceedingly dangerous.

Be careful of the foil material; it is extremely fragile.

The Experiment: Obtain rings of constant radii.   Use a gold foil.

From equation 3-13 and the constants immediately following it, measure the wave-length of the electrons.

From equations 3-6 and 2-12, compute the de Broglie wave-length and compare with the measured value.

REFERENCES

1. C. J. Davisson, Bell System Tech. Jr., **8**, 217 (1929).
2. L. de Broglie, Phil. Mag., **47**, 446 (1924).
3. Davisson and Germer, Phys. Rev., **30**, 705 (1927); Proc. Nat. Acad. Sci., **14**, 317, 619 (1927); Jr. Frank. Inst., **205**, 597 (1928).
4. G. P. Thomson, Proc. Roy. Soc., **119**, 651 (1928).
5. Schrödinger, Phys. Rev., **28**, 1049 (1926).
6. W. Heisenberg, Zeits. f. Physik, **43**, 172 (1927).
7. T. H. Johnson, Phys. Rev., **37**, 847 (1931).
   I. Estermann and O. Stern, Zeits. f. Physik, **61**, 95 (1930).
8. A. J. Dempster, Phys. Rev., **34**, 1493 (1929).
9. Finch and Quarrell, Proc. Phys. Soc., **46**, 148 (1934).
   L. H. Germer, Rev. Sci. Inst., **6**, 138 (1935).
   Morgan and Smith, Rev. Sci. Inst., **6**, 316 (1935).

GENERAL REFERENCES

A.—K. K. Darrow, Bell System Tech. Jr., **8**, 391 (1929).
B.—R. W. G. Wyckoff, *The Structure of Crystals*, Chem. Cat. Co., New York (1931).
C.—A. Sommerfeld, *Wave Mechanics*, Methuen & Co., Ltd. (1930).
D.—R. Beeching, *Electron Diffraction*, Methuen & Co., Ltd. (1936).
E.—Frohlick, *Electron Theorie de Mettalen.*
F.—Born, *Atomic Physics.*

CHAPTER 4

PHOTOELECTRIC EMISSION

4–1. Introduction.—Electricity is emitted by certain metals when ultra-violet light falls on their surfaces. This is one form of the photoelectric effect.

The existence of radio waves was predicted in 1864 by the brilliant theoretical work of Clerk Maxwell and was established, directly and for the first time, by Heinrich Hertz in 1887. During the course of his famous experiments, Hertz observed, though he did not understand, the photoelectric effect. In his transmitter, a spark was produced between two metal balls by an induction coil. His receiver consisted of a loop of wire whose ends were capped with small balls and placed close to each other to form a spark gap. When the induction coil was turned on and certain adjustments made, a spark appeared in the gap of the receiver, across the room from the transmitter. Hertz noted that a spark could be obtained at the receiver even though its gap was comparatively wide, provided the ultra-violet light from the spark of the transmitter was allowed to fall upon the small balls. An explanation of this peculiar phenomenon was offered the next year by Hallwacks, of Dresden, when he showed

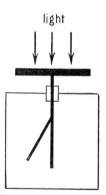

light

Fig. 4–1 The experiment of Hallwacks.

that the light which fell upon the spark gap of the receiver caused the emission of negative electricity and hence made it easier for the spark to start. In order to demonstrate this, he directed ultra-violet light upon a freshly polished zinc plate (and later many other metals) connected to an electroscope, as in figure 4–1. When the plate and electroscope were positively charged, there was no loss of electricity but, when negatively charged, the leaves collapsed. Thus negative electricity was repelled from the plate. As a consequence of this work, the photoelectric effect is sometimes referred to as the Hallwacks effect.

If a positively charged metal plate is placed near the illuminated surface, the negative electricity will be attracted to it and will constitute a flow of current. This may be measured by means of an electrometer, as in figure 4–2. In order to avoid the complicating effects of the gas between the two plates, Elster and Geitel located them in an evacuated bulb, as in figure 4–3. This was the first photo-electric cell. Many of the laws of photoelectricity were estab-lished by these men during the

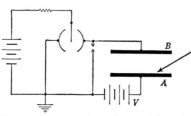

FIG. 4–2. Connections for studying the photoelectric effect.

years 1889 to 1892. For example, they showed that the photo-electric current, as measured by means of the galvanometer G of figure 4–3, is directly proportional to the intensity of the light. They observed that this current changed in amount when the plane of polarization of the light was rotated and they found certain substances which would re-spond to visible as well as to ultra-violet light.

The negative electricity flowing from an illuminated surface was identified as a stream of electrons by Lenard and Thomson in 1899 by means of magnetic and elec-tric deflecting fields. Lenard also proved that the total number of ejected electrons was directly proportional to

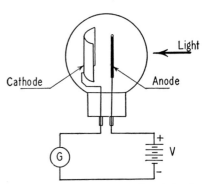

FIG. 4–3. A photoelectric cell and circuit.

the intensity of the light. On the other hand, he showed the important fact that the energy with which each electron leaves the surface is independent of this intensity.

In addition to the emission of electrons from the surface of various bodies, there is a *volume* photoelectric effect. For many years Gudden and Pohl have carried on extensive researches concerning the changes in electrical conductivity when various substances are illuminated. This is the *photo-conductive* effect.

A related phenomenon, known as the *photo-voltaic* effect, was discovered by Becquerel in 1893. He found that an electromotive force is produced between two similar electrodes in a suitable electrolyte when one of them is illuminated with light.

Photo-emissive cells have high internal resistance, give comparatively large voltage changes but only small current changes and are used frequently with vacuum tube amplifiers. Typical circuits are shown in figure 4–4. Photo-voltaic cells have low internal resistance (500–6000 ohms), deliver comparatively large

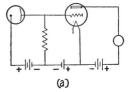 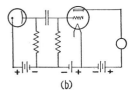

(a)   (b)

Fig. 4–4. Circuits for amplifying photoelectric currents.

currents into low resistance loads and hence may be used to operate relays directly. Photo-conductive cells are, in general, intermediate between the other two types.

4–2. The Number of Electrons Emitted.—In figure 4–3, the deflections of the galvanometer are proportional to the photoelectric currents which, in turn, are proportional to the number of electrons emitted each second by the cathode or sensitive surface. This number depends, for a given surface, on the intensity and the wave-length of the incident light. If the *intensity* I of a monochromatic beam of light is increased, the number of electrons also increases. If the intensity of the light is doubled, the current, i, is likewise doubled, etc. This linear relationship,

$$i = SI, \quad (\lambda \text{ constant}) \qquad (4\text{--}1)$$

where S is the proportionality constant, is exact over as wide a range as from 0.00007 to 10,000 foot-candles; from light intensities weaker than the eye can detect up to direct sunlight. It is true for thick and for thin sensitive surfaces; even when the material is no more than one atom thick. This linear relationship is also true when many wave-lengths of light are involved, provided the relative distribution of their energies remains unaltered as the intensity is changed. Apparent departures occur in photoelectric cells because of negative surface charges which form on the inside of the enclosing bulb at varying rates. The effect of these charges is reduced or avoided when the sensitive surface is mounted on a separate support away from the walls or when the photo-active material covers all of the inner walls of the bulb; except, of course, the clear spaces for the light to enter and for the lead wires.

The number of electrons emitted each second by a given surface varies in a complex manner with the color or *wave-length* λ of the incident light, as illustrated in figure 4–5. Here, the " yield " or " sensitivity," S, represents the photoelectric currents reduced to values which they would have if the light were of constant intensity in all parts of the spectrum, i.e.,

$$S = i/I. \tag{4–2}$$

The various curves shown here should not be compared in numerical value; their general shape alone has significance. One may note that there are large photoelectric currents (per unit of light intensity) at certain favored wave-lengths. This so-called *spectral selectivity* or preference for certain spectral regions is different for different sensitive surfaces. Compare the curves for potassium (K) and cesium (Cs). It is also different for a given material subjected to different treatments during the preparation of the cell. Thus, as shown in the figure, a cesium surface on cesium oxide on a silver base (Cs on CsO on Ag) has a totally different spectral distribution curve than a pure cesium surface. In like fashion, potassium and potassium hydride surfaces differ markedly from each other. A potassium hydride surface may be made which is more sensitive and stable than an untreated potassium layer. Obviously, certain types of cells are preferable for use in the ultraviolet, others in the infra-red and others in the region of maximum eye sensitivity (about 5555 angstroms; varies with intensity).

One of the important features of the curves in figure 4–5 is the fact that they plunge into the horizontal axis at a definite long-wave-length limit λ_o. The significance of this photoelectric *threshold* will be discussed later.

The energy radiated by different sources of light is distributed throughout the spectrum in different amounts, as indicated in

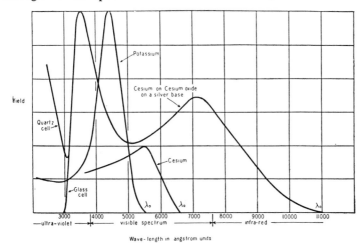

FIG. 4–5. Spectral distribution curves.

figure 4–6 for sunlight and for a tungsten filament operated at a specified temperature. Hence, the actual photoelectric currents

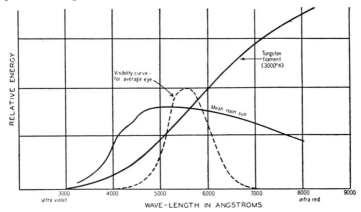

FIG. 4–6. Relative energies radiated at different wave-lengths.

observed at different wave-lengths depend also on the particular source of light and its operating conditions. The products of the ordinates of the spectral distribution curve of the cell (figure 4–5) and the ordinates of the relative energy curve of the source (figure 4–6) give the currents which are observed.

If, instead of a monochromatic beam of light, the total radiation from a source is allowed to fall upon a photoelectric surface, the current will be the integrated effect of all the separate wavelengths to which the surface responds, i.e., the area under the " observed " current curve mentioned in the preceding paragraph. If a metal cathode is exposed to the total radiation of a black body * operated at a temperature of T degrees absolute, the total or *complete* photoelectric current i_c from the surface is given by

$$i_c = aT^2\epsilon^{-\frac{h\nu_o}{kT}} \qquad (4\text{–}3)$$

where ϵ is the base of the Naperian logarithm system, a, h, and k are constants and ν_o is the threshold frequency corresponding to the long-wave-length limit λ_o.

If plane *polarized light* of a given wave-length and intensity falls obliquely on a given surface, the number of electrons ejected may be varied by rotating the plane of polarization. Whenever the electric vector of the light has a larger component which " cuts " into the surface, there is an increase in the number of electrons given off perpendicularly to that surface. Now, it has been noted that the amount of light absorbed by a surface changes as the plane of polarization of the incident light is rotated. Consider the photoelectric currents produced when the plane of polarization is at two different angles. If the ratio of the currents is not the same as the ratio of the amounts of light absorbed by the surface in the two cases, *polarization selectivity* is said to occur. Polarization and spectral selectivity very frequently occur together.

To specify the output of a photoelectric cell, it is necessary to include the intensity, the wave-length, the state of polarization and the angle of incidence of the light.

4–3. Measurement of the Sensitivity or Yield.—The spectral sensitivity or photoelectric yield is defined as the quantity of electricity liberated each second by unit intensity of absorbed

---

* For a source other than a " black " body, its *color temperature* may be used. This, in degrees absolute, is the temperature to which a perfectly black body would need to be heated to give the same appearance. It is not the actual temperature of the body. For example, the blue sky, which is cold, may have a color temperature of 25,000° K.

light of a given frequency. The measurement of the quantity of electricity emitted each second, i.e., the photoelectric current, is easily accomplished; but an absolute determination of the intensity of the light absorbed is more difficult. This " intensity," in basic form, is expressed as the number of ergs absorbed by unit area each second. Since 4.18×10^7 ergs are the equivalent of one calorie, the intensity measurement may be made in terms of the heat produced in a given body each second by the same monochromatic beam of light which is used to liberate the electrons. Thus one may use a thermocouple whose currents have previously been calibrated in terms of the number of calories of heat absorbed each second. The yield is then obtained in coulombs-per-second per calorie-per-second or, as usually expressed, in *coulombs per calorie*. The yield is also commonly expressed in *amperes per watt*. For example, the measured yield of a potassium surface, sensitized with hydrogen and irradiated with blue light of wave-length 4500 angstroms, was found to be 0.015 coulombs per calorie. This is equal to 0.00358 coulombs-per-second per joule-per-second or 0.00358 amperes per watt. The yield in commercial cells ranges from zero to ten microamperes of photoelectric current per microwatt of radiant energy.

For *comparative work*, where the general shape but not the absolute values of the curves in figure 4–5 are desired, the relative response at the different wave-lengths is specified as the ratio of the photoelectric current to the current produced by a black surfaced thermopile irradiated with the same light. This assumes that the thermopile currents are directly proportional to the heat absorbed each second. The black surface is used in order that the absorption of energy will be, as nearly as possible, complete at the various wave-lengths. Since the photo-cell surface itself is not black it will absorb differently than the thermopile at the different wave-lengths and the relative response curves obtained by this method will only approximate the true spectral distribution curves.

4-4. Practical Units.—A source of light is referred to as being " weak," like a candle; or " strong," like an electric light; or " intense," like the sun. Technically, one uses the term *luminous intensity*. This is an intrinsic property of a source of light. Its unit, arbitrarily established, is the International Candle.* Accurate specifications of the construction and of the rate of burning of this standard source of light have been established.   Secondary standards—electric lamps constructed and operated in a specified manner—have been built and are used in practice instead of the candle.   In order to determine the luminous intensity of a given source of light, photometers are used, whereby comparison is made with a standardized lamp.   We shall use C to stand for the luminous intensity in candlepower. C has the dimensions of power.

While the light is in transit from a point source to the receiver, energy radiates outward in all directions.   The rate at which this energy flows out from the source is called the *luminous flux* ($=$ "light flow").   It might be expressed as the number of ergs of energy radiating outward every second or as the number of joules per second (watts), but it has been found advisable to use a unit called the *lumen*.   One lumen is defined as the amount of light energy flowing out each second from a point source of one candle through a unit solid angle.   Thus, the unit of luminous flux is numerically equal to the intensity of the source.   The luminous flux through a solid angle of ω ster-radians is $L = C\omega$.   For example, from a point source of candlepower C, $4\pi C$ lumens are radiated in all directions; $2\pi C$ lumens are radiated in a hemisphere and $1 \times C$ lumens flow out through one ster-radian.

The amount of light energy received upon a given surface each second is called the *total illumination* (L) and is measured in lumens. (Notice that this statement does not mention what becomes of the light energy, whether it is absorbed, transmitted or reflected by the surface.)   Consider the special case of a point source of light or, in practice, the case where the distance to the illuminated surface is very great in comparison with the size of the source of light.   Let the surface of area A be everywhere normal to the light rays and at a distance d from the source.   Then A/d^2 is the solid angle made by the surface at the source.   The luminous flux

* The International Candle, referred to here, emits a total of 4π lumens.   For radiation of maximum visibility (when $\lambda = 0.00005560$ cm.) one lumen is equal to 0.001496 watt, or one watt is the equivalent of 668 lumens in this part of the spectrum.   The Hefner Candle has an intensity equal to 0.9 that of the International Candle.

reaching the surface is called the total illumination, and is given by

$$L = \frac{CA}{d^2}, \qquad (4\text{-}4)$$

where C is in candlepower. If A is in square feet, d must be in feet; if A is square centimeters, d must be in centimeters, etc. When a small, plane surface of area A' is placed so that its normal makes an angle θ with the incident light, then $A = A' \cos \theta$.

The *intensity of light* or *intensity of illumination*, I, which is often referred to simply as the illumination, is the total illumination divided by the area of surface: Thus, $I = L/A$. The student should be careful not to confuse the words " intensity of the light source " or " luminous intensity " with the words " intensity of light " or " illumination." The former deals with the source, the latter with the receiver. For a point source of light, and for a surface everywhere normal to the luminous flux,

$$I = \frac{C}{d^2}. \qquad (4\text{-}5)$$

There are several units of intensity of illumination. One of these is the lumen/cm². However, the unit most widely used in practice is called the *foot-candle*. One foot-candle is defined as the illumination received on one square foot of surface everywhere one foot away from a point source of one candlepower. In general, when one lumen of luminous flux falls uniformly and normally upon a surface whose area is one square foot, the intensity of illumination is one foot-candle. (Another unit sometimes used is the *lux*. This is the illumination on one square meter of surface everywhere one meter from a source of one candlepower.) For home lighting, the intensity of illumination should be 2 to 15 foot-candles; for office work, 5 to 30 and for detailed work, 15 to 100 foot-candles. A 60 watt, 110 volt frosted lamp, gives approximately 30 foot-candles at a distance of 14.5 inches from the center of the bulb. A light flux of 0.2 lumen passes through an aperture of one square inch illuminated by 30 foot-candles.

Ordinary photo-cells have a maximum sensitivity of from 15 to 135 microamperes per lumen. In modern sound-on-film equipment, the light flux varies from 0.01 to 0.04 lumen. The current output is then of the order of a few microamperes. A highly sensitive photo-cell has a sensitivity of 600 microamperes per lumen and will give 5.8×10^{-13} ampere for the smallest amount of light visible to the human eye (9.6×10^{-13} lumen, when the diameter of the pupil is 6 millimeters).

4–5. The Time Factor.—Lawrence and Beams[1] have used a pulsating light beam, operated by Nicol prisms and Kerr cells, in such a manner that a photoelectric surface was successively illuminated and darkened for periods of 10^{-8} seconds. The experiment showed that the photoelectric current starts within 3×10^{-9} seconds after the light is turned on and ceases within at least 10^{-8} seconds after the light has been turned off—the experimental limits of accuracy. In brief, a time lag in the surface photoelectric effect has never been observed.

The current from a gas-filled photoelectric cell decreases by as much as twenty per cent when the frequency of the fluctuations in the light intensity is increased from zero to ten thousand cycles per second; but this is due to the gas and to capacity shunting rather than to any finite emission time of the photo-electrons.

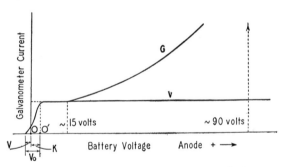

Fig. 4–7. Photoelectric currents for different voltages applied to a vacuum (V) and a gas-filled (G) cell.

4–6. Current-voltage Curves.—Figure 4–7 shows curves of the photoelectric current for different applied voltages when the incident light was of constant intensity and wave-length. See the circuit of figure 4–3. When the cathode or sensitive surface is only slightly negative, the currents are small. They quickly rise, however, to a saturation value. This is obviously a case where Ohm's law does not apply. Curve V is for a highly evacuated cell while curve G is for the case of a cell which contains a trace of gas, such as argon. The additional current in the latter case, at the higher voltages, is due to the ejection of electrons and positive ions from neutral gas atoms by collision with the accelerated photo-electrons. At the usual operating voltage, the effect of the gas is to multiply the photoelectric current (very) approximately four times.

The voltage applied to a gas-filled cell should not exceed the value where the current (G) rises rapidly, as indicated by the dotted arrow of figure 4–7. For commercial tubes, this potential is between 75 and 125 volts, usually about 90 volts, the higher values for the weaker light intensities. At still higher potentials, the positive ions bombard the cathode so vigorously as to destroy its sensitive surface in a short time.

4–7. The Energy of the Photo-electrons.—The kinetic energy of the ejected electrons may be measured by the use of magnetic and electric fields, as in the case of thermionic electrons described in chapter 2. The more usual method, however, is to apply a sufficiently negative potential to the collecting electrode to just reduce the photo-current to zero. The critical retarding potential $(V_o$ of figure 4–7) is proportional to the energy of the fastest electrons. The potential V of the *battery* in series with the photo-cell, which will thus stop the most energetic electrons, must be corrected by an amount K to give the true energy V_o. The contact potential,[2] K, is the inherent potential difference which exists between the two kinds of material forming the anode and cathode. It is positive in commercial photo-cells but may be positive or negative according to the materials used for the electrodes. The critical retarding potential, V_o, is thus equal to $V + K$. Then,

$$V_o e = (V + K)e = \tfrac{1}{2}mv^2_{\text{max}}, \qquad (4\text{–}6)$$

where e and m are the charge and mass of the electron and v_{max} their greatest velocity. The values of V, V_o, and K are indicated in figure 4–7. The horizontal part of the curve would extend left to the current axis, instead of decreasing as it does, if K were zero, i.e., if both anode and cathode were made of identical materials. The decrease of current at the lower voltages may be explained as due to the existence in the photo-current of electrons of all energies from zero up to a definite maximum amount; velocities from zero up to approximately 10^8 centimeters per second.   Thus, voltages immediately to the left of O' stop increasingly energetic electrons and V_o volts repel even the fastest ones.

From the shape of the curve to the left of O' in figure 4–7, it has been found possible to deduce the number of electrons which possess different velocities   The *velocity distribution* is as follows: there are very few electrons in the photoelectric current with velocities near zero and also very few near the theoretical maximum velocity.   Bewteen these limits, the number of electrons rises to a comparatively large, *most probable value;* about 0.4 of that of the maximum velocity.   As explained on the Sommerfeld theory of metallic conductors, the number of electrons with velocities near the maximum velocity does not suddenly reduce to zero except when the emitting surface is at zero degrees absolute. At room temperatures, the distribution curve, instead of plunging into the velocity axis, approaches it at an angle.   However, the slope of the curve is so great that, at least for rough work, it is easily possible to identify the maximum value.   Thus, in figure 4–7, the lower left end of the curve would cut sharply into the voltage axis at zero degrees absolute and does approach the axis fairly rapidly at room temperatures.

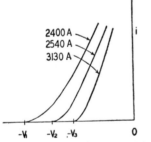

Films of silver of increasing thicknesses have been used as the emitting surface.   A critical thickness about one-hundred atoms deep has been found.   For thicker surfaces the electrons have a wide distribution of velocities, as pointed out above, but for films of lesser thickness, the electrons all have

FIG. 4–8.   Retarding potentials for light of different frequencies.

much more nearly the same velocity.   It is known that these thin metallic films are quite transparent to the ultra-violet light used. Hence, it appears that in the case of silver most of the photo-electrons originate in a surface layer one hundred atoms thick.

The extreme left end of the current-voltage curve has been studied in considerable detail.   Here the photoelectric currents are so small that an electrometer, rather than a galvanometer, must be used.   Figure 4–8 shows several curves for a given material, aluminum, irradiated with light of different wave-lengths. It is to be noted that the critical retarding potentials V_1, V_2, and V_3 are greater for the shorter wave-lengths or higher frequencies of incident light.

4–8. The Dualistic Nature of Radiant Energy.—In 1901, Planck introduced the idea that radiant energy, such as light or heat radiation, is emitted or absorbed by a black body in small, discrete amounts, rather than in a continuous manner. The amount of energy given out or absorbed at the surface of a body was considered to be an integral multiple of a certain small amount $\mathscr{E}$ (ergs) related to the frequency of the radiation ν (cycles per second) in the following simple manner,

$$\mathscr{E} = h\nu = \frac{hc}{\lambda}, \tag{4–7}$$

where h is a constant, now called Planck's constant and equal to 6.624×10^{-27} erg-second, c is the velocity and λ is the wavelength of the light. This idea of discontinuity in the processes of radiation and absorption of energy was used by Planck to derive an equation* for black body radiation which was found to agree very well with the observed facts.

In 1905, Einstein boldly extended Planck's discontinuity idea. He proposed that absorption or emission occurred in small but definite amounts because the radiation itself had a granular structure. Thus, radiant energy should be treated, under certain circumstances, not as a wave but as though made up of *quanta* or granules of energy. The energy content of each quantum or *photon* is given by equation 4–7. In preceding chapters it has been shown that the electron has a dualistic corpuscle-wave nature. Here, then, is the counterpart for x-rays, light and heat radiations; they are to be thought of as waves in certain experiments and as photons in others. However, there is a difference

---

* Planck's law states that the energy $\mathscr{E}(\lambda)$ radiated at a given wave-length each second in unit solid angle in a direction normal to unit area of a black body at a temperature T is

$$\mathscr{E}(\lambda) = c_1/\lambda^5(e^{c_2/\lambda T} - 1).$$

The more approximate radiation law of Wien

$$\mathscr{E}(\lambda) = c_1/\lambda^5 e^{c_2/\lambda T},$$

is useful to within 0.1 per cent when $T < 3000°$ K and $\lambda < 7000$ A.

between electrons and photons, since electrons can be deflected by magnetic and electric fields whereas light cannot; and also, the wave-length of the electron varies with its speed, the energy in each photon varies with the frequency of the radiation (equation 4–7).

From this *quantum theory*, Einstein was able to propose the following laws for photoelectric phenomena: first, the well-established fact that the number of electrons emitted each second should be directly proportional to the intensity of the incident light; second, that this number should be directly proportional to the wave-length of the incident light; and, third, that the kinetic energy of the fastest electrons leaving a surface should be directly proportional to the frequency of the incident light. A discussion of these laws will be given in the sections immediately following. The application of the quantum theory, by Bohr and Moseley, to predict the emission of light and x-rays from atoms and, by Compton, to predict the change of wave-length of an x-ray when it collides with a free electron, will appear later in this book.

4–9. Quantum Equivalence and Photoelectric Efficiency.— The principle of *quantum equivalence* states that one electron is emitted for each photon absorbed by a given material. In order to compute the number of photons absorbed in unit time, divide the total energy absorbed each second (the intensity, I) of a monochromatic beam of light of wave-length λ by the energy of each photon. The latter, from equation 4–7, is equal to hc/λ. Then, if quantum equivalence holds, the number of electrons ejected each second will be $I\lambda/hc$. If, on the other hand, y electrons appear when one photon is absorbed, the total number emitted each second will be $I\lambda y/hc$. This number, multiplied by the charge e of each electron, gives the photoelectric current i. Thus

$$i = \left(\frac{e}{hc}\right) I\lambda y, \qquad (4\text{–}8)$$

an equation which states the well-established fact that the photoelectric current is directly proportional to the intensity of the light ($i \alpha I$) and also that, for quantum equivalence, where $y = 1$, the current must be directly proportional to the wave-length of the light. As seen in figure 4–5, the sensitivity $S\,(= i/I)$ is not directly proportional to λ. Hence, for the surface photoelectric effect, quantum equivalence is not generally observed.

The *quantum yield* or *photoelectric efficiency*, y, of a surface is the number of photo-electrons emitted for each absorbed quantum of light. From equations 4–2 and 4–8,

$$y = \left(\frac{hc}{e}\right)\frac{S}{\lambda}. \tag{4-9}$$

The observed efficiency varies in an, as yet, unexplained manner with the wave-length of the light. At a given wave-length, however, it is a constant, irrespective of the intensity of the light. In the case of a potassium hydride surface irradiated with blue light of wave-length 4500 angstroms (as in Section 4–3), the energy in each photon is 4.37 micro-micro-ergs. The observed yield of 0.00358 coulombs per joule is equal to 1.56×10^{-21} coulombs per photon. Since the charge of each electron is 1.59×10^{-19} coulombs, the quantum yield y is 0.00977 electrons per photon. Approximately, then, one hundred photons were absorbed for each electron emitted; the efficiency was about one per cent of quantum equivalence; an unusually favorable case. As a further example: in the selective region (4360A) of a potassium surface, a sensitivity of 0.0345 coulombs per calorie was observed. Then, fifty photons were absorbed for each electron ejected. Again, in the case of a platinum surface, at $250\mu\mu(=2500$ angstroms), a sensitivity of 1.5×10^{-4} coulombs per calorie corresponds to about 5600 photons per electron. Values of $y = 10^{-4}$ are common. If the intensity of the light is increased, more electrons will be emitted but the ratio of the number of electrons ejected to the number of photons absorbed remains the same for a given surface and wave-length. The efficiency is a property of the surface.

4-10. Einstein's Photoelectric Equation.—In 1905, Einstein predicted that the *energy* of the fastest photo-electrons would be directly proportional to the frequency of the incident light. He stated this in the form of his famous equation,

$$\tfrac{1}{2}mv^2_{\max} = h\nu - \phi, \tag{4-10}$$

where m is the mass of the electron, $v_{\max}$ is the velocity of the fastest electron, ν is the frequency of the light, h is Planck's constant $(= 6.547 \times 10^{-27}$ erg-sec.) and ϕ is the energy required for an electron to escape from the surface of the emitting material. (ϕ is analogous to the action of gravity in preventing the escape of the atmosphere of the earth.) The magnitude $h\nu$ of each granule, quantum or photon of radiant energy depends directly on its frequency; the higher the frequency, the greater the energy in each quantum, and in direct proportion. This energy, given over to an electron, serves to remove it from the surface (ϕ ergs are required), after which the remaining energy is in the kinetic form.

Critical retarding potentials, proportionate to the maximum velocities of the electrons, were plotted against the frequency of

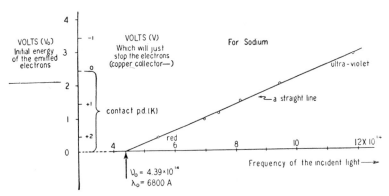

Fig. 4–9. Verification of Einstein's equation.

the light by Richardson and Compton and also by Hughes in 1912. However, it remained for Millikan and his associates, in 1916, to make the experimental proof of Einstein's equation entirely convincing by the great care which they used to eliminate all sources of error. The apparatus used was a veritable "machine shop in a vacuum." [3] Fresh surfaces of lithium, sodium and potassium were prepared in a vacuum by means of a knife and rotating mechanism. Contact potential differences were measured by the Kelvin method wherein an auxiliary battery is used to balance this potential; the two potentials were known to be equal when a movement of one of the electrodes no longer set up a current in their external circuit. Now, from equations 4–6 and 4–10,

$$V_o e = \tfrac{1}{2} m v^2_{\text{max}} = h\nu - \phi. \tag{4–11}$$

Hence, a plot of the retarding potentials V_o against the frequency ν, as in figure 4–9, should give a straight line whose slope is equal to h/e. In electro-static units,

$$\frac{h}{e} = \frac{\Delta V_o}{300 \Delta \nu}.$$ (4–12)

Millikan was the first to determine accurately the value of h/e, and hence of h. His value of $h(6.57 \times 10^{-27})$ is remarkably close to the now accepted value of

$$h = 6.624 \times 10^{-27} \text{ erg-sec.}$$

4–11. The Work Function and the Potential Barrier.—The energy required by an electron, in order that it may escape from the surface of a body, is called the work function ϕ of that surface. It is possible to determine a value of ϕ from the intercept of the straight line with the voltage axis in figure 4–9. This method is inaccurate since the extrapolation to zero frequency is very large. On the other hand, ϕ may be determined with reasonable accuracy by use of the intercept of this straight line with the frequency axis. If each of the incident light quanta contains an amount of energy $h\nu_o$ which is barely sufficient to remove an electron from the surface, then the emergent electron will have zero kinetic energy. The retarding potential V_o then required to stop this electron will likewise be zero. It follows, from equation 4–11, that

$$\phi = h\nu_o = hc/\lambda_o,$$ (4–13)

where c is the velocity of light. The critical frequency ν_o, or the long-wave-length limit λ_o, is referred to as the photoelectric *threshold*. It, and hence ϕ, may be determined not only from the retarding curves, as above, but also from the spectral distribution curves, as in figure 4–5.

The work function is expressed in a number of different units. We shall use ϕ to represent this quantity in general, irrespective of the units, and ϕ_1 to represent its value when measured in ergs per electron. Then, the number of ergs required to remove one unit of electrostatic charge will be $\phi_2 = \phi_1/e$, where e is the charge of the electron in e.s.u. Further, since 300 volts is the equivalent of one e.s.u. of potential difference, the number of volts (energy units) required to remove an e.s.u. of charge is

$$\phi_3 = \frac{300\phi_1}{e} \text{ volts/e.s.u.}$$ (4–14)

This latter is the unit most commonly used in practice. If numerical values are substituted in equations 4–13 and 4–14, it will be found that

$$\phi_3 = \frac{12336}{\lambda_o} \text{ volts/e.s.u.,} \qquad (4\text{--}15)$$

in which λ_o is measured in angstrom units.

Values of the work function for certain materials are listed in table 1 at the end of this book. They range from 1.8 to 6.3 volts per e.s.u., for various outgassed materials. However, the value which is found for any given material depends greatly on the condition of the surface. It is different for rough or smooth surfaces and is greatly affected by the presence of gases. It is smaller for surfaces exposed to such electro-positive gases as are readily adsorbed. Thus, larger photoelectric currents may be obtained from surfaces exposed to these gases. The effect of easily adsorbed electro-negative gases is just the reverse. The so-called "fatigue" observed in some photoelectric cells is due to changes in the gas impurities on the surface; a clean metal in a high vacuum shows no fatigue. Further, the addition of a very thin layer (perhaps only one atom thick) of other materials over a surface can greatly increase the photoelectric current. Alkali metals and alkaline earths are very effective, especially when treated with certain gases, such as hydrogen or oxygen. In these cases the surface layers are hydrides or pure metals on oxides, for example, potassium hydride, or cesium on cesium oxide on a silver base.

Experiments have shown that the contact potential difference between two surfaces in a vacuum, separated from each other, is equal to the difference of their work functions. Thus,[*]

$$K = \phi' - \phi''. \qquad (4\text{--}16)$$

Let us assume that there are free electrons moving among the atoms of a metal. There is ample evidence for their existence, as we shall see in the next chapter. The energy which a free electron possesses in the metal is called the *inner energy* and shall be denoted by $\mathcal{E}_i$. It varies, from electron to electron, from zero to a maximum of approximately 10^{-11} ergs, when the metal is at

---

[*] The Peltier coefficient should be added to the right-hand side of equation 4–16 but was omitted since it amounts to only a few milli-volts, while $(\phi' - \phi'')$ is of the order of a few volts.

room temperature. This *maximum energy*, $\mathscr{E}_m$, corresponds approximately to six volts and would be sufficient to allow the faster electrons to escape from the metal were it not that a *potential barrier* of energy $\mathscr{E}_p$, greater than ϕ, exists at the surface to restrain the electrons. A free electron of energy $\mathscr{E}_i$, in the metal, which absorbs one photon of energy $h\nu$, has then a total energy ($\mathscr{E}_i + h\nu$)

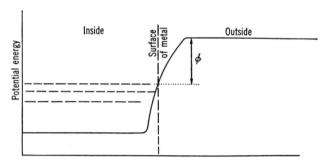

Fɪɢ. 4–9A. Potential barrier at surface of metal. Dotted lines show energy-levels of electrons inside metal and ϕ represents the work-function, or energy which must be given to the electron for it to escape.

just before emission. As it passes out of the metal it gives up an energy equal to $\mathscr{E}_p$ in overcoming the surface forces and retains a kinetic energy $mv^2/2$. Thus,

$$\mathscr{E}_i + h\nu = \mathscr{E}_p + \tfrac{1}{2}mv^2, \tag{4-17}$$

and

$$\mathscr{E}_m + h\nu = \mathscr{E}_p + \tfrac{1}{2}mv^2{}_{\text{max}}, \tag{4-18}$$

or

$$h\nu = (\mathscr{E}_p - \mathscr{E}_m) + \tfrac{1}{2}mv^2{}_{\text{max}}. \tag{4-19}$$

Then, from Einstein's equation, (4–10),

$$\phi = \mathscr{E}_p - \mathscr{E}_m. \tag{4-20}$$

It is thus seen that the work function is the difference between the potential barrier energy $\mathscr{E}_p$ and the energy $\mathscr{E}_m$ of the most energetic electrons inside of the metal. The quantity $\mathscr{E}_p$ is that measured in the experiments on the reflection of electrons from crystals described in chapter 3. (See section 3–7.)

The electrons inside the metal may be thought of as being kept in by a "potential barrier" at the surface of the metal. Schematically we may represent this by figure 4-9A. The dotted line shows the surface of the metal and the parallel horizontal lines on the left show the various energy-levels $\mathcal{E}$ occupied by the electrons. The photoelectric work-function ϕ is the amount of energy which must be supplied to raise the electrons to such a level that they may get out.

4–12. The Photo-ionization of Gases and Vapors.—Under certain conditions, electrons are ejected from the atoms or molecules of a gas through which light is passed. The atoms or molecules are then left with an excess of positive charge; the gas is said to be ionized and the process is called *photo-ionization.* If a potential is applied across two electrodes in the gas, the electrons move toward the anode and the heavier, positively charged ions are attracted to the cathode. The resultant photoelectric current, which is less than 10^{-11} amperes, is very much smaller than that observed in the case of emission from the surface of solids.

Figure 4–10 shows the photoelectric currents produced by light of different wave-lengths for the case of cesium vapor at a temperature of 182° C. The energy of the photon is used in the removal of an electron from its normal state in the atom and, if sufficiently great, to add kinetic energy to the electron. From other experiments it is known that an energy $h\nu_o$, equivalent to a wave-length of 3184 angstroms, is required to remove an electron from a cesium atom.

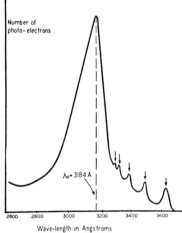

Fɪɢ. 4–10. The photo-ionization of cesium vapor.

This threshold value is indicated in the figure. It was found that on the short wave-length side of this theoretical limit, an increase in the pressure of the vapor in the tube caused an increased current and that all the light absorbed could be accounted for as having been used up in the production of ions, thus establishing the fact that the absorption of one quantum of light results in the ejection from an atom of one electron. This is a case of quantum equivalence. The peaks to the right of the threshold, in figure 4–10, occur at the wave-lengths of the principal-series lines in the emission spectrum of cesium. However, the ionization of the gas at these points is necessarily accomplished by an indirect process (by cumulative ionization) since the energy in each photon at these wave-lengths (above the threshold) is less than that required to remove an electron from a cesium atom. This indirect process of ionization occurs in the following manner: first, the energy of one photon is used to raise an electron in the cesium atom into a higher energy state where it can remain for a comparatively long interval of time. The act of collision of this excited cesium atom with another neutral cesium atom results in the formation of a positively charged molecule and a free electron. In this way, the photo-electron is obtained at the expenditure of the energy of one photon plus that liberated when two cesium atoms combine to form a charged molecule.

4–13. Photo-conductivity.—In figure 4–11, a crystal, such as zincblende, diamond or colored rock salt, at room temperature, is

placed between two metal electrodes connected to a battery. There is no flow of electricity unless ultra-violet light enters the crystal. Then, electrons are freed from certain favored centers. In this *photo-ionization* process, one electron is set free for each absorbed quantum of light; a case of quantum equivalence. It seems probable that the electrons move rapidly toward the anode while the positive charges

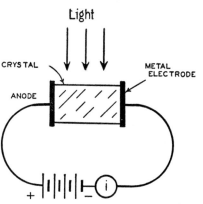

Fig. 4–11. A photo-conductive circuit.

which are left move slowly toward the cathode. A positive space charge is thus built up in the crystal and serves to retard the movement of the electrons so that the photo-current decreases with continued exposure to the light. The existence of a positive space charge may be shown when the crystal is mounted close to an electrode connected to the leaf of an electroscope. Continued exposure to the light causes the leaf to move in such a direction as would be caused by the accumulation of a positive charge. If the crystal is exposed to infra-red rays or is heated, the positive space charge is decreased. With this decrease in the space charge, it is found that the total or *primary current* is increased.

As the primary current passes through the crystal, the number of free electrons is increased and the original or natural resistance of the crystal is lowered. An additional, *secondary current* is then added to the primary current. In some crystals, notably *selenium*, the secondary current is so large as to mask the primary current. Selenium which has been properly " annealed " after solidification, at a temperature between 100° C. and 217° C., is used in thin layers between conducting supports to form selenium cells and shows marked changes in conductivity when irradiated with light. The resistance varies greatly in different types of cells, and in some cases, drops from dark values of ten to twenty million ohms to approximately one million ohms when exposed to light. Such cells, however, are comparatively sluggish in their response to changes of light intensity. When the light is turned on, the resistance drops sharply at first and then continues to fall slowly, for as much as several minutes and even hours, depending on the previous history of the cell. Similarly, the final dark resistance is not attained until an appreciable time interval after the light has been turned off.

The basic process in the formation of the invisible or latent image of a photographic film is due to the combination of photo-electrons with silver ions to form silver atoms. It has been found that one silver atom, approximately, is set free for each quantum of light absorbed. Upon development, each separate silver atom becomes the nucleus around which more silver atoms collect to form the black area of the visible image.

4-14. The Photo-voltaic Effect.[5]—Electromotive forces of the order of magnitude of tenths of a volt may be produced by the unsymmetrical illumination of two similar electrodes separated by an appropriate electrolyte. For example, an e.m.f. of 0.25 volt was produced by intense illumination of one of two similar platinum electrodes in a fluorescent solution. Potential differences of 10 to 20 microvolts were similarly generated when platinum, copper, mercury, silver or gold electrodes were used in non-fluorescent electrolytes such as copper sulphate.   The kind of electrolyte used has no effect on the electromotive force.

The *barrier-layer*, *dry-disc*, or photo-voltaic cells produce an electromotive force of their own when exposed to light and can be used to drive a current through a resistance without the use of an external battery.   In one type,* a film of properly annealed selenium is formed on a thick base of iron.   Light which passes through the thin layer of selenium causes electrons to move from the iron to the selenium; in the conventional sense, the iron forms the positive and the selenium forms the negative terminal. Curve *A* of figure 4–12 shows the spectral distribution as compared to the average sensitivity of the human eye (curve *C*).

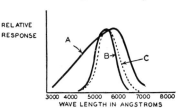

Fig. 4–12.   Spectral distribution curves of barrier-layer cells.

These cells can deliver the comparatively large current of one-quarter of one milliampere through an external resistance of three ohms when the illumination is only 170 foot-candles, and hence may be used to operate meters and relays directly without the use of vacuum tube amplifying equipment. The currents produced by photo-voltaic cells are directly proportional to the intensity of the incident light provided the external resistance is sufficiently low.   When the external resistance exceeds a few hundred ohms, and especially when the illumination is great, large departures from linearity are observed.   The output then falls short of the low resistance values because of the shunting effect of the internal resistance of the cell which decreases with increase of illumination.   Due to the comparatively large capacity between the electrodes, these cells do not respond equally to light intensity fluctuations of different frequencies; the current is shunted more and more by the cell capacity until the output is negligible at a few thousand cycles per second.

Grondahl has shown that a thin layer of cuprous oxide on a heavy base of copper serves as a rectifier, permitting current to pass more readily from the cuprous oxide to the copper than in the reverse direction.   The unit may also be used as a self generating

* The " photronic " cells are of the selenium-iron type while the " photox " cells are of the copper cuprous-oxide photo-voltaic type.

or photo-voltaic cell, in the absence of an external battery. The incidence of light releases electrons at the boundary; the cuprous oxide becoming the positive and the copper the negative electrode. Currents are thus in the opposite direction to those in the rectifier. In curve *B* of figure 4–12 the sensitivity of such a cell is seen to be remarkably similar to that of the human eye.

4–15. X-ray Photoelectric Effects.—Inasmuch as x-rays are the same, except in frequency, as light rays, it is to be expected that they should be able to eject photo-electrons from a substance. Einstein's equation should be and is applicable. However, the frequency of an x-ray is very great, of the order of 3×10^{18} as compared with 10^{14} for light rays. Therefore, the energy in each x-ray photon is so great that the work function ϕ is negligibly small and may be omitted.   In addition, the electrons are ejected with such high velocities that the relativistic expression for their kinetic energy, given by equation 2–26, must be used.   With these changes, it is found that the photoelectric equation for x-rays is

$$h\nu = m_o c^2 \left(\frac{1}{\sqrt{1 - v^2/c^2}} - 1 \right) + W_i. \qquad (4\text{–}21)$$

Here, h is Planck's constant, ν is the frequency of the x-rays, m_o is the rest mass and v the velocity of the electron, c is the velocity of light and W_i, the energy (roughly 1 to 100 volts) required to remove electrons from the so-called K, L or M energy levels deep down inside the atoms of the material upon which the x-rays are impinging. The frequency of the x-rays can be measured by the use of crystals or gratings and the kinetic energy of the ejected electrons, the first term on the right hand side of the equation, can be measured in the following manner.   In figure 4–13, a magnetic field of strength H oersteds, perpendicular to the paper, bends the electrons in a vacuum chamber into a circular path of radius r. Then

$$Hev = mv^2/r. \qquad (2\text{–}1)$$

Also

$$m = m_o/\sqrt{1 - v^2/c^2} \qquad (2\text{–}25)$$

from which a value of v^2/c^2 may be obtained and used in equation

4–21. In this manner, values of W_i have been obtained and found to agree with those measured by other methods.

The still higher frequency gamma rays spontaneously emitted by certain radioactive substances have also been used in experiments of this type and have been found capable of ejecting photoelectrons even from the deepest (K) levels of the heaviest (uranium) atoms. Gamma rays also produce photoelectric effects in the nuclei of atoms, as will be discussed later in this book.

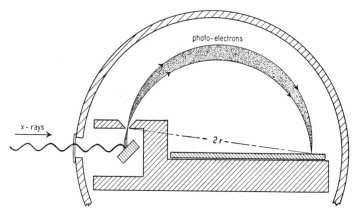

Fɪɢ. 4–13.   To measure the energy of x-ray photo-electrons.

An inverse photoelectric effect may also be observed with x-rays. When electrons from a hot filament are suddenly stopped by a metal, the anti-cathode of an x-ray tube, a continuous range of x-rays are produced with frequencies from a comparatively low value to a sharply defined upper limit ν_{max}. If V is the potential used to accelerate the thermionic electrons, then

$$h\nu_{max} = Ve. \tag{4–22}$$

This is known as the law of Duane and Hunt. The contact potential difference need not be considered except in the most precise work as it is negligibly small in comparison to values of V (tens of thousands of volts). This equation has been used to determine h/e, the ratio of Planck's constant to the charge of the electron, with great precision.[6] Thus

$$h/e = 1.379 \times 10^{-17} \text{ erg. sec./e.s.u.}$$

EXPERIMENT 4–1

A STUDY OF PHOTOELECTRIC CELLS

Purpose.—Photoelectric currents from a high vacuum and a gas filled cell are to be measured for different light intensities and applied voltages.

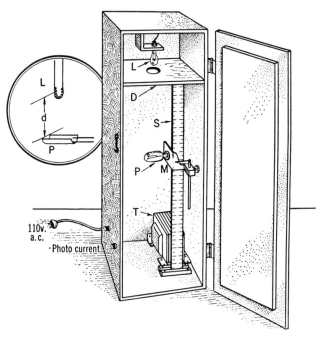

FIG. 4–14. To study photo-cells.

Apparatus.—A light source, photo-cell, scale and diaphragm are mounted in a light-tight box as shown in figure 4–14. The box may be 30 in. tall, 10 in. wide and 9 in. deep. All holes and cracks must be carefully covered and the inside painted a dull black. The light source L may consist of a 32-candlepower, 6–8 volt auto headlight, mounted at the top-center, and operated from the 110-volt line through a step-down transformer T. The diaphragm D, of three-ply plywood, is located 10 cm. below the filament of the light bulb. It contains a central hole 1 in. in diameter. These dimensions are such that the cone of light from the filament, passing through the diaphragm, does not touch the side walls—not even near the bottom of the box—yet it is sufficient to entirely cover the sensitive surface of the photo-cell P at its highest position. The socket for the photo-cell is carried on a sliding mount M on a vertical meter stick. The mount is provided with a lock screw so that it can be fixed at various positions up and down in the box. It is also provided with an adjustable index which permits establishing the scale reading at the sensitive surface of the photo-cell, as shown in detail in figure 4–14. The meter stick can be slid a short distance in horizontal grooves, top and bottom, for sideways displacement, in order to permit centering of photo-cells of different dimensions. The meter stick is cut at the top so that its zero is at the filament of the light bulb. Minor adjustment is made with the mount which holds the socket of the light bulb. Lead wires from the photo-cell socket are brought out to binding posts on the outside of the box.

Precautions.—(1) The distance from the light source to the photo-cell—d in figure 4–14—should never be less than 20 cm. (2) The voltage applied to a gas-filled cell should not exceed 80 volts. (The manufacturer's maximum is usually 90 volts. However, with a gas-filled cell, the photo-current rises very rapidly in the region between 80 and 90 volts, especially when the intensity of the light falling on the cell is great, and the danger of damaging the cell and the meter is great. If it is desired to increase the voltage to 90, it should be done with the greatest care and a resistance of not less than one megohm should be connected in series between the cell and the voltmeter. Be sure to subtract the ir drop in this protective resistor from the voltmeter reading when determining the voltage applied to the cell itself.)

Experiment.—1. Connect as shown in figure 4–14A. The rheostat and the voltmeter V should be of high resistance. The current meter i should be a sensitive milliammeter, a microammeter or a galvonometer with its shunt.

2. Using a vacuum type photo-cell, set the applied voltage at some fixed value, say 80 volts or 250 volts or at some value in between. Vary the distance of the photo-cell from the light source in steps (10 will be sufficient), recording the photo-current i and

the distance d from the source to the front plane of the sensitive
surface, as indicated in figure 4–14.

3. Using a gas-filled photo-cell and *not more than* 80 volts,
repeat (2).

4. Light intensities are inversely proportional to the square
of the distance d Plot the photo-currents i vertically and $1/d^2$
values horizontally.   If a light intensity meter is available, direct

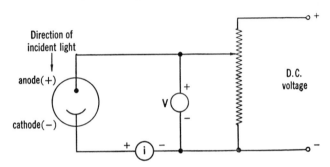

Fɪɢ. 4–14A.   Circuit for study of photo-cells.

measurements may be made and used as abscissae instead of
$1/d^2$ values.   Plot the data for the vacuum and the gas-filled cells
on the same graph and study their comparative values and shapes.

5. Set the vacuum cell at a fixed distance of 50 cm. from the
light source.   Vary the applied voltage, say in 10 steps, from 0
to 80 or 250 volts.   Record the current i and the voltage V at
each step.

6. Repeat (5) using a gas-filled tube.   The current will rise
rapidly as the voltage is raised.   Proceed with caution at voltages
above 60 and do not exceed 80 volts.   Shift to a higher range
meter (i) if necessary.

7. Plot the data of (5) and (6) on the same graph; i vertically
and V horizontally.   Compare the two curves and explain their
differences.

Additional.—The apparatus may be used for numerous experiments other than the study of the photoelectric cell itself: for
example, (1) light intensity of a lamp operated at various voltages,
(2) comparison of the output of various lamps or other sources of
light, (3) the effect of various reflectors back of or around the lamp,

and (4) measurement of the absorption of smoke or translucent screens in the path of the light rays. With alterations of the apparatus, studies may be made of the reflecting power of various substances and the angular distribution of light around a source.

EXPERIMENT 4–2

A STUDY OF A PHOTO-VOLTAIC CELL

Purpose.—To study the current output of a photo-voltaic cell at various light intensities.

Apparatus.—The apparatus of experiment 4–1 may be used.

Precaution.—Do not use a battery or external voltage source in the photo-cell circuit.

Experiment.—1. Connect as shown in figure 4–14B. It is

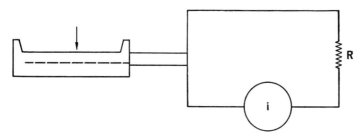

FIG. 4–14B.   Circuit for study of a photo-voltaic cell.

necessary to keep the circuit resistance approximately constant, since the output of the cell is influenced by the resistance across it. Examination of the microammeter *i* will show its resistance on the various ranges. If the resistance of the meter is not the same on all the ranges, add a dial box *R* in series and use such resistance in the box as is necessary to keep the sum of the resistances of the meter and box constant. Keep the total circuit resistance as low as possible.

2. Vary the distance of the photo-cell from the light source in, say 10 steps, recording the photo-current *i* and the distance *d* from the filament of the light source to the sensitive surface just under the cover glass of the cell. These cells have an appreciable

time lag. Do not take your readings until the current has had time to settle to a steady value. This may amount to as much as 30 seconds; longer times are required when the light on the cell is brighter. Keep cell 20 cm. or more from source at all times.

3. Plot photo-electric currents i vertically and light intensities $1/d^2$ horizontally.

4. Repeat, with an additional resistance of a few thousand ohms in series with the cell. Plot on the same graph with (3). Why is one of the lines curved?

Additional.—(1) If a light chopper (a slotted rotating disc) is available, or a fluctuating light source, plot relative response from 0 to 5000 cycles. (2) Support the cell horizontally in a thermos bottle, a few centimeters above a cooling solution. With constant light intensity and with cooling solutions such as salt in ice water, carbon dioxide snow and liquid air, determine the relative response at various temperatures. A copper-constantin thermo-junction may be used with a 0 to 5 milli-voltmeter and an ice water cold-junction to determine the temperature. Calibration data for these metals will be found in the Handbook of Chemistry and Physics or in the International Critical Tables. Use calcium chloride as a drying agent to avoid the water vapor condensed out of the air upon the cell surface at the low temperatures. The current will be found to remain approximately constant or rise a little, according to the strength of the light source (try a 5 watt clear 110 volt lamp 2 feet away) until the temperature lowers to somewhere between −70° and −140° C., when a sudden drop in the current will be observed. (3) With a light source consisting of a 100 watt lamp bulb about 4 feet away, expose the cell continuously and observe the gradual decrease of current output, i.e., the fatigue effect.

EXPERIMENT 4-3

THE SPECTRAL DISTRIBUTION CURVE OF A PHOTOELECTRIC CELL

Apparatus.—In order to secure various monochromatic beams of light whose wave-lengths are distributed over the visible spectrum, use one of the three following methods: the first is comparatively inaccurate but is cheap, the last, much better but expensive.

(1) A projection lantern with lenses removed, and having a 400 to 500 watt lamp which sends light to the photo-cell through the filters listed below.

TABLE 4–1.—SOME FILTERS FOR PHOTOELECTRIC WORK

Corning 5 × 5 cm.	Effective wave-length in angstroms
Heat transmitting ⚹ 254............................	8000
H. R. traffic red ⚹ 245 plus Aklo ⚹ 397..............	6500
Sextant green ⚹ 401 plus Aklo ⚹ 397................	5500
Signal blue ⚹ 556 plus Aklo ⚹ 397.................	4500
Red purple Corex A ⚹ 986 plus Aklo ⚹ 397.........	3500

The filters should be located, preferably, just in front of the cell housing in order to filter not only the direct light from the lamp but also any stray or scattered light. The effective wave-lengths listed in the table are only approximate, so that great accuracy should not be expected.

(2) Construct a crude monochromator, as in figure 4–15; other combinations of lenses and prisms may obviously be used; the arrangement shown reduces scattered light from the edges of the lenses, particularly those near the source. The apparatus is used in a darkened room. Use a lantern slide projector with a 400 to 500 watt lamp, with the projection lenses removed. The lenses of figure 4–15 may be very crude, such as from the five and ten cent stores. The prism P is a large, glass or carbon disulphide (CS_2) type with faces four centimeters or more on the side, the larger the better. Liquid solder has been found satisfactory in sealing the glass sides to the framework of a CS_2 prism. The slits should be about as long as the side of the prism. S_1 may have a width of 0.7 centimeter. Slits S_2 and S_3, in cardboard screens, are used to select portions of the spectrum and are curved to fit the curvature of the colored light. S_3 is used to reduce the amount of stray light which reaches the cells; it may be 2 centimeters wide. The slits are of such width as to select a spectrum band about one hundred angstroms wide, except for the blue region,

when greater widths are necessary due to the low sensitivity of the thermo-couple for these wave-lengths. One may use variable widths for S_2 of say one millimeter in the red, seven millimeters in the green and two centimeters in the blue. The average wave-length of each band is measured by means of the calibrated spectroscope W.

(3) For accurate work, one may use the more expensive commercial monochromators in order to secure a very narrow band

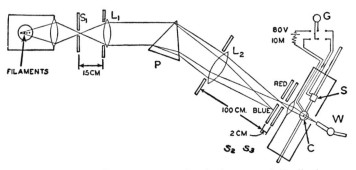

Fig. 4–15. Top view of an arrangement for plotting spectral distribution curves of photoelectric cells.

of wave-lengths, or single spectrum lines from sources such as the mercury or sodium arcs.

The photoelectric cell C and the standard S of figure 4–15 are mounted on a slide inside a black box so that either one may be shifted easily into the path of light. The standard may be either: (1) a photo-cell of different nature than the one under test (a potassium or a cesium cell, for example) which has a known spectral distribution curve (supplied by the instructor or the manufacturer), or better, (2) a thermocouple of good sensitivity operating into a galvanometer of low resistance, about 10 ohms.

Experiment.—Observe the galvanometer deflections due to the currents of the photoelectric cell C and the standard S for each of five or more wave-lengths chosen uniformly over the visible spectrum. "Galvanometer readings" should be the difference between deflections when the lamp is on and when it is turned off. Plot the ratio of the photoelectric to the thermoelectric currents as ordinates and the wave-lengths as abscissae.

If the standard is a photoelectric cell, the ratio of the current of the unknown cell to that of the standard gives their comparative responses; and this ratio, multiplied by the yield of the standard, at each wave-length, gives the yield of the cell under test. Plot the yield-wave-length curve.

EXPERIMENT 4-4

THE RATIO OF PLANCK'S CONSTANT TO THE CHARGE OF THE ELECTRON

98375

The value of h/e is to be determined from measurements of retarding potentials for light of different frequencies. See figure 4-8 and equation 4-12.

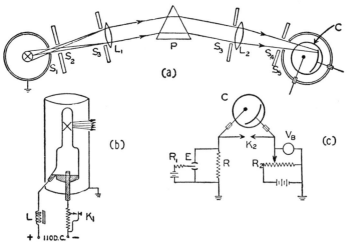

Fig. 4-16. Apparatus for the measurement of h/e.

Apparatus.—A diagram of the apparatus is shown in figure 4-16. Variations, such as the use of other spectrometer equipment, sources of light, the use of filters, etc., will occur to the student.

In the figure, the source of light, X, is a mercury arc, details of which are shown in (*b*). The bulb is of pyrex, tungsten leads are used to contact the mercury, which was distilled into the apparatus while a good oil pump (fore pump) exhausted the tube. The key K_1 shorts out part of the series resistor in order to facilitate the starting of the arc. The choke L may be used, although it is not essential, in order to steady the light by reducing fluctuations in the line voltage. If an alternating current arc is used its enclosing shield *must* be grounded.

The prism P is a large glass or CS_2 type with faces four centimeters or more on the side. Liquid solder has been found satisfactory in sealing the glass sides to the framework of a CS_2 prism.

The lenses L_1 and L_2 are cheap reading glasses of 20 to 40 centimeters focal length. L_1 has its focus at approximately $S_1 S_2$ and L_2 is arranged to give a streak of light on the edge of the sensitive surface of the photo-cell C. The width of this streak is kept constant at approximately 2 millimeters. The reason for not illuminating the entire cathode may be explained as follows: if the cathode is not concentric with the anode, differing components of the motion of the electrons from various parts of the surface will be effective, and retarding potential values will not be sharp. It is to be noted in the figure that the light does not strike the anode and produce photo-electrons at this point. The slit openings are as follows: S_2, 1 millimeter by 2.5 centimeters, S_3, one centimeter by 2.5 centimeters, S_4, 3 millimeters by 2.5 centimeters, S_5, 7 millimeters by 2.5 centimeters. Slit S_4 should be curved if the spectral lines are curved. The apparatus should be covered with black paper or cloth to cut out stray light and the experiment carried out in a dark room.

The photo-tube C may be a G–M 71AV, with the base removed. The glass is carefully cleaned with alcohol or ether and paraffined around the base. The bottom of the tube and all leads are carefully insulated; clean paraffin proving satisfactory. In (c) of figure 4–16, the electrometer, E, should have a sensitivity of 100–800 millimeters per volt; the current through the high resistance R (about 10^{10} ohms, S. S. White Dental resistor), is approximately 10^{-13} amperes, minimum. The protective resistance, R_1, may be 10,000 ohms; the needle voltage on a Dolezalek type electrometer, 180 volts. Use only direct current for the light of the electrometer: a.c. induces fluctuating currents in the electrometer circuits which are rectified by the non-linear character of the foot of the photo-current-voltage curves, and contribute false d.c. currents. Let the electrometer readings reach a steady value before recording the deflections. R_2 is a 1200 ohm slide wire rheostat; the battery across it is a bank of two or three dry cells. The voltmeter V_b (0 to 1.5 or 3 volts) should have a scale which may be read in intervals of 0.02 volt or less.

Experiment.—Adjust the electrometer and plot its calibration curve; i.e., deflections *vs.* quadrant voltages, with a fixed needle potential. Readjust the instrument if this is not a straight line over an appreciable range of the scale, say 0 to 10 centimeters. With the photo-cell in the circuit, as in figure 4–16(c) and with a fixed wave-length of incident light, record the electrometer deflections (d) for various potentials (V_b) from 0 to 3 volts which make the sensitive surface positive with respect to the collecting electrode. Repeat, using a different wave-length. Plot as in figure 4–17 and calculate h/e, using equation 4–12. Compare with the accepted value of 1.379×10^{-17} erg · sec/e.s.u.

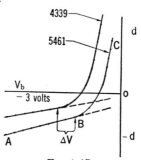

FIG. 4–17.
Retarding potential curves.

Discussion.—Unless special cells are constructed and numerous precautions taken, the retarding potential curves will appear as in figure 4–17, rather than as in figure 4–8. In the absence of light on the cell, a "dark current" occurs whose value increases linearly as the voltage across the cell is increased. The straight line AB in figure 4–17, is found to be parallel to but below the dark current line, the displacement increasing as the intensity of the incident light is increased. This may be summarized, roughly, by saying that the "leakage" current through and around the cell increases with applied voltage and decreases with light intensity. In general, the lines (AB) do not extrapolate back to the origin. The "leakage" currents are further complicated with an inverse current due to electron emission from the "anode" (which is now negative with respect to the sensitized surface). These effects probably account for the reverse currents ($-d$) observed with the commercial cell used. Together with the thermal curvature at the lower end of the photo-currents (BC), it is not to be expected that the value ΔV in figure 4–17 is a precise value for use in equation 4–12. However, with the method described, the student will obtain a value giving the correct order of magnitude of h/e and, probably, not in error by more than 10 per cent.

REFERENCES

1. E. O. Lawrence and J. W. Beams, Phys. Rev., **32**, 478 (1928).
2. W. A. Zisman, Rev. Sci. Inst., **3**, 367 (1932).
3. R. A. Millikan, *Electrons* (+ *and* −). The University of Chicago Press (1935).
4. A. L. Hughes, Rev. Mod. Phys., **8**, 294 (1936).
   F. C. Nix, Rev. Mod. Phys., **4**, 723 (1932).
5. L. O. Grondahl, Rev. Mod. Phys., **5**, 141 (1933).
6. J. Dumond and V. Bollman, Phys. Rev., **51**, 400 (1937).
   B. Lange, *Die Photoelemente*, Part I. Barth (1936).

GENERAL REFERENCES

A.—A. L. Hughes and L. A. DuBridge. *Photoelectric Phenomena.* McGraw-Hill Book Co. (1932).
B.—L. B. Linford, Rev. Mod. Phys., **5**, 34 (1933).
C.—H. Simon and R. Suhrmann, *Lichtelectrische Zellen.* Springer (1932).
D.—N. R. Campbell and D. Ritchie. *Photoelectric Cells.* Pitman & Sons (1929).
E.—V. K. Zworykin and E. D. Wilson, *Photocells*, Second Edition. Wiley & Sons (1934).
F.—J. D. Stranathan, *The Particles of Modern Physics.* The Blakiston Co. (1942).

CHAPTER 5

THERMIONIC EMISSION

5-1. Introduction.—A glass bulb containing a filament F and a metal plate P, as in figure 5-1, is evacuated to a high degree. In the process of evacuation, gases are given off continuously by the walls of the glass bulb and by the metals of the filament and plate. In order to hasten the process, each of these parts is heated as hot as possible while the pumps are in operation. The bulb is finally sealed off when the pressure has been reduced to 10^{-5} millimeter of mercury or less. There are still a large number of gas molecules left in the bulb but, when compared with the number at atmospheric pressure, there are so few that the phenomena of thermionic emission which we shall study in this chapter, will not be measurably influenced. That there are very few carriers of electricity left in the tube may be shown by increasing the plate voltage V, when the filament is cold. Many thousand of volts are needed before a current of electricity will start to flow through the tube across the vacuum.

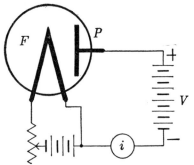

Fig. 5-1. A two-electrode vacuum tube.

In 1883, Thomas Edison found that if the filament was heated and the plate was positively charged, electricity would flow through the tube. He did not use a plate battery (V of figure 5-1) but connected the return wire from the plate, alternately to one side and then the other of the filament battery. Current was observed in the milliammeter i when the connection was made to the positive side but not when the connection was made to the negative side. When the filament was cold, no current could be observed. It is evident that electricity is given off by the filament and that it is of the negative kind, since it can only pass through the tube when the plate is positive.

The two-electrode vacuum tube, or *diode* may be used as a rectifier of alternating currents since the flow of current through it can only take place in one direction, namely, from the hot filament to the cold plate.*

5–2. The Shot Effect.—In this section we shall examine the proof that the negative electricity which leaves a hot filament in a vacuum is made up of many discrete charges rather than of an unbroken stream of electricity. Assuming this to be true for the time being, then the small electrical charges can be thought of as bombarding the positively charged plate of figure 5–1 like the small shot from a shot gun. The number of particles which reach the plate each second would be a constant when averaged over a sufficiently long period of time. This is found to be true since the milliammeter readings, i of figure 5–1, do not fluctuate. If the current could be examined during a very short time interval and with a sufficiently delicate instrument, it would be found to increase and decrease slightly around a mean value. It would further be found that the changes around the mean value take place in an irregular manner. In figure 5–2, the excesses and deficiencies above and below the mean are shown by the step-like curve. The

Fig. 5–2. Irregularities in the plate current.

---

* It is customary in electrical discussions to speak of the flow of current as from positive to negative outside the battery or generator. However, in the work on thermionics presented here, the direction of flow will be that of the moving electrons, which is from negative to positive.

changes are very small in comparison to the total current since they are due to a change of only a few particles in billions.

Since the variations in the plate current are too small and take place too frequently to be observed directly, an indirect method of proof must be used. The changes of current are used to set up oscillations in an inductance-capacitance circuit, LC of figure 5–3. A momentary increase in the charge in the condenser occurs as the plate current undergoes a slight increase. This additional quantity of electricity discharges through the inductance in the usual oscillatory manner. The oscillations thus produced occur at a frequency equal to $1/2\pi \sqrt{LC}$, the natural or resonant frequency of this circuit. In other words, the irregular changes of plate current set up oscillations in LC by "shock excitation."

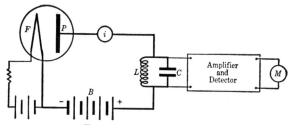

Fig. 5–3. The shot effect.

The result of the continued shock excitation of the LC circuit is that an "average" voltage is developed across the condenser C which is amplified and measured. The amount of this voltage depends on the type of emission assumed to take place from the filament. Schottky[1, 2, 3] assumed that the charged particles all carried the same charge e, and also that the probability of escape of any one of the particles into the vacuum would not be influenced by other charges. From statistical considerations, he then derived an equation for the voltage to be expected across the condenser. When solved for e, this equation is

$$e = \frac{2RC^2\overline{V^2}}{Li_s} \tag{5–1}$$

where R is the resistance in ohms of the LC and plate circuits in parallel with each other. This is largely the resistance of the coil and the tube in parallel with each other. C is the capacity of the condenser in farads, L is the inductance of the coil in henries and $\overline{V^2}$ is the average of the squared voltages across C. The latter is deduced from the gain of the amplifier and the reading of the meter M. The reading of the plate milliammeter, i_s amperes, carries the subscript s to denote an important condition in the experimental procedure, namely, that the voltage of the battery B shall be sufficiently high (several hundred volts) that all electrons emitted by the filament shall be drawn over to the plate; no " space charge" is left in the vacuum.

Hull and Williams[4] measured the charge e, using equation 5–1.* They found the value

$$e = 1.586 \times 10^{-19} \text{ coulombs} \quad \text{or}$$

$$= 4.758 \times 10^{-10} \text{ e.s.u.}$$

which is within a fraction of one per cent of the accepted value for the charge of the electron. The voltage developed across the condenser would have been equal to zero if the electricity had been emitted by the filament in a steady stream and would have been 1.4 times as large as that which was observed had each of the charges leaving the filament been twice that of an electron. These extremes of voltage are well beyond the experimental errors. In the light of this work and the e/m experiments, we see that *electrons* are emitted by a hot filament in a vacuum.

A noise[5] will be heard in a loud speaker used in place of the meter M of figure 5–3, due to the shot effect. If a space charge exists between the filament and plate, due to too low a voltage at B, as is usual in amplifiers, the *shot noise* is lessened. In addition to the shot effect, there are a number of other causes for amplifier noises. It is assumed, of course, that the disturbances due to poor connections, batteries, resistors, etc., have been eliminated. Among these additional noises may be mentioned the erratic changes in plate current resulting from the evaporation of the filament material itself, called the *flicker effect*, and from the emission of secondary electrons and positively charged particles.

* In this work, they developed the screen grid tube which has become so useful in modern radio sets. They did so in order to obtain high amplification at radio frequencies, since the resonant frequency of the LC circuit was in the broadcast range. In one case, 750 kilocycles or 400 meters wave-length was used.

The latter noises are usually more pronounced for audio than for radio frequency amplifiers. Finally, there exists a *thermal noise* which will be discussed in the next section and which is of the order of one-third that of the shot effect if there is no space charge. Under the usual operating condition of an amplifier, a space charge does exist, in which case the thermal noise is considerably greater than the shot noise.

5-3. Free Electrons in a Metal.—In a given sample of metal there are small crystals of microscopic size, arranged sometimes in a haphazard fashion and sometimes in a regular manner, according to the treatment which the metal has received. Frequently there are impurities in the spaces between the crystals. Each of the crystals contains atoms arranged in various geometrical configurations or "space lattices," as revealed by x-ray crystal analysis methods. The atoms are bound in essentially fixed positions and contain within themselves electrons which are in rapid motion. It is assumed that some of the electrons are able to escape from their atoms and move about with more or less freedom inside the metal. The metal, as a whole, remains neutral since the negative charge of the free electrons is counterbalanced by the positive charge of the atoms from which they have escaped. The number of free electrons depends on the ease with which they may escape from the atoms. Thus, in insulators there are but few of these charged carriers, whereas in metals there is one electron per atom, perhaps even more, free or nearly free to move about.

A free electron in a metal may travel a distance of several hundred atoms before "colliding" with other particles. It then changes its velocity and direction. Thus the free electrons are in a continuous state of thermal agitation, moving in tortuous paths and entering and leaving atoms. Statistically, a condition of thermodynamic equilibrium results between the moving free electrons and the atoms. At a given instant there are slow and fast electrons, with all gradations between.

The application of an electromotive force between the ends of a wire superimposes a drift motion on the thermal movements of the free electrons. We may use the following analogy to make clear the phenomena of metallic conduction. A stream of water is allowed to fall into one side of a bowl full of water. Almost instantly, water spills out at the opposite side even though the individual water particles in the bowl have moved but little and at a comparatively low velocity. As water continues to pour in from one side, the discharge continues from the other side until finally some of the water particles have actually travelled across the bowl. In a straight wire, the effect of the application of an electromotive force is propagated with the velocity of light, or just a little less, even though the drift motion of the free electrons is only a few centimeters per second. Conceivably, a free electron at one end of the wire might eventually reach the other end.

The concept of free electrons in a metal has been used to explain the transfer of heat from one point to another. The Wiedemann-Franz law states that the ratio of thermal conductivity K to electrical conductivity ρ is a constant at a given temperature. Thus,

$$K/\rho = (\pi^2 k^2/3e^2)T, \qquad (5\text{--}2)$$

where k is Boltzmann's constant, e is the electronic charge and T is the absolute temperature of the wire. In other words, a substance which is a good conductor of electricity is also a good conductor of heat.

The idea that there are free electrons in a solid has also been used in the interpretation of the small values of the specific heats of metals at low temperature, in studies of the reflection of light from metals, in the emission of photo-electrons, as in the preceding chapter, and in the phenomena of thermionic emission in this chapter.

On the average, over comparatively long time intervals, there is uniformity of the thermal movements of the free electrons. Considered during a very short time interval, however, there are regions of greater or less density than the average. The movements of "clouds" of free electrons of slightly greater or less charge density than the average results in exceedingly small, temporary potential differences between two points, the ends, say, of a wire. These varying potentials may be used to charge a condenser, which in turn discharges through an inductance in an oscillatory manner, as in the "shot effect." Johnson [6] has detected these thermal effects by connecting a coil and condenser in the grid circuit of a three electrode tube, followed by a high gain amplifier and a meter. The *thermal noise* heard in the loud speaker of a high gain amplifier of the usual type, which originated in the movements of the free electrons in the grid circuit of the first tube, sets a lower limit to the possible signal-to-noise ratio. This noise has been found to be proportional to the resistance of the grid circuit and to the width of the frequency band which is to be amplified.

As stated before, some of the free electrons in a metal are travelling faster than others. Consider, first, only a portion of these electrons, those which have velocities in an exceedingly small velocity range dv. Next, compare the number of electrons in one velocity range with the number in other ranges. Sommerfeld [7, 8, 9] has shown that a distribution law discovered by Fermi and Dirac must be used to express these numbers when dealing with an *electron gas* in a metal. The form of this law differs

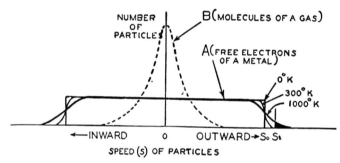

FIG. 5-4. The distribution laws of, A, Fermi Dirac and, B, Maxwell.

markedly from the Maxwellian distribution law used in the Kinetic Theory for the atoms or molecules of a gas. It has proved successful in several fields of work with metals where the Maxwellian law has failed. In photoelectric and thermionic emission effects, the components of velocities perpendicular to the surface of the metal are of chief importance rather than the total velocities. In curve A of figure 5–4, the ordinates are the number of free electrons having a normal velocity component in a range ds and the abscissae are the corresponding speeds s for which these numbers are counted. Curve B shows a Maxwellian distribution curve for gas molecules. In this figure, abscissae to the right of O are velocity components for particles approaching the surface and those to the left of O are for particles receding from the surface.

In the case of the Fermi-Dirac law, A of figure 5-4, the number of free electrons with normal velocity components in the range ds is constant for the different speeds s from zero to a sharp maximum s_0 when the metal is at zero degrees absolute. The effect of heating the metal is to speed up a comparatively small number of the electrons, as shown by the curves for 300 and 1000 degrees absolute. It is only the faster electrons, the shaded area above s_t, which are given out in photoelectric and thermionic emission.

5-4. Richardson's Equation.[7,8,9]—Let the potential of the plate of a diode be sufficiently great to draw over to it all electrons emitted by the filament, even at the maximum operating temperature. Then the current of electricity i_s which passes from the hot filament to the cold plate is equal to the product of the number of electrons emitted each second and the charge on each. The number of electrons which can escape from the metal at room temperatures is too small to be measured since the kinetic energy even of the faster ones inside the metal is less than the critical amount required to overcome the surface forces. Thus, at room temperatures, the velocities of the free electrons are all less than the value s_t of figure 5-4. As in the photoelectric effect, the work to remove an electron from the metal is expressed by the symbol ϕ and is equal to the difference between the barrier energy $\mathscr{E}_p$ of the surface and the inner energy $\mathscr{E}_m$ of the fastest electrons at zero degrees absolute. $\mathscr{E}_m$ is the kinetic energy corresponding to the velocity s_0 in figure 5-4.

When the filament is raised to higher temperatures, some of the electrons acquire kinetic energies greater, by an amount ϕ, than their low temperature values and are able to escape. The hotter the metal, the greater the number of electrons with velocities perpendicular to the surface in excess of this critical value. The Fermi-Dirac distribution law is a quantitative statement of the number which have certain velocities in the metal and hence may be used to predict the number which will succeed in escaping through the surface at a given temperature. It has been used to derive the following, slightly modified form of Richardson's equation.

$$i_s = AT^2 \epsilon^{-\phi/kT}. \tag{5-3}$$

Here, i_s is the saturation current in amperes per square centimeter of the filament surface, A is a constant for a given filament, ϵ is the base of the Naperian system of logarithms ($= 2.718\ldots$), T is the absolute temperature of the filament ($= 273 + °$ C.), ϕ is the work function of the filament metal in ergs per electron and k is Boltzmann's constant ($= R/N = 8.315 \times 10^7/6.064 \times 10^{23} = 1.371 \times 10^{-16}$ ergs per degree).

The exponential form of equation 5-3 has been tested and found to be correct over an exceedingly wide range of temperatures. It is shown graphically in figure 5-5 by the heavy line OA. In case the plate voltage is not sufficiently great to withdraw all emitted electrons from the vicinity of the filament, curves OV result. These space charge limited currents will be discussed in the next chapter. Richardson's equation deals only with the total or emission current to the plate.

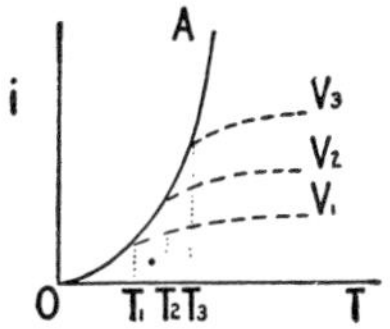

Richardson was the first to derive this law. He considered the free electrons in the

FIG. 5-5. Plate current vs. filament temperature.

metal to be sufficiently separated from each other and sufficiently small that they could be treated as though they formed a perfect gas. The well known kinetic theory laws for a perfect gas passing through a constraining boundary surface into a complete vacuum were used. The Fermi-Dirac distribution law had not been discovered at this time and Richardson assumed that the customary Maxwellian law for gas molecules was applicable to the electron gas. The difference between the equations resulting from the two laws lies in the interpretation of the constants A and ϕ. We have already seen in the photoelectric chapter that ϕ is not the total potential barrier at the surface, as Richardson thought, but the difference between this and the inner energy of the electrons. The use of the Fermi-Dirac law leads to the relation

$$A = 2(2\pi emk^2/h^3)(1 - R) \qquad (5\text{--}4)$$

where e and m are the charge and mass of the electron and h is Planck's constant (6.55×10^{-27} erg seconds). The value of the reflection factor R for pure outgassed metals is approximately equal to $\frac{1}{2}$. Then $A = 60.2$ amperes per square centimeter per degrees squared, in agreement with experimental values. For other filaments, certain complications enter and further work is needed to interpret the experimental values of A. It is to be remembered, however, that A, as well as ϕ, is a constant for a given surface.

In his first derivation, Richardson assumed that the number of free electrons per cubic centimeter inside the metal was independent of the temperature and obtained an equation containing $\sqrt{T}$ instead of T^2. This is a question as to the number of "free" electrons per atom in the metal, i.e., of the binding forces between the semi-free electrons and the atoms. Later, Richardson assumed that the number of free electrons increased as the three-halves power of the absolute temperature and arrived at the T^2 form of the equation. Dushman also derived the T^2 form from thermodynamic rather than kinetic theory considerations. However, the effect of T in the exponent of equation 5–3 so greatly overshadows the effect of $\sqrt{T}$ or T^2 in determining the value of i_s that it has not yet been found possible to determine experimentally which is correct. In testing Richardson's equation (experiment 5–1) the student may verify this for himself. In view of the successes of the Fermi-Dirac law (which gives T^2), the Dushman form with T^2 is preferred.

5–5.   Testing Richardson's Equation.—By taking logarithms of both sides of equation 5–3, we get

$$\log_\epsilon i_s = \log_\epsilon A + \log_\epsilon T^2 - \phi/kT. \qquad (5\text{–}5)$$

Changing to common logarithms and rearranging, gives

$$\log_{10} \frac{i_s}{T^2} = \log_{10} A + \left(-\frac{0.4343\phi}{k}\right)\frac{1}{T}. \qquad (5\text{–}6)$$

$$\underbrace{\phantom{\log_{10}\frac{i_s}{T^2}}}_{y} \;=\; \underbrace{\phantom{\log_{10}A}}_{b} \;+\; \underbrace{\phantom{-\frac{0.4343\phi}{k}}}_{m}\;\underbrace{\phantom{\frac{1}{T}}}_{x} \qquad (5\text{–}7)$$

Here, i_s may be measured with a milliammeter and T with an optical pyrometer, (see experiment 5–1). The left hand side of equation 5–6 is plotted on the vertical axis while $1/T$ is plotted on the horizontal, as in figure 5–6. If the exponential form of Richardson's equation is correct, this will be a straight line corresponding to the linear equation 5–7. Here, b is the y-intercept and m is the slope of the line. The value of A may then be obtained from the y-intercept ($b = log_{10}A$), provided the current i_s is expressed in amperes per square centimeter of surface of the filament. On the other hand, it is not necessary to know the area of the filament in order to prove that Richardson's equation is of the correct form; or to determine the value of the work function ϕ. The negative slope of the straight line in figure 5-6 is equal to $\Delta y/\Delta x$ and involves the difference Δy between two values of $\log_{10}(i_s/T^2)$. Then the area of the filament drops out and observed currents for the particular filament under test may be used. When ϕ is in ergs per electron ($\equiv\phi_1$, of chapter 4), the slope m is equal to $0.4343\phi_1/k$. Changing to volts per e.s.u., by the use of equation 4-14, we find

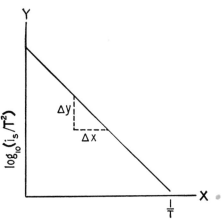

FIG. 5-6.   Testing Richardson's equation.

$$\phi_3 = \frac{slope}{5040} \text{ volts/e.s.u.} \qquad (5\text{-}8)$$

Values of ϕ for various materials will be found in Table 1. The smaller the value of ϕ, the more copious the emission of electrons, other conditions being the same. In general, the work function is smaller for those substances whose atoms are large. Additional discussion of the work function will be found in the preceding chapter on the photoelectric effect.

5-6. **Various Filaments.**[10, 11]—A tungsten wire which contains a trace of thorium is first heated to about 2800° K. Metallic thorium, from its oxide in the metal, diffuses to the surface and slowly evaporates. After this "flashing," the temperature is lowered until the rate of diffusion of the thorium to the surface, along the grain boundaries inside of the tungsten, and the rate of evaporation from its surface are such as to leave a layer of thorium approximately one atom thick over the surface. This occurs somewhere between 2000° K and 2200° K. In practice, these *thoriated* *filaments* are usually operated near the temperature, 1900° K, at which temperature the diffusion is so slow that only patches of the surface are covered with thorium. The advantage of thoriated over pure tungsten filaments is that the work function is lowered from 4.52 to about 2.6 volts.

Wehnelt found that a drop of sealing wax on a platinum filament increased the electron emitting power, so that larger emission currents could be obtained even when operating at lower temperatures, with attendant increase in life. There are, today, a number of similar *coated filaments* which have low work functions. For example, a mixture of three parts of barium carbonate ($BaCO_3$) and two parts of strontium carbonate ($SrCO_3$), formed into sticks with a binder such as beeswax or paraffin, may be used. This is rubbed on a warm (100–200° C.) platinum filament and "flashed" in air, at or near 1000° C. It is then sealed into the tube and the evacuation process carried out. These are of the so-called *combined type* of coated filaments, since, probably, a layer of barium and strontium platinides exists under a monatomic layer of barium and strontium atoms. In the *uncombined type*, a fifty-fifty mixture of the carbonates, supported by cellulose nitrate, is sprayed at 100–200° C. onto a supporting metal; or one may dip the metal into the coating mixture. The "flashing" is not carried out until the filament is sealed into the tube and the evacuation well under way. The barium and strontium oxides do not then combine to form compounds with the platinum or other supporting metal. It is probable that a layer of their oxides is formed. These are referred to as " oxide " coated filaments. Since there is no chemical combination with the supporting material, this base metal may consist of platinum, nickel, or alloys such as konel metal or platinum-nickel mixtures. The base metal is chosen to have the desired tensile strength and electrical resistance at the operating temperature rather than for its electron emitting ability. Cesium has also been used on metal surfaces in order to lower the work function.

As a rough indication of the improved efficiency of these "dull emitter" filaments over the pure metals, it may be stated that a square centimeter of tungsten filament operated at 2370° K. will give 3 milliamperes of electron current per watt of heating energy, a thoriated filament at 1900° K. will give about 100 milliamperes per watt, a combined filament at 1200° K. will give 18 and an uncombined filament at 1100° K. will give 30 milliamperes output per watt input. It is to be understood that these are only approximate figures and that other factors such as life and durability of the coating must be considered in choosing a filament.

5-7. Field Emission.—If the voltage on the plate of a two-electrode vacuum tube or diode is very great, the current which passes through the tube will be found to be noticeably greater than that given by Richardson's equation. The electric field between the plate and the filament adds to the number of electrons which can escape from the filament at a given temperature. This so-called *field emission* is very small at the usual voltages used with ordinary vacuum tubes but may become greater than the thermionic emission when high field intensities are used. According to the theory developed by Schottky,[12] there are two forces acting simultaneously on an electron as it attempts to escape from the metal. First, there is an opposing force set up as an electron rises above the surface which is due to an equal but oppositely charged "image" electron induced in the metal and second, there is an attracting force due to the electrostatic field of the plate potential. Electrons which escape must have sufficient energy that, aided by the attracting force, they can overcome the opposing force. From these considerations Schottky derived the following equation for the total current, I (amperes per square centimeter),

$$I = i_s \epsilon^{4.389\sqrt{E}/T},\qquad(5\text{--}9)$$

where i_s is the saturation current given by Richardson's equation (5–3), T is the temperature of the filament in degrees absolute and E is the field intensity in volts per centimeter. In absolute units, $4.389 = e^{3/2}/k$. For a diode consisting of a cylindrical anode of one centimeter diameter, at a potential of 43.5 volts and with a tungsten filament whose diameter is 0.01 centimeter, at a temperature of 2000° K., the field intensity close to the filament would be 1890 volts per centimeter and the total current would be ten per cent greater than that due to temperature emission alone. If the field intensity were increased one hundred fold, the total current would be 8000 times greater. In other words, *the Schottky effect* becomes increasingly important and greatly overshadows the thermionic effect when extremely high field intensities are used.

The Schottky equation (5–9) has been tested experimentally over a wide range and found to be satisfactory for clean metals but not for thoriated or coated filaments.

When an external field is applied, the picture of the electrons in a metal, held in by a potential barrier, is modified as in figure 5–7A. As soon as an electron gets past the potential barrier at the surface, the field pulls the electron away from the metal. In this case, the modern quantum-mechanics has demonstrated the

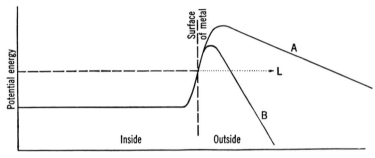

Fig. 5–7A. Potential energy distribution at surface of metal when external field is applied. *A* is case for weak field, *B* is case for strong field. Slope of line at right is field-strength. Dotted line *L* shows possibility of " leak " of electron out through barrier, which occurs in case of " field emission " at high fields.

probability (which can be calculated) that, without needing to go " over the top " of the barrier, the electron may actually penetrate through it. The probability that the electron will " leak through " is a sensitive function of the thickness of the barrier, i.e., depends on the strength of the field. Figure 5–7A shows the situation, diagrammatically, for two different field-strengths. Thus, quantum-mechanics justifies by theory the experimental fact that high fields do pull electrons out of metals, and, moveover, makes possible the computation of the magnitude of the effect in individual cases. Field emission can occur at low temperatures if the field is high enough, and is sometimes called " cold electron emission." This type of emission is particularly troublesome in the design of high-voltage equipment such as Van de Graaff machines, where it is overcome by potential-distributing rings   It is also sometimes observed at the tips of lightning rods during thunderstorms.

EXPERIMENT 5–1

TEST OF RICHARDSON'S EQUATION

Three things are to be done: (1) Establish saturation of the plate current in the particular two-electrode high-vacuum tube used, i.e., find the plate voltage which is sufficiently great to draw to the plate all electrons emitted by the filament at its highest temperature; (2) measure these saturation currents i_s; (3) Measure the temperature T of the filament at each point where i_s is determined.

First, connect the circuit. Have it checked by the instructor and then apply the voltages. Start with the maximum voltage E_f (or current I_f) on the filament which you are to use (see details below) and zero plate voltage. Take data and plot a curve of the plate current (I_b, plot vertically) against plate voltage (E_b, plot horizontally), continuing until the curve is essentially horizontal, i.e., until the saturation current i_s has been reached. It is impossible to obtain completely saturated plate currents, even with pure tungsten filaments, because of the field emission. Find the value of E_b where I_b seems to remain fairly constant.

Second, hold E_b at the value just found. Record i_s and measure the temperature of the filament (details below). Decrease E_f (or I_f) to a new value and record the value of i_s and T. Repeat for 10–20 points.

The temperature of the filament may be measured with an optical pyrometer. This consists of a calibrated lamp in the eyepiece of a telescope and is adjusted so that the standard filament and that of the two-electrode tube are in focus at the same time. The current through the standard is varied until the two intensities are the same, and its value recorded. The calibration chart gives the temperature in terms of this current.* Since it is true that the filament is always cooler near the supports, the calibration is usually made at the center of the wire. This same point must be used in determining an unknown temperature. For measuring the higher temperatures, a more accurate comparison is possible if a green or a red glass is used over the eyepiece of the

* This calibration was determined by matching the filament intensity with that of various metals raised to melting point in a vacuum. The melting points of different substances will be found in published tables of physical constants.

pyrometer, provided, of course, that the calibration has been made under these conditions. For very high temperatures, a rotating sector may be used in front of the pyrometer. A calibration chart, made with this in operation, does not depend appreciably on the speed of the shutter provided it exceeds some sixteen times a second. It does depend on the relative areas of the shutter and open space. If the glass walls of the two-electrode tube are darkened by some deposit, correct values for the temperature of the filament will not be obtained but the test of the form of Richardson's equation will not be invalidated.

If an optical pyrometer is not available, the temperature of a pure tungsten filament may be determined in terms of its resistance. It can be shown[13] that, in this case

$$R/R_0 = (T/T_0)^{1.2}, \tag{5-10}$$

where R is the resistance of the filament at the temperature T and R_0 is the resistance at zero degrees centigrade ($T_0 = 273$). It has been found sufficiently accurate to measure R_0 at room temperature ($T_0 = 273 + °$ C.) by means of a Wheatstone bridge. The current used to operate the bridge will heat the filament appreciably unless a high resistance is used in series with a single dry cell and the current is only flashed through the filament for a brief instant while obtaining the balance. It is possible, if greater accuracy is desired, to measure R_0 with various observed bridge currents and extrapolate back to zero current. The high temperature resistance R may be measured by means of an ammeter in series and a voltmeter in parallel with the filament. Ohm's law is then used to give R.

Using an FP85 tube.—The circuit is shown in figure 5–8.

Procedure.—1. With $E_f = 6$ volts, get data and plot I_b vs. E_b from $E_b = $ zero to full saturation.

2. Keep E_b constant where saturation exists. Determine i_s vs. T by varying E_f from 4 to 6 volts only. Take 10 points with i_s varying from 0–1 ma, and 10 more points above 1 ma. The filament temperature can be determined by measuring the filament watts ($= I_f E_f$) and using the table in figure 5–8.

3. Plot i_s vs. T. Also plot on semi-log paper, i_s/T^2 vs. $10^4/T$ and note whether a straight line results. If so, you have established that the exponential form of Richardson's equation is correct.

4. Compute the work function from the slope of the last plot and

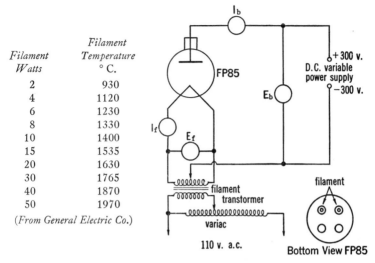

Filament Watts	Filament Temperature ° C.
2	930
4	1120
6	1230
8	1330
10	1400
15	1535
20	1630
30	1765
40	1870
50	1970

(*From General Electric Co.*)

FIG. 5-8. Test of Richardson's equation using an FP85 tube. Filament: tungsten. Rated filament voltage: 10 volts. Rated filament current: 5 amps. Filament diameter: 0.0085″. Lighted length of filament wire: 3.937″ = 10.00 cm.

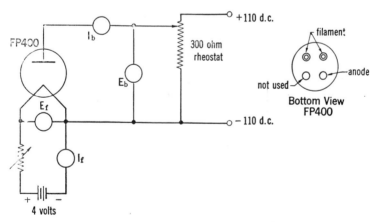

FIG. 5-9. Test of Richardson's equation using an FP400 tube. Do not pass more than 2.25 amperes through the filament. Filament and anode dimensions are held to close tolerances and the electrodes are carefully aligned. Dimensions are supplied with the tube by the manufacturer (G. E. Co.).

equation 5-8. Also compute A. Compare with accepted values.
Using an FP400 tube.—The circuit is shown in figure 5-9.
Experiment.—Data for $I_b E_b$ curves are to be taken with $E_f =$

4.0, 3.75, 3.5, 3.25 and 3.0 volts. (E_b from 0 to 110 volts, and I_b *never over 25 ma.*) Simultaneously, record values of I_f at all points. Plot the five curves on the same graph. Measure the room-temperature resistance R of the filament with a Wheatstone bridge and compute the five values of the filament temperature T using equation 5–10. Plot the i_s—T or Richardson equation. Also plot on semi-log paper i_s/T^2 vs. $1/T$ and note whether a straight line results. If so, you have established that the exponential form given by Richardson is correct. One may also compute the work function ϕ from the slope of the last plot and the application of equation 5–8. The y intercept of the plot also permits calculation of A. Compare with accepted values.

Using an 01A Tube.—An *01A triode* may be used, with grid and plate connected together. The cathode is of the thoriated tungsten type, in which case the exponent of equation 5–10 varies, usually from 1.1 to 1.3, for different tubes. Whatever its value, provided it remain constant, the logarithmic test (figure 5–6) of Richardson's equation should yield a straight line. To insure saturation, let $E_p = 200$ or more volts and vary the filament voltage from, say 2 to not more than 3.7 volts. A convenient plate current meter reads 0–5 or 0–10 milliamperes.

REFERENCES

1. W. Schottky, Ann. d. Physik., **57**, 541 (1918).
2. T. C. Fry, Jr. Frank. Inst., **199**, 216 (1925). A rigorous derivation.
3. R. Fürth, Phys. Zeit, **23**, 354 (1922). A simplified derivation.
4. A. W. Hull and N. H. Williams, Phys. Rev., **25**, 147 (1925).
5. G. S. Pearson, Bell System Tech. Jr., **13**, 634 (1934), or Physics, **5**, 233 (1934). Amplifier Noises.
6. J. B. Johnson, Phys. Rev., **32**, 97 (1928), and reference 5.
7. A. Sommerfeld, Naturwiss., **21**, 374 (1928).
8. S. Dushman, Rev. Mod. Phys., **2**, 381 (1930).
9. K. K. Darrow, Rev. Mod. Phys., **1**, 90 (1929).
10. L. R. Koller, *The Physics of Electron Tubes.* McGraw-Hill Book Co. (1934). Also Reference 8.
11. H. A. Jones and I. Langmuir, Gen. Elec. Rev., **30**, 310, 354, 408 (1927).
12. W. Shottky, Zeits. f. Physik, **14**, 63 (1923).
13. Worthing and Forsythe, Phys. Rev., **18**, 145 (1921).

GENERAL REFERENCE

A.—E. L. Chaffee, *Theory of Thermionic Vacuum Tubes.* McGraw-Hill Book Co. (1933).

CHAPTER 6

HIGH VACUUM, LOW-VOLTAGE TUBES

6-1. Space Charges.—If the voltage on the plate of a diode is comparatively small, the observed current will be less than that given by Richardson's equation, as indicated by the dotted portion of the curve OV_1 in figure 5–5. This is due to the repellent action of electrons in the region between the filament and plate on the outcoming electrons. The electrons in transit, repel other electrons which are behind them and may even drive them back into the filament. Thus a cloud of electrons forms in the space between the filament and plate, with greater charge density near the filament. Although electrons are continually entering and leaving this *space charge*, its density at a given point remains essentially constant if the voltage and temperature remain constant. The space charge limits the flow of electrons to the plate and is analogous to the vapor accumulated above a liquid in an enclosed vessel. If a higher plate voltage is used, say V_2 in figure 5–5, a higher filament temperature T_2 is required before the space charge effect becomes prominent, as in curve OV_2.

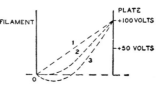

FIG. 6–1. Potential gradients in a diode with *plane* electrodes.

The potential gradient between the filament and the plate is no longer linear when a space charge exists in this region. In figure 6–1, it is assumed that the filament is at zero potential and the plate +100 volts. For a cold filament, the potential drop per centimeter between the filament and the plate across the vacuum is constant as in curve 1; the mid point, for example having a potential of 50 volts. But when the filament is sufficiently hot and a space charge is present, curves of the form of 2 and 3 result. Then the potential gradient is greater near the plate; it may be zero for some distance out from the filament, as in 2, or even nega-

121

tive as in 3. In the latter case, electrons are able to escape from
the filament only because of their initial velocities of emission.

The phenomena due to space charges may be shown in another
fashion, as in the next section.

6–2. **Plate Control of the Space Charge.**—Let the temperature
of the filament of a diode be held constant and the voltage on its
plate be increased. The space-charge-limited current will then
increase and eventually equal the emis-
sion value i_s given by Richardson's
equation. As shown in figure 6–2, the
current does not increase linearly with
voltage, as in the case of Ohm's law for
metallic conduction. Child and Langmuir [1] have deduced from theoretical
considerations that the voltage must
be raised to the three-halves power.
Thus,

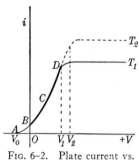

FIG. 6–2. Plate current vs.
plate voltage.

$$i = BV^{\frac{3}{2}} \qquad (6\text{–}1)$$

where B is a constant which includes the square root of the charge-
to-mass ratio of the electron.

It is to be noted that a small current passes to the plate when
it is slightly negative. This is due to the fact that the electrons
have a small initial velocity as they leave the filament, sufficient
to carry them to the plate against a few volts retarding potential,
and to the contact potential difference which exists between the
metals of the filament and plate. The shape of the curve AB may
be deduced from the Maxwellian law. It will appear as a straight
line if logarithms of the current are plotted against voltages.

The second part of the curve, C, is given by the three-halves
power law, where a space charge limits the current. In order to
test this, take logarithms (to either the base ϵ or the base 10) of
both sides of equation 6–1. Then

$$\log i = \log B + \tfrac{3}{2} \log V. \qquad (6\text{–}2)$$

This is the equation of a straight line when values of $\log i$ are used
as ordinates and values of $\log V$ as abscissae. As in figure 6–3,
$\log B$ is the y intercept and 3/2, the slope.

In the experimental work of testing the three-halves power law, values of V should be taken as those of the voltmeter plus the voltage OV_o of figure 6–2 (about 1.5 volts). For the smaller voltages, near the lower end of the line in figure 6–3, variations from linearity may occur due to the choice of a slightly incorrect value of V_o. The cooling effect of the heavy lead-in wires of the filament may also alter the emission sufficiently so that the line is not straight near the lower end. For higher voltages near the upper end, the line will curve over, approaching the horizontal as saturation sets in. It is only in the middle that the line will be straight in practice. Further, if a diode is used which has a directly heated rather than an indirectly heated filament, there will be an IR drop along its length. The electrons from one end of the filament will then be acted upon by a higher potential than those from the other end. In this case one may use the voltmeter reading from the plate to the center of the filament as an "average." If the potential drop in the filament is comparable to the plate voltage, the slope of the line will be found to be somewhere between $3/2$ and $5/2$. It is,

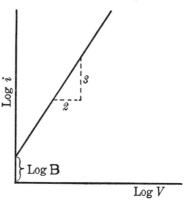

Fig. 6–3. Testing the "three-halves power" law.

therefore, preferable in this test to use a uni-potential cathode (indirectly heated).

To sum up, the current-voltage relation of a diode is a combination of four distinct phenomena; first, the current due to the initial velocities, which is usually small; second, the space current which is limited by space charges and follows the $3/2$ power law, third, the emission current where all emitted electrons pass to the plate, as given by Richardson's equation and finally, the field emission currents which prevent the realization of complete saturation and are given by the Schottky equation (the line DT_1 of figure 6–2 is not strictly horizontal but rises slowly to the right).

6–3. Grid Control of the Space Charge.—A more effective method than plate voltage variation for the control of the space

charge was discovered by Lee de Forest [2] in 1907. He introduced
into the tube a third electrode which consisted of a grid of wires
located between the filament and the plate, as at G in figure 6–4.
This three-electrode vacuum tube is referred to as a *triode*.   A posi-

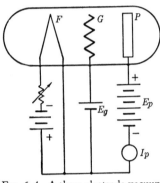

tive potential on the grid, with
respect to the filament, serves to
reduce the space charge and increase the plate current. On the
other hand, a negative grid adds
its effect to that of the space charge
and reduces the plate current.

That the grid is more effective
in controlling the plate current than
is the plate, appears reasonable since
the grid is placed directly in the
region of the space charge. It has
been found that in a given tube, for
example, the plate voltage had to

FIG. 6–4. A three-electrode vacuum
tube.

be changed by ten volts in order to produce the same change in
plate current as could be accomplished by a change of only one
volt of the potential on the grid.

The variation of plate current I_p with grid voltage E_g is shown

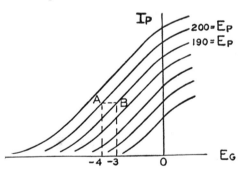

FIG. 6–5.   Characteristic curves of a triode.   Plate current vs. grid voltage.

for different plate voltages E_p in the family of *characteristic curves*
of figure 6–5. As indicated by the horizontal line between A and
B, a change of ten volts on the plate may be counteracted by a
change of only one volt on the grid. The ratio of these voltage

changes (10 to 1) is known as the amplification constant of the tube.

6-4. The Voltage Amplification Constant μ.—The voltage amplification constant or magnification factor μ of a vacuum tube is the ratio of the change of plate voltage ΔE_p to the change in grid voltage ΔE_g for zero change in the plate current, $(\Delta I_p = 0)$. Thus, in absolute value

$$\mu = \frac{\Delta E_p}{\Delta E_g}, (I_p = \text{constant}). \tag{6-3}$$

The amplification constant ranges from 1 to 100 for the various commercial triodes. From equation 6-3 it is seen that a voltage ΔE_g applied to the grid may be replaced by an equivalent change of $\mu \cdot \Delta E_g$ volts in the plate battery.

The amplification constant may be obtained from characteristic curves, as in the preceding section, or it may be measured directly by means of the Miller[3] balance method of figure 6-6. An

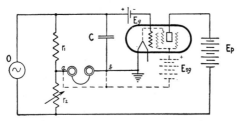

Fig. 6-6. Measurement of the voltage amplification constant μ.

alternating voltage, developed across the resistance r_1, is applied to the grid and causes a change in the plate current whose effect in the phones is neutralized by means of the voltage developed across the resistance r_2. The voltages of the grid, filament and plate are first adjusted to their normal operating values. The 1000 cycle oscillator O is then turned on and sends a current $I \sin \omega t$ through r_1 and r_2. The voltage drop thus created across r_1 is $Ir_1 \sin \omega t$. This is superimposed on the fixed grid voltage E_g (the "C" bias), causing a change in the plate current as indicated by the 1000 cycle note heard in the phones. The change of grid voltage is the equivalent of a change of $\mu Ir_1 \sin \omega t$ volts in the potential of the "B" battery E_p and may be counterbalanced by the voltage drop

$Ir_2 \sin \omega t$ occurring across r_2.   A small compensation for the grid-plate capacity of the triode is made by means of the condenser C. After adjusting r_2 and C until there is no sound in the phones,

$$\mu Ir_1 \sin \omega t = Ir_2 \sin \omega t, \qquad (6\text{--}4)$$

$$\mu = r_2/r_1. \qquad (6\text{--}5)$$

Values of μ will be found to be essentially constant for a given tube over considerable ranges of grid, filament and plate voltages.

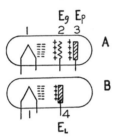

FIG. 6–7.   A diode B equivalent to a triode A.

It is convenient to imagine a triode replaced by an *equivalent diode*. The combined effect of the plate and grid charges upon the space charge is to be replaced by that of a single anode.   Thus, in figure 6–7, A represents the triode and B its equivalent diode.   The plate (4) of the diode is to have a suitable potential E_l such as will replace the total effects of the grid potential E_g and the plate potential E_p of the triode. We may consider the electrodes as the plates of condensers.   The charges per unit area in the two cases must be equal, so that

$$C_{14}E_l = C_{12}E_g + C_{13}E_p, \qquad (6\text{--}6)$$

where the C's are the capacity coefficients for the electrodes, corresponding to their subscripts.   Inasmuch as C_{14} is nearly equal to C_{12} in actual tubes, we may write

$$E_l \doteq E_g + \frac{C_{13}}{C_{12}} E_p. \qquad (6\text{--}7)$$

Thus the *lumped voltage* E_l of the equivalent diode is approximately that of the grid of the triode plus a fraction of that of the plate. This fraction, C_{13}/C_{12}, is called the *penetration factor* and is customarily represented by the symbol D.*   Its reciprocal is the voltage amplification constant μ.   Then,

$$E_l = E_g + \frac{E_p}{\mu}. \qquad (6\text{--}8)$$

* " Durchgriff," in German.

Equations for μ have been derived from equations for C_{12} and C_{13} and used in the design of triodes.[4] It is found, both theoretically and experimentally, that μ is greater when the grid-filament distance is much less than the grid-plate distance and when the grid is made of large wires, close together. In some tubes, called *variable mu or super control-tubes*, the grid is constructed with the wires close together near its ends and with considerably greater spacing in its middle. The result is that the lower left end of the characteristic curves approach the grid-voltage axis much more slowly and only reach it at a large negative grid potential. Tubes with a *"sharp cut-off"* have great uniformity in the spacing of the grid wires and in axial symmetry with the filament and plate.

6–5. The Plate Resistance r_p.—It has been found possible to treat the three-electrode tube, when used as an amplifier or oscillator, in a simple manner by replacing it with the circuit of figure 6–8

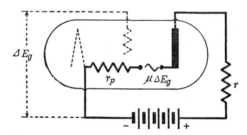

Fig. 6–8. Plate resistance of a three-electrode tube.

(the solid lines). Let a small change of potential ΔE_g be applied to the grid. This is equivalent to the addition of a voltage $\mu \Delta E_g$ ($= \Delta E_p$) in the plate circuit which will increase or decrease the normal plate current by an amount ΔI_p according to whether it is in the same or opposite direction to the plate voltage. We may then write as a theorem,

$$\Delta I_p = \frac{\mu \Delta E_g}{r + r_p} \qquad (6\text{–}9)$$

where r is the external resistance and r_p the so-called plate resistance (or plate impedance) of the tube. This equation is true provided we interpret r_p as

$$r_p = \frac{\Delta E_p}{\Delta I_p}, \qquad (6\text{–}10)$$

which is seen to be the reciprocal of the slope of the curve of figure 6–9 at the point P, the increments ΔE_p and ΔI_p being taken as small as possible. It is to be noted that this differs from the *dc* definition of resistance which would be the reciprocal of the slope of the line OP, i.e., E_p/I_p.

Since the curve of figure 6–9 is never exactly a straight line, r_p varies as the voltage of the plate battery is changed but, with

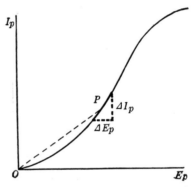

FIG. 6–9.   Plate current-plate voltage curve of a three-electrode tube.

fixed voltage, may be taken as a constant in applying equation 6–10. Values of r_p at normal operating voltages range in different commercial triodes from 800 to 150,000 ohms.

The plate resistance may be measured by means of a bridge circuit[3] such as that in figure 6–10, where the normal operating

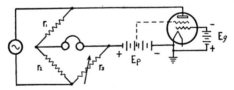

FIG. 6–10.   Measurement of the plate resistance r_p.

grid, filament and plate voltages are applied to the tube. The resistances r_1, r_2, and r_3 are varied until there is no sound in the phones. Then the usual Wheatstone bridge equation is applicable. Thus,

$$r_p = r_1 r_3 / r_2. \tag{6–11}$$

6-6. The Mutual Conductance g_m.—The mutual conductance g_m, or as it is sometimes called, the trans-conductance s_m, expressed in mhos, is defined as the change of plate current per volt change on the grid. Thus,

$$g_m = \frac{\Delta I_p}{\Delta E_g}.$$ (6-12)

It is a measure of the effectiveness of voltage fluctuations on the grid in causing changes in the plate current. Dividing equation 6-3 by 6-10 shows that

$$g_m = \mu/r_p.$$ (6-13)

Since r_p changes with plate and grid voltages, so also does g_m. Values of g_m for different commercial triodes range from 200 to 5000 micromhos.

The mutual conductance may be measured[3] with the circuit of figure 6-11. The drop across r_1, of amount $\Delta E_g = Ir_1 \sin \omega t$

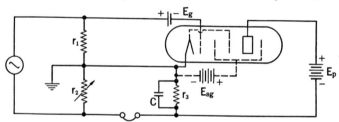

FIG. 6-11.   Measurement of the mutual conductance g_m.

is applied to the grid of the tube and causes a change of plate current of amount $g_m Ir_1 \sin \omega t$ to flow through the phones. This is counterbalanced by the current $Ir_2 \sin \omega t/r_3$ due to the voltage drop $Ir_2 \sin \omega t$ in r_2. It is assumed that r_3 is very large compared to r_2 and that the phones have low resistance. Then, for no sound in the phones,

$$g_m Ir_1 \sin \omega t = Ir_2 \sin \omega t/r_3,$$ (6-14)

$$g_m = r_2/r_1 r_3.$$ (6-15)

Equation 6-15 is to be multiplied by $r_3/(r_2 + r_3)$ if r_3 is not great compared to r_2, or if increased accuracy is desirable.

6–7. Tetrodes.—A tetrode is a four-electrode vacuum tube. The conventional tetrode contains two grids, the second or outer of which is called a " screen grid." This grid serves to *screen* the control grid from voltage changes of the plate. See figure 6–12. It is evident that the voltage on the plate is less than that of the

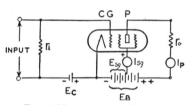

INPUT

FIG. 6–12. A screen-grid tube.

battery E_b by an amount equal to the potential drop in the load resistance r_0. When a voltage, applied to the input terminals, causes a change i_p in the plate current, the potential across r_o, and hence also on the plate, changes by an amount $i_p r_o$. This change of plate voltage would induce a voltage on the control grid were it not for the screen grid which acts in the manner of a Faraday cage. The capacity between the control grid and the plate is reduced by the screen, in a typical case, from 8 to only 0.008 micromicrofarad. With a triode, the voltages induced on the control grid because of the feedback from the plate can be sufficiently great to start and maintain oscillations. This is especially true at high frequencies, where the reactance ($1/\omega C$) formed by the capacity between the electrodes is small. The screen grid greatly reduces this possibility.

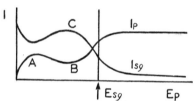

FIG. 6–13. Current-voltage curves of a screen-grid tube.

Tubes of the screen-grid type are characterized by high plate resistance, of the order of a million ohms, and by high voltage amplification constant, as great as 800. Circuits for the measurement of μ, r_p and g_m are shown in figures 6–6, 6–10 and 6–11. The plate (I_p) and screen grid (I_{sg}) currents for various plate voltages E_p are shown in figure 6–13 and can be obtained with the circuit of figure 6–12 if r_o is removed so that $E_p = E_b$. It is to be noted that when the plate has a lower voltage than that of the screen grid, as in the region *AB* of figure 6–13, that the plate current decreases as the plate voltage increases. Over this region the tube is said to have a *negative resistance*. This feature has been made use of in the so-called dynatron oscillators and tube voltmeters. When the tube is used as an amplifier in the usual manner, the plate voltage is made greater than that of the screen. The interpretation of the curves in figure 6–13 will be given in the next section.

Another type of tetrode is the "beam power tube." Here a flattened arrangement of electrodes is used and a pair of plates is put in at the sides, so that the electrons go from the cathode to the plate in sheets or beams. The result of this arrangement is that large amounts of power can be handled and power-sensitivity is increased. These tubes are employed in high-power audio-output amplifiers, in radio transmitters and in a variety of control-devices.

6–8. Secondary Emission.—The plate current, I_p in figure 6–13 of the preceding section, does not increase continuously over the region AB as the plate voltage is increased because secondary electrons are ejected from the plate by the primary electrons from the filament. The secondary electrons are attracted to the screen grid which is more positive than the plate. That this is true is shown by the increase in the screen grid current at C. Since electrons are travelling both toward and away from the plate, curve I_p represents the net electron current to the plate. As the plate voltage is increased, more secondary electrons are ejected and pass to the screen. It is even possible that each primary electron may eject more than one secondary electron, in which case the plate current is reversed; more electrons are flowing from it to the screen than approach. Under these conditions, the curve AB crosses the voltage axis at a point where the number of secondary electrons is equal to the number of primary electrons. When the plate has a sufficiently high potential to draw the secondary electrons back to it, (as at E_{sg} in figure 6–13), the plate current rises in the usual manner to its saturation value and the screen not only fails to attract secondary electrons but also fails to capture as many primary electrons as before.

Let S be the number of secondary electrons produced by each primary electron. It has been found[6] that

1. as the velocity of the primary electrons is increased from zero to a few hundred volts, S increases from a low value, perhaps zero, to a maximum S_m. With still further increase in the energy of the primary electrons, S slowly decreases.

2. The curve of S for different voltages accelerating the primary electrons (1, above) is not smooth but has small maximae and minimae.

3. S_m is about 1.0 to 1.5 for outgassed ordinary metals, about 3 to 4 for untreated metals and may be as great as 8 to 10 for alkali metal films on an oxidized metal plate.

4. S, in general, is reduced by heat treatment of a surface and is increased by contaminations, especially by electro-positive impurities. S depends greatly on the condition of the surface.

5. Moderate temperature changes have but little effect on the value of S.

6. The velocity of the secondary electrons are usually only a few volts, even when 1000 volt primary electrons are used.

7. The secondary electrons appear to leave the surface at random in all directions.

8. Secondary emission can occur from insulators, such as glass. With high velocity primary electrons, S may be greater than unity, in which case the surface of the insulator acquires a positive instead of a negative charge.

6–9. Pentodes.—A five-electrode vacuum tube is called a pentode. In one form, the additional electrode is called the suppressor grid and is located between the screen grid and the plate, as in figure 6–14. The suppressor grid is at the potential of the

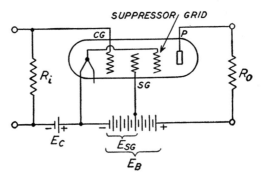

Fig. 6–14. A pentode.

cathode and hence serves to repel secondary electrons, driving them back into the plate from which they were ejected by primary electrons. As a result, the negative resistance region (AB of figure 6–13) is largely eliminated and the tube may be used for greater power output with small input grid voltage. The plate resistance of various pentodes in normal operation is moderately high and ranges from 22,000 to 2,000,000 ohms. The mutual conductance is high and ranges from 400 to 6000 micromhos and the amplification constant ranges from 70 to 1500. These constants may be measured with the circuits of figures 6–6 and 6–11.

In another form of pentode, the lead wire of the third grid is brought out of the tube. There are then, obviously, many combinations possible. For example, the grid nearest the filament can serve as a space charge grid, the next as the control grid and the one nearest the plate as a screen grid.

In the so-called beam power tubes, the suppressor grid is supplanted by the negative space charge produced by electrons which, en route to the plate, are concentrated between the screen grid and the plate. Although the tube serves the same purpose as a pentode, there is no physical suppressor in the path of the electrons, and the tube is classed as a tetrode.

6–10. Electron Multiplier Tubes.—The phenomenon of secondary emission is used in electron multiplier tubes to gain large current amplification. Figure 6–15 shows the principle of operation.[7] The photoelectric or thermionic cathode K emits electrons which are directed against the plate P_1 by electric, magnetic or combined fields. The plate may consist of oxidized silver, zirconium or beryllium coated with a layer of cesium so as to be a good emitter of secondary electrons. The secondary electrons from P_1 are directed onto a second plate P_2, which in turn multiplies the number of electrons. This is repeated as many as ten times and the final, comparatively large current reaches the output plate P from which it passes into the load circuit. The usual noises in a well-constructed high-gain amplifier using ordinary vacuum tubes are largely due to the thermal effect. Since this is reduced in multiplier tubes, except at the input end, the signal to noise ratio is improved sixty to one hundred fold. These tubes are useful over wide ranges of frequency and can be used as " linear " or d.c. amplifiers.

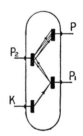

FIG. 6–15. An electron multiplier tube.

In another form of multiplier tube,[8] electrons are oscillated back and forth between two surfaces which are good secondary emitters. This is accomplished by means of a battery connected to an anode ring around the center of the tube and an external radio frequency oscillator of low power. At each impact of the electrons with the cathode surfaces, the number of electrons is appreciably multiplied.

6–11. Electron Coupling.—Tubes have been constructed which contain a filament, a plate and four or five grids. The latter are called *penta-grid converters*. The first grid, near the filament, is used as the control grid of a triode whose "plate" is the second grid. This triode is used as an oscillator in one of the many forms of vacuum tube oscillators. As a result of the fluctuating grid voltage, the current to the "plate" (grid number 2) is alternately increased and decreased. The number of electrons which penetrate the second grid and enter the remainder of the tube is thus increased and decreased periodically. It is as though it were possible to have a (virtual) cathode which emitted a periodically varying number of electrons by alternately heating and cooling. There are various uses to which the pulsating stream of electrons can be put in the remainder of the tube, such, for example, as the modulation of a radio frequency signal in a super-heterodyne receiver. The modulated portion of this penta-grid converter is said to be *electron coupled* with the oscillator, as contrasted with the usual inductive or capacitative coupling methods.

6–12. Electron Optics.—The analogy between light beams and electron beams is two-fold; first, the deflection of charged particles by electric and magnetic fields is analogous to the deflection of light rays in refractive media, as treated in the study of geometrical optics and second, the diffraction, interference, etc., of electron waves corresponds to the same phenomena for light waves as studied in the subject of physical optics. Let us now consider the first analogy in some detail.

In section 2–9 it was seen that a magnetic field, directed along the axis of a diverging bundle of electrons, caused them to follow a helical path and come to a focus on a fluorescent screen. By analogy, we may think of the magnetic field as a converging lens which, if it extends along the entire path, has a focal length l given by equation 2–23. Thus,

$$l = \left(\frac{2\sqrt{2}\pi 10^4}{\sqrt{e/m}}\right)\frac{\sqrt{V}}{H_c}\cos\beta, \text{ cm.,} \qquad (6\text{–}16)$$

where V is the accelerating potential in volts, H_c is the magnetic field strength in oersteds and e/m is in e.m.u. Thus, the focal length is short when a strong magnetic field acts upon slow electrons and vice versa.

A short solenoid, placed axially with the beam, but covering only a portion of its path, serves as a convergent lens [9] whose index of refraction, like the magnetic field strength, varies from point to point. In this case, electrons which diverge at a large angle from the axis do not come to the same focus as those which travel more nearly along the axis and *spherical aberration* occurs.

When electrons of various velocities pass between the charged plates of a condenser, the slower ones are deflected more than the faster ones; the electrons are dispersed in a manner analogous to

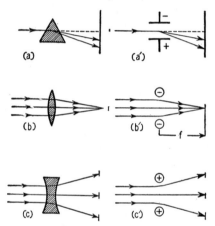

FIG. 6–16.   Light and electron ray analogs.

the dispersion of various colors of light as they pass through a prism.   See figure 6–16 (*a*) and (*a'*).

The use of electro-static fields for the purpose of converging electron beams has proved more flexible than the use of magnetic fields, and may be understood from the following elementary considerations.   In figure 6–16 *b'*, a parallel stream of electrons approaches two, fixed, negatively charged pith balls.   Since the lines of force around the balls are the paths along which free charges would tend to move, it is only the momentum of the electrons which carries them past the balls.   Since those electrons which pass nearest the balls are in stronger fields, they are deviated more than those near the axis.   In order that they shall all come to a common focus it is necessary that the deflecting force should increase in direct proportion to its distance off the axis.

We shall now see that the "index of refraction" of an electric field for electron rays is directly proportional to their velocity. At the instant when electrons are entering an electric field at an angle, as in figure 6–17, we may consider the incident velocity v_1 to have a component v_{1x} parallel to the boundary surface, and the velocity v_2 in the field to have a similar component v_{2x}. Since v_{1x} is unaltered by the field, sin $r =$ $v_{2x}/v_2 = v_{1x}/v_1$. Also, sin $i = v_{1x}/v_1$. Therefore sin $i/$ sin $r = v_2/v_1$.

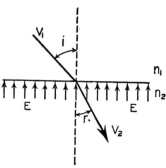

FIG. 6–17. The refraction of light and electron rays.

But, according to Snell's law for the refraction of light rays, this ratio is equal to the ratio n_2/n_1 of the respective indices of refraction. It follows that the *index of refraction for electron rays* is

$$n = \frac{v}{c},\qquad(6\text{–}17)$$

where v is the velocity of the electrons in the electric field and c is arbitrarily chosen equal to 3×10^{10}. For electrons whose velocities exceed a few thousand volts, the index of refraction is given by

$$n = \frac{v/c}{\sqrt{1 - v^2/c^2}}.\qquad(6\text{–}18)$$

The amount of refraction or bending which an electron ray undergoes when passing through the boundary between two electric fields is proportional to the ratio of the velocities in the two fields. The change of velocity is dependent on the incident velocity and the electric field gradients at the boundary.

When the shapes, positions and potentials of all electrodes are known, the equi-potential surfaces around them are calculated[10] or measured.[11] In contrast with the usual optical cases, the index of refraction of electron lenses is not constant throughout the refractive medium. The medium may, however, be considered as built up of layers, each of constant index, with boundaries at the equi-potential surfaces. In further contrast with optical systems, it is necessary for accurate work to consider the mutual repulsion between the electrons in the beam, their alteration of the fields and the effects of other space charges such as gaseous ions.

The focal length f of the *double-gauze lens* of figure 6–18a is given by

$$f = R/(1 - \sqrt{V_1/V_2}),   \text{(6–19)}$$

where R is the radius of curvature of the gauze and V_1 and V_2 are

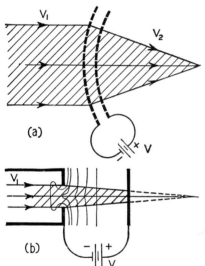

(a)

(b)

FIG. 6–18.   Electron lenses.

the respective incidence and emergence speeds of the electrons, in volts. As shown, the lens is convergent but, with reversed voltage (V), it may diverge and even reflect the electrons.

The focal length of the *diaphragm-hole lens* of figure 6–18b, has been given by Davisson and Calbick[12] as

$$f = 4V_1/(G_2 - G_1),   \text{(6–20)}$$

where V_1 is the speed of the incident electrons at the hole, in volts, and $G_2 - G_1$ is the difference between the electrical potential gradients on the emergence (G_2) and incidence (G_1) sides of the diaphragm. These gradients are counted as positive when they serve to accelerate the electrons. If a slit, rather than a circular hole, is used in the plate, a factor 2 is used instead of 4 in the equation above and the system forms a cylindrical rather than a spherical lens. As an example of a spherical lens; the electrons are accelerated by a potential of 1000 volts, pass through the field free space ($G_1 = 0$) in a parallel bundle and are then accelerated by 1000 volts applied across a distance of 10 centimeters ($G_2 = 100$ volts/$cm.$). The focal length is then + 40 centimeters. If V were reversed, the focal length would be — 40 centimeters, the image would be virtual and the electrons would diverge as they passed the hole.

Combinations of two or more diaphragm lenses of the type shown in figure 6-18 (*b*) have been used in *electron-microscopes* to produce magnified, inverted, real images of the surface of the filament, permitting detailed studies of the emissive properties of various cathodes.

In the *double-cylinder lenses*[13] of figure 6–19 (*a*) and (*b*), a parallel bundle of electrons, travelling at a fixed velocity, enters the electrostatic field near the end of the first cylinder and is converged toward the point *O*. When, however, they pass through the field near the second cylinder, they are diverged. Due to the accelerating voltage *V*, the electrons are travelling faster in the latter field and the divergence is less than the previous convergence. Hence the electrons tend to focus farther down the tube. In figure 6–19 (*b*), the focal length is shorter than in (*a*).

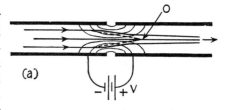

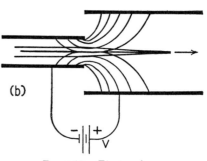

FIG. 6-19.   Electron lenses.

In figure 6–20, the *electron gun*[14] is composed of the cathode *K*, the grid *G*, which chiefly controls the number of electrons which pass through the gun, and two cylinder anodes *A*₁ and *A*₂. The second anode has a larger radius than the first in order that the field near it shall have but small divergent action on the electrons. The focussing action is controlled by the ratio of the potentials on the anodes.

The *electron telescope* consists of a photoelectric surface upon which an optical image of a distant object is sharply focussed. The number of electrons ejected from the various parts of this surface is proportional to the intensity of the image. It is to be

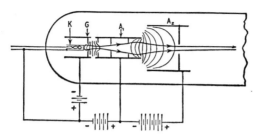

Fig. 6–20. The electron gun of a cathode-ray oscillograph.

noted that ultra-violet or infra-red rays may be used as well as visible light on the photoelectric surface. Short cylinder lenses are used to focus the electrons upon a fluorescent screen at the opposite end of the tube, producing a sharply defined image of visible light.

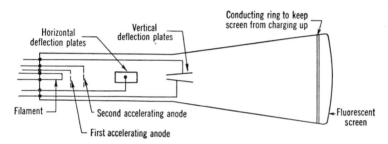

Fig. 6–21. Schematic diagram of typical cathode-ray tube.

Experiment 6–1

CHARACTERISTIC CURVES OF TRIODES

The connections are shown in figure 6–22. Three circuits are involved, the filament, plate and grid, supplied by the *A*, *B*, and *C* batteries, respectively. It is desired to study the various currents in these circuits as the voltages are changed. However, to observe the principal phenomena involved, only three such relations need be observed. These are:

Plate Current and Filament Voltage (or Current).—Disconnect the grid circuit and join the plate and grid. Apply the normal voltage (say 45 for type O1A tubes) to the plate. Vary the filament voltage in steps of about one-half volt from zero to normal (5). If filament currents are used, vary in steps from zero to normal (0.25 amp.). Read filament voltage (or current) simultaneously with plate current and plot with the latter as ordinates.

Plate Current and Plate Voltage.—Disconnect the grid and plate and complete the grid circuit. Adjust the grid to zero potential and set the filament at normal voltage (or current). Vary the B battery voltage in steps of about three volts from zero to maximum (say 135) recording its value simultaneously with plate currents. Plot, with the latter as ordinates.

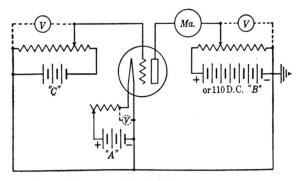

Fɪɢ. 6–22.   Connections for obtaining the characteristic curves
of three-electrode tubes.

Plate Current and Grid Voltage.—With connections as in figure 6–22, adjust the plate voltage (45) and filament voltage (5) to normal values. Note plate currents as grid voltages are varied from −10 to +10 volts. The points should be taken more frequently wherever the curves bend sharply. Repeat with various plate voltages, say $22\frac{1}{2}$, 90 and 135, and plot all data on one graph with plate currents as ordinates. These are spoken of as the *static characteristic curves.* All will be shifted slightly if the *A* battery is reversed or the filament rheostat is connected in the other lead. If the plate voltage is small (10 volts) and the grid voltage high (vary it from zero to plus 90), *secondary emission* may be observed. Tubes using alternating current for heating the filament may be studied as above. The plate current-grid voltage curves will be straighter and have a smaller slope if resistances (5,000 to 1,000,000 ohms) are included in the plate circuit because of the potential drop in them—but this is a phenomenon belonging to the plate circuit rather than to the tube itself.

TETRODE CURVES

The connections are shown in figure 6–23. With all voltages constant as shown, vary E_p from 0 to 150 volts and plot plate and screen currents as in figure 6–14. Since the secondary current is

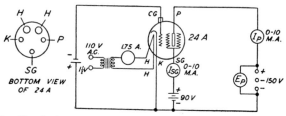

Fig. 6–23. Circuit for studying the characteristic curves of a screen-grid tube.

subtracted from the plate and added to the screen-grid current, the sum (I_t) of the plate and screen currents should be a constant, equal to the total current which passes the control grid, i.e., $I_t = I_p + I_{sg}$. Test this relationship.

CONSTANTS OF VACUUM TUBES

The circuits are shown in figures 6–6, 6–10 and 6–11. Particular care should be taken that the ground is connected as shown in each case. The oscillator O may be an electrically driven tuning fork of say 1000 cycles per second or a vacuum tube oscillator. There should be a grounded electro-static shield between the primary and secondary of its output transformer or there should be one-half megohm potentiometer across the secondary with its sliding contact grounded. In figure 6–6, r_1 may be 10 ohms for low mu tubes and one ohm for high mu tubes. The potential drop across r_1 should not exceed 1 or 2 volts. A dial box may be used for r_2. By-pass condensers of low impedance should be used around all batteries and rectifier-filter systems must be avoided. Since the batteries have capacity to the ground, they should be located in such a manner as to reduce this effect to as small a value as possible. For screen-grid tubes, connections are to be made to point a and for pentode tubes, to the point b in figure 6–6. Condenser C is used to sharpen the balance point by introducing a small phase shift. In figure 6–10, this may be accomplished by means of a small capacity in parallel with r_3. In this circuit the resistances r_1, r_2 and r_3 should be kept as small as possible. In figure 6–11, the phones should have a comparatively low resistance and the phasing condenser C may be omitted with pentodes. Here r_1 may be 50 to 1000 ohms, r_2 of the order of 100 ohms and r_3 much greater, perhaps 20,000 ohms. It will be found that less care is required by the student when triodes are used in the circuits above than with tetrodes or pentodes.

Measure the voltages amplification constant of a tube operated under normal conditions, determine and plot values of either the plate impedance or mutual conductance for various plate voltages.

REFERENCES

1. See L. Page and N. I. Adams. *Principles of Electricity*. D. Van Nostrand Co. (1931).
2. U. S. Patents, No. 841387 (1907); No. 879532 (1908).
3. J. M. Miller, Proc. I. R. E., **6**, 141 (1918).
   General Reference B, Chapter VII.
4. General Reference C, pages 34–44.
   General Reference A, pages 177–191.
5. L. R. Hafstad, Phys. Rev., **44**, 201 (1933).
6. See K. T. Compton and I. Langmuir, Rev. Mod. Phys., **2**, 171 (1930).
7. Zworykin, Morton and Malter, Proc. I. R. E., **24**, 351 (1936).
   L. A. Kubetsky, Proc. I. R. E., **25**, 421 (1937).
8. P. T. Farnsworth, Electronics, **7**, 242 (1934).
9. See V. K. Zworykin, Jr. Frank. Inst., **215**, 535 (1933).
10. General Reference D, page 61 et seq.
11. W. Estorff, Zeit. f. Electroteck, **37**, 63 (1916).
    E. D. McArthur, Electronics, **4**, 192, June (1932).
12. C. J. Davisson and C. J. Calbick, Phys. Rev., **38**, 585 (1931).
    L. H. Bedford, Proc. Phys. Soc., London, **46**, 882 (1934).
13. W. W. Hansen and D. L. Webster, Rev. Sci. Inst., **7**, 17 (1936).
    P. Kirkpatrick and J. G. Beckerley, Rev. Sci. Inst., **7**, 24 (1936).
14. I. G. Maloff and D. W. Epstein, Proc. I. R. E., **22**, 1386 (1934).
    D. W. Epstein, Proc. I. R. E., **24**, 1095 (1936).

GENERAL REFERENCES

A.—E. L. Chaffee, *Theory of Thermionic Vacuum Tubes*. McGraw-Hill Book Co. (1933).

B.—F. E. Terman, *Measurements in Radio Engineering*. McGraw-Hill Book Co. (1935).

C.—E. V. Appleton, *Thermionic Vacuum Tubes*. Dutton & Co. (1931).

D.—E. Brüche and O. Scherzer, *Geometrische Elecktronenoptik*. J. Springer (1934).

E.—Zworykin, Morton, Ramberg, Hillier and Vance, *Electron Optics and the Electron Microscope*, John Wiley & Sons (1945).

CHAPTER 7

THE OUTER PARTS OF THE ATOM

7–1. Introduction.—Two spheres are said to collide with each other when they just touch, i.e., when the distance between their centers is equal to the sum of their radii. This definition of a " collision " is not satisfactory when small bodies such as electrons or atoms are considered since these particles carry electrical charges capable of repelling each other even at comparatively large distances. For such cases, we shall consider an *elastic collision* as one in which the charged bodies are deflected from their normal paths without loss of energy; both the total energy and the momentum shall be conserved. On the other hand, we shall say that an *inelastic collision* has taken place between charged particles when one of them gains energy at the expense of the other. We shall see that the study of collisions between charged particles has yielded a great deal of information as to the nature of the bodies themselves.

An electron gun is used to direct a beam of electrons through a chamber filled with gas at a low pressure. Occasionally the electrons collide with the gas atoms and are " absorbed," either by loss of energy, scattering or by combination with the atoms. Let λ be the average distance or *mean-free-path* which an electron will travel between collisions and let A be the *effective-cross-section* of a gas atom for the electrons. It will be of interest to compare the measured values of these quantities with those computed from the kinetic theory; a theory which treats the atoms as solid spheres.

The thermal velocities of the atoms of a gas at ordinary temperatures are very small in comparison with the usual velocities of free electrons; their root-mean-square values are equivalent to approximately one one-thirtieth of an electron volt. Also, the " radius " of an electron (about 10^{-13} cm.) is negligibly small compared with that of an atom (about 10^{-8} cm.). Hence, the kinetic

144

theory expressions for the mean-free-path of electrons in a gas may be reduced[1] to the following simple form:

$$\frac{1}{\lambda_k} = n(\pi\rho_k{}^2) = nA_k, \tag{7-1}$$

where the subscript k implies that these are values given by this theory, n is the number of atoms per cubic centimeter and ρ_k is the effective-radius of an atom for an electron. It has been found by calculation that electrons travel through a gas $4\sqrt{2}$ ($=5.656$) times as far, on the average, before a collision takes place, as do the gas atoms or molecules among each other.

The effective-cross-section of an atom for an electron may be determined experimentally by a measurement of the number of electrons which enter and the number which emerge from a gas of thickness x. Let a parallel beam of electrons enter a gas containing n atoms in each cubic centimeter.* Now, nA is the total effective-cross-section of all the atoms in one cubic centimeter of the gas for one electron and $nAdx$ is the total effective-cross-section for each electron, of the atoms in a layer dx centimeters thick and one centimeter on each side. Of a total of N electrons, a certain number, dN, will be "absorbed" as they traverse this layer of the gas. Thus,

$$dN = -(nAdx)N. \tag{7-2}$$

The negative sign is used to indicate that the electrons decrease in number as the beam passes through the gas. From this,

$$\frac{dN}{N} = -nAdx. \tag{7-3}$$

Integration gives

$$\log_\epsilon N = -nAx + \text{constant}. \tag{7-4}$$

But when $x = 0$, $\log_\epsilon N_o = \text{constant}$, so that

$$\log_\epsilon \frac{N}{N_o} = -nAx \tag{7-5}$$

or

$$N = N_o\epsilon^{-(nA)x} = N_o\epsilon^{-\mu x}, \tag{7-6}$$

* It is customary to specify a pressure of 1 mm. of mercury at $0°$ C. Then, $n = 2.705 \times 10^{19} (1/760) = 3.56 \times 10^{16}$/cc.

where N_o is the original number of electrons entering the gas and ϵ is the base of the Naperian system of logarithms. The absorption coefficient μ is given thus as

$$\mu = nA = \frac{1}{\lambda}. \tag{7-7}$$

It will be a comparatively large number whenever the electrons are easily absorbed.

A comparison of effective-cross-sections, A, determined experimentally by the use of equation 7–6, with those (A_k) calculated by the kinetic theory has shown agreement over a range of intermediate velocities of the electrons. However, for electrons with velocities less than a value of approximately 4×10^8 centimeters per second ($=50$ e.v.), there has not been agreement [2] in many cases, thus showing that for these collisions, the atom cannot be considered as a solid sphere. It may be seen in figure 7–1, that

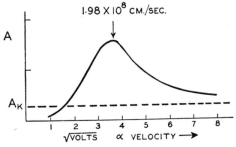

FIG. 7–1. Effective-cross-section (A) of argon atoms for electrons of various velocities.

for certain velocities of the electrons, the argon atom offers a much greater barrier to the electrons than that given by the kinetic theory (the dotted line). The decrease in A to the left of the maximum, for the slower electrons, is true for a number of gases and is known as the *Ramsauer effect*.

It will be recalled that Lenard found that cathode rays which had penetrated a thin aluminum window were capable of travelling through the air for distances as great as three to five centimeters. He noted the large difference between these ranges and the average distance or mean-free-path of the air molecules between their mutual collisions (about 10^{-5} centimeters) and concluded that the atoms were not solid spheres.

Since atoms cannot be considered as solid spheres, we proceed to a discussion of their inner structure.

7-2. The Nuclear Atom.—The experiments in which the charge-to-mass ratio of electrons was measured (Chapter 2) indicated that negative electricity exists inside the atoms. If the atom contains negative electricity alone it would tend to fly apart under the forces of repulsion between like charges. Thus, the presence of a restraining positive charge is necessary. Many attempts were made in the past to secure a satisfactory geometrical distribution of these positive and negative charges such that a stable atom would result and various known properties of the atom would be explained. Obviously, the total negative charge had to be equal to the total positive charge if the atoms were to be electrically neutral.

In 1911, Rutherford proposed his *nuclear atom*.[3] This consisted of a heavy, positively charged nucleus, surrounded by negative electrons in such number as to make the total charge equal to zero. He and his colleagues tested this model by studies of the scattering of alpha particles from thin foils, as discussed in the next section. In 1913, Niels Bohr used this model successfully to predict the frequencies of the light radiated from hydrogen atoms and in 1914, Moseley used the same model to deduce the frequencies of x-rays emitted by different elements.

As we shall see in this book, the nuclear atom satisfies the three requirements of an atom model; namely,

1. An outer region associated with chemical valence, visible and near-visible spectra and with critical potentials,
2. An intermediate section associated with x-rays,
3. A nuclear region which determines the kind of element at hand and is associated with natural and artificial disintegrations.

7-3. The Scattering of Alpha Particles by Thin Foils.—A simplified diagram of the apparatus used by Rutherford to establish the nuclear atom is shown in figure 7–2. A radioactive source, placed at X, spontaneously emits alpha particles. These particles have very nearly the mass of the helium atom, carry a positive electrical charge whose value is twice that of the electron and travel with velocities of approximately 10^9 centimeters per second. Some of them travel through the collimating holes SS' in a narrow beam to the thin metal foil F. As they pass through the foil, they are deflected and scattered in various directions. The number which emerge at the angle ϕ is counted by means of the scintillations which they produce on a fluorescent screen O. The arrows in the figure are intended to give a very rough idea of

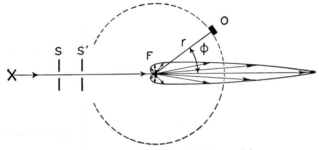

FIG. 7–2.   The scattering of alpha particles.

this number: a vast majority of the particles suffer only a small deviation.

Of great significance, however, is the fact that a few of the particles are deflected through large angles; even greater than 90°. There must, then, be comparatively large reactions occurring between the alpha particles and the atoms of the foil. This would be possible if the atom has a comparatively large mass and large positive electrical charge concentrated in its center. Rutherford assumed that the repellent force between the alpha particle and the nucleus was directly proportional to the product of their charges and inversely proportional to the square of the distance between them. He also assumed that the electrons in the outer parts of the atom did not appreciably deflect the alpha particles and that the nucleus was so massive that it did not move appreciably under the impact of the alpha particle. He then computed the path which the particle might be expected to traverse in its encounter with the nucleus, and also the fractional number of particles that might be expected at the various angles. Thus,

$$N = \frac{N_o e^4}{M^2 v^4} \underbrace{}_{\text{source}} \cdot \underbrace{ntZ^2}_{\text{foil}} \cdot \underbrace{\frac{cosec^4(\phi/2)}{r^2}}_{\text{observation position}} \tag{7-8}$$

where N is the number of alpha particles each second which reach one square centimeter of a screen located r centimeters from the center of the foil and at the angle ϕ. N_0 is the corresponding number at zero angle when the foil has been removed. The charge of the electron is e while M is the mass and v the velocity of the alpha particle. Z is the number of electron units of charge on the nucleus, n is the number of atoms per cubic centimeter and t is the thickness of the foil in centimeters.

This equation has been subjected to extensive tests[4] and proven to be correct under the conditions for which it was derived. It is, therefore, to be concluded that the basic assumption of a nuclear atom, upon which it rests, has also been established.

Let the chemical elements be arranged in sequence, from the lightest, hydrogen, to the heaviest, uranium, and numbered 1, 2, 3, etc. These are the *atomic numbers* of the elements. The scattering experiments gave corresponding numbers for the quantity Z of equation 7–8, thus proving that the atomic number is equal to the number of electron charges on the nucleus. There will then be a nucleus of positive charge $Z \cdot e$, surrounded by Z negative electrons.

It was just stated that equation 7–8 had been tested and found to be true under the conditions for which it was derived. This is true provided the alpha particle does not approach the nucleus closer than approximately 10^{-12} centimeter, a distance which is much less than the diameter of the atoms. The assumption of an *inverse square law* was found to be satisfactory to within approximately 4×10^{-12} centimeter of the center of uranium nuclei and to within approximately 1×10^{-12} centimeter for copper nuclei. It is interesting to note that the wave-length of an alpha particle is about 7×10^{-13} centimeter.

It must be added that discrepancies were found between theory and experiment with the lighter elements, even after corrections had been made for the recoil of their nuclei. In the light of later studies of the construction of the nucleus, these apparent discrepancies in the scattering of alpha particles by light atoms can be interpreted as evidence of large binding forces operating over short distances and serving to keep the parts of the nucleus from flying apart.

7–4. The Scattering of Electrons by Gases.[5]—An electron gun is used to direct electrons in a narrow beam through a chamber filled with mercury vapor at a pressure around 10^{-3} millimeter. Electrons which are deflected or *elastically scattered* by the mercury atoms pass through several slits into a faraday chamber and are recorded by means of an electrometer. Various potentials are applied to the slits so as to exclude from the chamber all positive charges and also all electrons which have lost energy at their encounter with the gas atoms (i.e., inelastic collisions). Most of the electrons suffer but little deviation in their elastic scattering. This is shown by the great height of the central peak in the curve of figure 7–3. The humps in the curves at the larger angles on either side of the original beam suggest diffraction patterns, such as those observed when a light ray passes through a fog, and justly so, since the wave-length of the electrons is of the same order of magnitude as the effective-cross-sections of the atoms. From the wave equations, theoretical curves can be plotted which agree with those obtained experimentally.

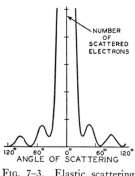

Fig. 7–3. Elastic scattering of electrons by gas atoms.

If the potentials on the slits of the apparatus just described are properly adjusted, *all* electrons scattered by the atoms in a given direction may be obtained. Their energies are then measured by means of electric deflection methods. It is found that, in addition to those which possess the same energy (V) as in the original beam, there are other groups which have suffered *definite* losses of energy. In these *inelastic collisions*, the energies lost by the electrons were absorbed by the atoms. For example, after passing through helium, the electrons were found to have energies of V, $(V - 21.12)$, $(V - 22.93)$, and $(V - 23.63)$ electron volts and hence the helium atoms absorbed 21.12, 22.93, and 23.63 electron volts of energy.   The significant point is this: the atoms absorbed particular amounts of energy, not any amount, suggesting an inner structure in the atoms, of finite rather than continuous energy values.

7–5.   Ionizing Potentials.[6, 7]—We shall now see some of the methods used to prove that the electrons in undisturbed atoms are bound to the nucleus by fixed forces and require the addition of definite amounts of energy to remove them from their normal state to the outside of the atom.

In the discussion of thermionic emission and vacuum tubes, as presented in chapters 5 and 6, it was assumed that there was

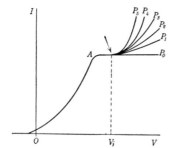

Fig. 7–4.   The effect of gases in a
two-electrode tube.

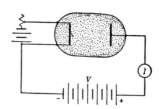

Fig. 7–5.   Circuit for obtaining
the curves in figure 7–4.

no gas present in the tube.   Under such a condition, the current-voltage curves showed a saturation value, all electrons emitted by the filament being drawn over to the plate as indicated by AP_o in figure 7–4.   The circuit for obtaining such a curve is given in figure 7–5.   If a gas such as helium at a pressure of one or two millimeters is introduced in the tube, curve OP_1 results.   The increase of current is due to the creation of ions when the electrons collide with neutral gas particles.   The potential V_i, where this added current first becomes evident, is one of the *critical potentials*. In particular, it is the *minimum ionizing potential*.   If the distance between the filament and plate is less than one centimeter, the minimum ionizing potential is independent of the pressure if this remains less than two millimeters for diatomic gases and ten millimeters for monatomic gases. This may be shown by increasing the pressure, when the curves OP_1, OP_2, etc., may be obtained. These are found to rise above OP_o at the same potential (V_i) as in the former case.

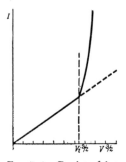

FIG. 7–6. Replot of data for figure 7–4.

This method is not very satisfactory since the potential at which OP_1, OP_2, etc., rise above the gas-free curve OP_o is not sharply defined. It may be brought out more clearly by heating the filament to such high temperatures that a space charge always exists between it and the plate. Now, when positive ions and electrons are produced from neutral gas particles by collision, the electrons are rapidly drawn away and the slower positive ions tend to neutralize the space charge, resulting in much greater current flow.* With the presence of a space charge, Langmuir's equation $I = BV^{3/2}$ holds true. Hence, plotting I against $V^{3/2}$ gives a straight line. As ionization by collision sets in, there will be a deviation from this straight line as indicated in figure 7–6. This

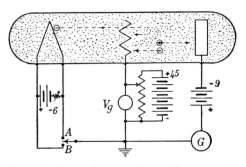

FIG. 7–7. Circuit for measuring ionizing potentials.

" kink " is more pronounced than the one in figure 7–4. Correction must be made for the initial velocity of emission of the electrons, contact potentials, filament drops of potential, etc.

* The large increase in current which results when positive ions reduce an electron space charge offers a very sensitive method for the detection of small amounts of ionization.

A better method of measuring the minimum ionizing potential, originated by Lenard in 1902, involves the use of a three-electrode tube.   The circuit is shown in figure 7–7.   Here the grid is made positive so that electrons are accelerated toward it and pass into the space between grid and plate where they are reversed by a small negative potential on the plate and return to the grid.   The voltage of the grid is increased so as to speed up the electrons until they have sufficient energy to ionize the gas between grid and plate. This is made known by observing the current flowing to the plate by means of the galvanometer G.   Thus in figure 7–8, this " par-

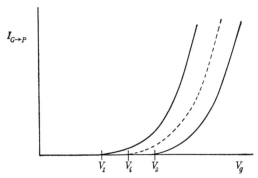

Fig. 7–8.   Ionizing potential measurement.

tial " or positive ion current begins to flow when the grid is given a voltage V_1 or V_2, according to whether the switch is on A or B. The two curves are taken in order to correct for the potential drop in the filament.   The ionizing potential V_i (uncorrected for emission velocity and contact p.d.) is the mean of V_1 and V_2.

The high velocity electrons may be deflected (elastic impact) on approaching a neutral atom or they may give up their energy to the atom (inelastic impact).   This latter will disturb the normal positions of the electrons in the atom, changing the energy from a value $\mathscr{E}_1^0$ to a value $\mathscr{E}_n^0$ by an amount

$$10^8 V e = \tfrac{1}{2}mv^2 \qquad (2\text{–}6)$$

where V is the accelerating potential in volts, e is the charge of the incident electrons in e.m.u., m the mass of the electron, and v the velocity.   If the energy of the incident electrons is just equal to

$10^8 V_i e$ ergs, the atom will be ionized by the ejection of one of its electrons. If the energy is greater than this amount, the atom's electron will be ejected and, in addition, possess kinetic energy equal to $10^8 V e - \mathcal{E}_1$ ergs.

The minimum ionizing potential V_i, expressed in volts, gives a measure of the energy required to remove the most loosely bound electron from the atom and hence is numerically equal to the energy of this electron in its normal state in the atom. For example, it requires 3.88 electron volts to remove an electron from the cesium atom, whereas, the value for the energy of an electron in its normal state in the helium atom is 24.5 electron volts. Values for various elements are listed in Table 2 at the end of this book. It may be seen that they range between the values quoted for cesium and helium, that they are periodic functions of the atomic number of the elements, that they are higher for the rare gases, lower for the alkali metals and that they usually decrease in any column of the periodic table with increasing atomic number.

The *probability* of ionization,[8] i.e., the number of positive ions created per collision, rises very rapidly from a zero value just at the ionizing potential. It reaches a maximum value at 210 electron volts for helium, 340 for neon, 140 for argon, 145 for hydrogen, 175 for nitrogen and 135 electron volts for mercury vapor. For electrons of greater than the maximum energy, the ionization probability decreases slowly.

7–6. Energy Levels—Excitation Potentials.—In 1914, Franck and Hertz used a three-electrode tube somewhat like that in figure 7–7 but so constructed that the grid was much closer to the plate. The potential of the plate was made positive with respect to the filament but slightly negative, say 0.5 volt, with respect to the grid. Electrons of energy greater than 0.5 volt were then able to reach the plate against this small retarding potential whereas those of lesser energy were returned to the grid. As the grid was made increasingly positive from zero, the current to the plate was found to vary in the manner represented in figure 7–9. The form of this curve may be explained in the following manner. As the grid becomes increasingly positive, an increasing number of electrons can reach the plate against its small retarding potential, as shown by the region OA. At A, however, some of the faster electrons have acquired sufficient energy to collide *inelastically* with the atoms somewhere near the grid and give up all their energy. This is true even though their energies are less than the minimum ionizing potential. If the electrons had retained an energy greater than 0.5 volt, they would have been able to reach the plate and the current would not have decreased as from A to B. As the potential of the grid is still further increased, the electrons will acquire sufficient energy to cause an inelastic collision in front of the grid and then acquire an additional velocity in the remainder of the potential gradient to the grid. Thus, they are able to pass to the plate against the 0.5 volt retarding potential; whereupon,

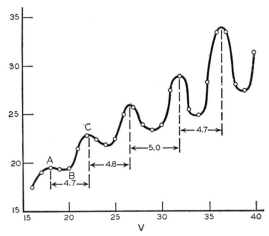

Fig. 7–9. Excitation potential for mercury vapor.

the current increases, as from B to C. At C, two inelastic collisions with the atoms occur, one well in front of the grid and the other near it. The successive peaks are separated from each other, as indicated, by the voltage (energy) which the electron must acquire to bring about an inelastic collision. This energy (4.9 volts in the case of mercury) is also one of the critical potentials and is called an *excitation potential* V_x.

The point of significance is that an inelastic collision can only occur and the atom can only absorb energy in specified amounts. In the case of mercury, only one of these favored values has been made apparent by the experiment described. Other experiments, however, have shown that there exist a number of excitation potentials for mercury between 4.9 volts and the ionizing potential of 10.4 volts. The existence of excitation potentials for the atoms of other elements and for molecules has been established in similar fashion.

The minimum excitation potential is called the resonance potential V_r.* Some values of V_r will be found in Table 2 at the end of this book. It may be concluded that the electrons in the atom may be shifted from their normal state only into *definite* higher energy levels.

The collision between an electron and an atom may occur head on or at a glancing angle. Hence, the type of collision may be expected to determine whether or not the transition from a normal state to a higher one will occur. It can be shown[9] that the probability that an atom will be excited is zero just at the value V_x but rises rapidly to a maximum as the energy of the bombarding electrons is increased. Beyond this maximum it decreases again. The maximum is not displaced as far from V_x as the maximum probability of ionization is from the minimum ionizing potential V_i.

7-7. Energy Levels—Radiation of Light.[D, E]—When an atom absorbs energy equal to an excitation potential, one of its electrons is raised to a definite higher energy level. As the electron returns to its normal level, the atom emits an amount of energy equal to that which it absorbed. This appears in the form of an electromagnetic radiation corresponding to one frequency or wave-length in the x-ray, ultra-violet, visible or heat spectrum. The energy of the impinging electrons is then the same as the difference in energy $\mathscr{E}_1 - \mathscr{E}_n$ between the two atomic states. This voltage is spoken of as the *radiation potential* (V).

The quantum theory states that the energy in each radiated photon is equal to the difference of energies of the electron in the atom. Thus,

$$h\nu = \mathscr{E}_1^{\mathcal{Q}} - \mathscr{E}_n^{\mathcal{Q}} \qquad (7\text{-}9)$$

where h is Planck's constant ($=6.624 \times 10^{-27}$) and ν is the frequency of the radiated light. Instead of the frequency (ν), the wave-length (λ) may be used; $(\lambda = c/\nu$, where c is the velocity of

---

* In the case of mercury, the 4.9 value is not the resonance potential since a meta-stable state exists at 4.6 volts.

light). Often, however, the wave-number $\tilde{\nu}$ is used. This is the number of waves per centimeter of path; i.e., $\tilde{\nu} = 1/\lambda$.

In terms of the energy of the bombarding electron, we may write

$$h\nu = Ve. \tag{7-10}$$

Substituting numerical values for the constants, we find

$$V = \frac{12,395}{\lambda} \tag{7-11}$$

and

$$\tilde{\nu} = 8,068V \tag{7-12}$$

where V is the radiation potential in volts, λ is the wave-length in angstrom units and $\tilde{\nu}$ is the number of waves per centimeter of path.

Very accurate measurements of the wave-length (λ) may be made with optical gratings. From the values so obtained and the equations above, it is possible to calculate the energy differences ($\mathscr{E}_1 - \mathscr{E}_n$) between the various electron energy levels in atoms with great precision. From inter-relationships between the values of ($\mathscr{E}_1 - \mathscr{E}_n$) for any one element, it has been found possible to deduce the separate values $\mathscr{E}_1$, $\mathscr{E}_2$, etc., of the energy levels. This type of work, *spectrum analysis*, has expanded to such large proportions that it cannot be treated adequately even in an entire chapter. There are a number of books on this subject, a few of which are listed in the references at the end of this chapter.

7-8. Collisions of the Second Kind.—So far we have dealt with inelastic collisions in which an electron gives up some of its kinetic energy in exciting an atom to a higher energy state. These are called " collisions of the first kind." Collisions of the " second kind " may be described in the following manner. When *an excited atom collides* with an electron, it may lose energy which does not appear as a photon but serves to (1) increase the relative kinetic energy with which the two particles separate from each other, (2) excite or ionize the atom or molecule, or (3) dissociate the molecule and if the energy is sufficient, to add to the kinetic energies of the particles.

7-9. Conclusion.—We may now say that the atom contains a massive, positively charged nucleus around which negative electrons are confined in known energy levels.

EXPERIMENT 7-1

MINIMUM IONIZING POTENTIALS

The purpose of this experiment is to measure the minimum ionizing potentials of various gases such as nitrogen, hydrogen, helium and argon using three-electrode tubes.

Preparation of the tube may be made by the instructor or by the advanced student in the following manner. Secure a radio tube such as the O1A and make a small hole in its top either with a flame or by cutting off the tip. Seal on a piece of soft glass tubing which contains a constriction a short distance from its end. Then seal this to a good vacuum system, blowing through a drying tube, and evacuate until an electrical discharge can no longer be made to pass through the system. (Note: If the filament is left exposed to the air for more than a few hours, water vapor will ruin it.) If possible, it is advisable to outgas the grid and plate. (See the chapter on Vacuum Technique.) Now admit a little of the gas to be tested and re-evacuate as thoroughly as possible. Let in a little of the gas again and start the evacuation but close off the system from the pumps when the pressure is around one-half mm. Anywhere from 1.0 mm. to 0.005 mm. will serve. The lower pressures are better although the amount of the positive ion currents measured will be small. The degree of evacuation may be crudely estimated by the distance between the striations. This will amount to about 1 mm. for a pressure of 1 mm. and 1 or 2 cm. for a pressure around 0.05 mm. The constriction is now closed, using as small a flame as possible, and the tube removed from the system. It is now ready for use. Of course the experiment may be carried out without removing it from the evacuation system.

Connect as in figure 7-7. The grid-voltage potentiometer should permit variations of 0.1 to 0.5 volts. A 3000 ohm potentiometer will serve. The grid voltmeter should be accurate and should have a finely divided scale. The usual B and C batteries used in radio serve nicely for the grid and plate voltages. The galvanometer may be one of the usual wall type with a sensitiveness around 10^{-8} amperes and should be provided with a shunt.

With the switch on A and normal filament current or voltage, slowly increase the grid voltage from zero, observing its values simultaneously with the deflections of the galvanometer. Plot with grid voltages as abscissae and positive ion currents (galvanometer readings) as ordinates. A larger number of readings should be made where the galvanometer first shows a deflection. The galvanometer should be made as sensitive as possible in this region, no attempt being made to measure the large currents which are produced after ionization has set in. From the graph, determine the lowest grid voltage V_1 at which the galvanometer shows any deflection.

Repeat with the switch on B to obtain the voltage V_2. The mean of these two is the minimum ionizing potential of the gas in the tube, neglecting corrections for the initial velocity of emission, contact potentials, etc. These usually amount to about one-half volt.

The experiment may be performed using the ac tubes such as type 26 (low potential drop in the filament), when the values V_1 and V_2 will be closer together or by using ac tubes of the 27 type. In the latter, the emitting cathode is heated by an auxiliary filament operated on either ac or dc and hence is all at the same potential. The switch AB is dispensed with and the final graph is like the dotted curve in figure 7–8.

Correction for initial velocities, etc., may be made if the tube is left on the vacuum system and filled with different gases. Be careful to re-evacuate and flush out with the new gas each time. A gas of known ionization potential is first used. The difference between the carefully determined experimental value and the correct value is the desired correction and may be applied to each of the succeeding gases.

Minimum Ionizing Potential of Argon.—This may be measured with an 885 tube connected as in figure 7–7A. The grid and plate are connected together and act as the anode. The voltage E_b

between the cathode and anode is to be increased until a marked change occurs in the plate current I_b. The voltage where this occurs is the desired potential. Since theory indicates that the plate current is proportional to the three-halves power of the plate potential, a plot of $I_b^{2/3}$ as ordinates and E_b as abscissae should yield two straight lines whose intersection is the minimum ionizing potential.

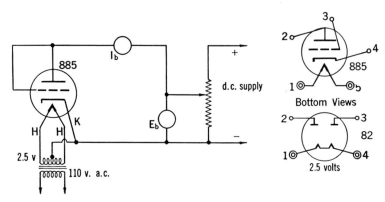

FIG. 7–7A.   Circuit for the measurement of minimum ionizing potentials.

Experiment.—Have the circuit checked by the instructor before turning on any voltages.   The heater is to be turned on one minute or more before the plate voltage and is not to be turned off until the plate voltage has been made zero.   Start with $E_b = 10$ volts and proceed in 1-volt steps up to 15 volts; then in $\frac{1}{4}$-volt steps up to about 16 volts.   Stop before I_b reaches 70 milliamperes. Plot values of $I_b^{2/3}$ vertically and E_b horizontally.   Extend the straight portions toward each other and record the ionizing potential as the value of E_b where they intersect.   Compare with the accepted value for argon.

Minimum Ionizing Potential of Mercury.—One half of a type 82 tube is used in the circuit of figure 7–7A.   Proceed as in the previous experiment on argon, but use 1-volt steps from 4 to 8 volts; then $\frac{1}{2}$-volt steps to about 12 volts.

EXPERIMENT 7–2

IONIZATION AND EXCITATION POTENTIALS OF MERCURY

Apparatus.—The circuits are shown in figure 7–10. The filament of the FG–17 tube operates on 2.5 volts and 5 amperes. The filament must be of the flat spiral rather than the V type.* The tube is operated in a vertical position in an electrical furnace wound non-inductively. A rheostat (r) is used in series with the furnace to vary the temperature. The mercury or thermocouple thermometer should be capable of reading up to 250° C.

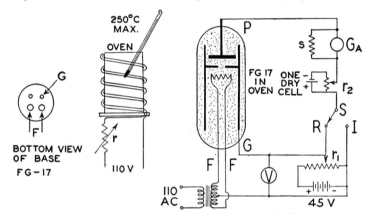

Fig. 7–10. Circuits for measuring critical potentials of mercury.

The galvanometer G_a must be sensitive (10^{-9} to 10^{-10} amperes per millimeter on a scale one meter away) and is provided with a shunt (s). The retarding potential on the plate may be 0.5 to 1.5 volts for the V_x measurements. The voltmeter (V) may have a range of 0 to 50 volts.

Precautions.—1. Heat the filament before applying the grid voltage. 2. After heating the tube to a given temperature (with the filament hot) wait one-half hour before taking readings in order to insure temperature equilibrium. 3. Start at the higher voltages on the grid and quickly run down to the lower voltages, not attempting to repeat readings.

* This was pointed out to the author by Dr. J. S. Thompson.

Radiation Potential.—Heat the tube to approximately 230° C. Connect the switch (S) to contact (R). Observe the galvanometer currents at one volt intervals of V from 45 volts to zero. Plot galvanometer deflections vertically and voltages horizontally. The curve should look like that in figure 7–9. The difference in voltage between the peaks is equal to V_r. The correction voltages (contact pd, etc.) are equal to the voltage of the lowest peak minus V_r. Compare V_r with the correct value of 4.86 volts ($\lambda = 2536.52A$).

Ionization Potential.—Heat the tube to approximately 110° C. and connect switch (S) to contact (I). Plot the galvanometer deflections from $V = 15$ volts to zero, taking readings more frequently as the current approaches zero. The voltage when the current just equals zero is the uncorrected value of V_i. Correct this value by subtracting the correction voltage measured in the V_r experiment. Compare with the accepted value of 10.39 volts.

REFERENCES

1. General Reference A, page 47.
2. K. K. Darrow, Bell System Tech. Jr., 9, 668 (1930).
3. E. Rutherford, Phil. Mag., 21, 669 (1911).
4. General Reference B, Chapter VIII.
5. General Reference A, Chapter VI.
6. K. T. Compton and F. L. Mohler, Bulletin National Research Council, 48, pages 3–9, 17–18, 42–47, 61–64 (1924).
   H. D. Smyth, Products and Processes of Ionization by Low Speed Electrons, Rev. Mod. Phys., 3, 347 (1931).
7. General Reference A, Chapter II.
8. General Reference A, Chapter IV.
9. General Reference A, Chapter III.

GENERAL REFERENCES

A.—F. L. Arnot, *Collision Processes in Gases*. Methuen & Co. (1933).

B.—Rutherford, Chadwick and Ellis, *Radiations from Radioactive Substances*. Macmillan (1930).

C.—R. B. Brode, Rev. Mod. Phys., 5, 257 (1933).

D.—R. F. Bacher and S. Goudsmit, *Atomic Energy States*. McGraw-Hill (1932).

E.—H. E. White, *Introduction to Atomic Spectra*. McGraw-Hill (1934).

CHAPTER 8

THE PASSAGE OF ELECTRICITY THROUGH GASES

8-1. Introduction.—When electricity passes through a gas many new phenomena are observed which do not exist for metallic conduction. The particles of the gas are in rapid motion, some are charged while others are neutral. Both positive and negative charges are free to move, whereas in a metal the free electrons alone serve to carry the current. Some of the charged particles in the gas drift slowly under the applied potential, others rapidly. New charges are created at various points along the gaseous path while others recombine with charges of opposite sign and are lost as electrical carriers, whereas in a metal there are no " sources " or " sinks," the current is the same from point to point. The emission of light from a wire occurs only when the current is comparatively large, whereas it is a familiar phenomenon in gas conduction. It is as though the slender wires were greatly enlarged and illuminated so that the details can be studied not only along the length of the path but at the various parts of a given cross-section. As a result of the multiplicity of phenomena which occur at the same time in gas conduction, the known laws are largely empirical and approximate. Ohm's law is valid in only a few limited cases. The amount of electricity which passes, and hence the conductivity, changes markedly with the pressure of the gas.

In this chapter, the passage of electricity through gases at atmospheric pressure will be considered first. This will be followed by a discussion of the phenomena observed as the pressure of the gas is reduced.

8-2. Sparking.[1]—At atmospheric pressure a gas, such as air, is a very poor conductor of electricity unless the potential is very high. Ordinarily to break down the resistance requires thousands of volts. Then a great surge of electricity occurs, accompanied by a brilliant flash of light. The potential needed to cause sparking depends on the shape of the electrodes, the gas between them and their distance apart.   This phenomenon offers a means of measuring high potentials in terms of the length of a spark gap.

8–3. Ionization.—However, a gas may be made slightly conductive for low potentials by many methods.   For example, when a flame is brought near a charged electroscope, charges of opposite sign, which are in the gas, move to the leaves, neutralize their charge and cause them to collapse.   These charges may be filtered out by passing the air from the flame through a glass wool or cotton plug in a metal tube (Fig. 8–1) or through a long narrow tube.   These experi-

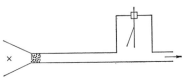

FIG. 8–1.   The conductivity of gases.

ments indicate that the charges diffuse readily to the walls of bodies very close to them.   The charges may also be filtered out by passing the gas between two charged metal plates.   The process of rendering a gas a conductor of electricity is called

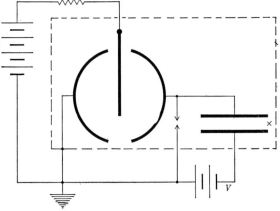

FIG. 8–2.   Connections for studying ionization currents.

ionization and may be accomplished in a variety of ways.   For example, X in figure 8–1 may be a source of x-rays, ultra-violet light, a hot filament, a bunsen burner or the radiations from radioactive substances.

A more detailed study of the charged particles, called *ions*, may be accomplished by ionizing the gas between two parallel plates.

The plates are charged to various potentials and the flow of current (of ions) between them is observed with an electrometer, as in figure 8–2. The curve in figure 8–3 results. This curve of ionization current (i) and potential (V) will be considered in three parts. The first part is OA where the current rises as the voltage is increased. When the gas is ionized by the source X (Fig. 8–2) both positive and negative particles are produced. With no potential between the plates, these move about at random, occasionally passing near an opposite charge when *recombination* to form a neutral particle may take place. Occasionally some may *diffuse* to the plates.

When, however, a potential is applied, the charged particles move, the positive to the cathode and the negative to the anode.

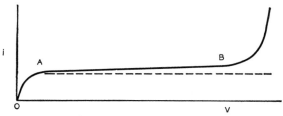

FIG. 8–3. Ionization currents and applied potentials.

The electrometer then shows a current made up of these two streams. Recombination and diffusion still take place and the shape of the curve OA depends on the relative importance of these two factors and on the velocity of the particles.

When all ions which are formed in the gas are being drawn to the plates, a further increase in the potential cannot increase the current. This *saturation current** is represented by AB, figure 8–3. Since this is a measure of the total number of ions produced by the source at X it gives a measure of the strength of the source. Thus the intensity of x-rays, radioactive substances, etc., can be measured. The use of currents below the saturation point, i.e., along OA, will obviously give erroneous results since they do not repre-

* Due to the effects of recombination and electron or ion diffusion, it is never possible to bring about complete saturation. The curve AB of figure 8–3 is fairly flat in practice but does rise slowly above the horizontal dotted line. Saturation is never quite complete when there is an appreciable density of ionization.

sent the total number of ions produced by the source, and the recombination rates may be different in different cases.

The potential which must be applied across the plates of the ionization chamber in order to insure a degree of saturation sufficiently complete for practical purposes is different in different experiments but may be roughly stated as between 50 and 200 volts per centimeter for ions produced by the beta and gamma rays of radioactive substances. In these cases, the ions are produced uniformly in the gas in the ionization chamber, but with alpha particles the ions are produced in high concentration along a narrow beam. Rapid recombination results, requiring the use of several thousand volts per centimeter to give saturation. Further, the potential necessary to produce saturation depends on the density and kind of gas being ionized, the distance between the plates and the presence of dust or moisture. However, if the saturation current is given in amperes per volt per cubic centimeter of air at standard pressure and temperature, it is an accurate specification of the intensity of the source of ionization. For uniformly ionized gases the value of the saturation current increases as the total mass of gas between the plates is increased.

If, now, the potential is still further increased the particles travel with greater and greater velocities (particularly the negative charges) until they acquire sufficient energy to break up neutral atoms at a collision. Thus new positive and negative charges are formed which also move under the applied field and increase the current. This is represented by the curve to the right of B in figure 8–3. This rapid increase continues until, with rising potential, a brush discharge or spark occurs. These large currents cannot be measured with the electrometer. As it is difficult to observe *ionization by collision* at atmospheric pressure, it is better to partially evacuate the region between the plates.

Finally, it is to be noted that the curve does not rise sharply from the saturation value when ionization by collision sets in. This is due to the fact that not all the particles are traveling with exactly the same velocity. Some are moving faster and some slower than the majority.

There are three general ways in which ionization may be produced:

1. By direct impact by moving positive or negative charges.
2. By electromagnetic radiation such as x-rays, ultra-violet light or gamma rays.
3. By heat or thermionic emission.

In order to learn more of the nature of ions, we shall now study in greater detail their recombination and mobility.

8–4. Recombination.[2]—This is measured by the rate of decay of the ionization after the ionizing source has been removed. Since the charges are in motion, they do not all recombine at the same time. Rutherford has determined the rate of recombination in several cases by the following method.

A gas is passed at a known rate through a metal tube, as is shown by the arrows in figure 8–4. All ions are filtered out by a

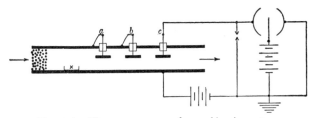

Fig. 8–4. The measurement of recombination rates.

cotton plug as the gas enters the tube. The gas is then ionized by a radioactive source at X. During its passage down the tube, recombination is taking place so that the number of ions existing at a is greater than the number at b, which, in turn, is greater than the number at c, as indicated by the saturation currents measured with an electrometer. From these readings and the time required for the gas to pass between the electrodes a, b and c, the rate of recombination is calculated. This method is very inaccurate. On the other hand, precision measurements require equipment of considerably greater complexity.[3]

It is found that the number (dn/dt) of recombinations each second is approximately the same for different gases and decreases as the pressure is reduced. It is proportional to the square of the number of ions of one kind present at a given time in a unit volume and represents the number of collisions of ions which result in recombination to form neutral particles. The value of dn/dt so found for oxygen is $1.6 \times 10^{-6} \times n^2$, whereas for uncharged particles the kinetic theory gives the number of collisions per second per cc. as $1.25 \times 10^{-10} \times n^2$. Consequently, due to electrical attractions, the number of collisions resulting in recombination is 10,000 times greater than the number of collisions between neutral particles.

8–5. Mobility.[4]—The mobility of an ion is defined as its velocity in centimeters per second under an accelerating potential of one volt per centimeter. This is the average velocity of drift of the ions due to the electrical field and it is superimposed on the irregular kinetic motions of the charged particles.

There are two basic schemes for measuring the mobilities of ions, called the *flow* and the *alternating current* methods. A modification of the Zeleny flow method has been used by Erickson[5] to

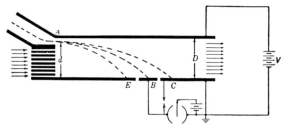

FIG. 8–5. Erickson's method of measuring the mobility of ions

study the aging of ions (see figure 8–5). An ionized gas is introduced into a high-velocity, uniform air current at the point *A*. As the ions are carried along they are deflected to the metal plate *EBC* by means of the high voltage *V*. A small part *B* of this plate is insulated from the rest and connected to an electrometer. The ions with high mobility will fall at *E* and those with low mobility will reach *C*. The time (*t*) for the particles to travel from *A* to *B* is obtained from the velocity of the air current which is determined by means of a pitot tube. Their actual velocity under the electrical field in the direction *d* is given by $v = d/t$ and their velocity under unit field is given by

$$k = \frac{v}{V/D} = \frac{dD}{tV} \tag{8-1}$$

centimeters per second per volt per centimeter, at a pressure of one atmosphere. If the atmospheric pressure decreases, the ions suffer fewer collisions and travel faster.

A simple modification of the Rutherford alternating current method is shown in figure 8–6. The ions are produced in a gas in the region immediately above a metal gauze B by some ionizing source such as a radioactive substance at X. Some of these are drawn upward to the metal plate A by the fixed potential v, while those of opposite sign are drawn to the gauze B and, because of their momentum, pass through its meshes into the region above the metal plate C. On applying an alternating potential of square wave form between B and C (by means of the commutator D)

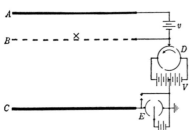

these ions are attracted or repelled from C each half cycle. The procedure is to adjust the voltage V, the frequency of the applied potential and the distance BC until a current is first observed in the electrometer E. Under these conditions the velocity of the ion is such that it can just travel the distance BC during one-half cycle. Knowing the distance the ion travels in a known time, its actual velocity and also its velocity under unit field may be calculated.

Fig. 8–6. The measurement of the mobility of ions.

Neither of the methods just described is accurate to better than 10 or 20 per cent. Accurate values may be obtained with the latter method, however, by the following modifications. In figure 8–6, A is removed, B is a solid metal plate and the ions are formed between the two plates B and C, in a layer of definite thickness, at a definite position and for a definite time. This is accomplished by means of flashes of x-rays which have passed through a slit in a rotating lead disc. The commutator D is mounted on the same shaft as the disc. Then the ions are started on their trip to the opposite plate from a known point at a known instant and greater accuracy results. This modification has been used with success by Bradbury.[6]

In the Powell and Brata method,[7] accurate measurements of ion mobilities are made as follows: An alternating potential is used to send pulses of ions, one each half-cycle, through a metal grid into an electric field. They are drawn by the field to a second grid, which they reach after the lapse of a definite time, depending on their mobilities.   The same alternating potential used to produce the pulses of ions is used to prevent their continued passage beyond the second grid to a collecting plate and electrometer, except during the time when the latter attracts rather than repels the ions.   This occurs when the period of the alternations is equal to the time for the ions to travel from the first grid to the second, or some integral multiple thereof.

The mobility of " old " ions in dry air is 1.6 for the positive and 2.18 for the negative, as measured by Loeb and his collaborators.   For most gases the positive ions move more slowly than the negative.   However, for freshly formed positive ions in air, the mobility is just as great as for the negative.   The mobility of ions is inversely proportional to the pressure over wide ranges and is independent of the inertia of the ion.   In certain gases such as hydrogen, helium, nitrogen and mercury vapor, the electron formed by ionization remains free.   The mobility of electrons is very great, ranging from several hundred to many thousand centimeters per second per volt per centimeter.   In other gases (the electro-negative) such as oxygen, chlorine and water vapor, the electron attaches itself to a neutral molecule and forms a negative ion.   " The ion in general consists of the initially charged positive or negative molecule or atom and, according to the nature of the surrounding gas and the electrochemical affinity of those gas molecules, may have one to three foreign molecules attached, the combinations being specific electrochemical products such as the positive molecule-ammonia ion, positive molecule-methyl amine ion, positive molecule-ether ion, or the negatively charged molecule plus chlorine, hydrochloric acid, water vapor, or alcohol molecule.   It must be emphasized that the ion will shed one impurity attached and take another one which is more strongly attracted.   Thus ammonia replaces some unknown constituent in ordinary air and makes a less cumbersome ion.   In turn, however, if there is a trace of ether present, the ether will replace the ammonia and make a very cumbersome, slow ion.   There is no evidence for the old concept of a cluster ion which is a loosely bound aggregate of six to twenty molecules." [8]

8–6. Conductivity at Reduced Pressures.—At atmospheric pressure a gas does not conduct electricity unless very high potentials are used or the gas is ionized by some agency such as x-rays, radioactive rays, or ultra-violet light. However, as the pressure is lowered it is found that a gas becomes conductive, reaching a maximum and then, at very low pressures again becoming an extremely poor conductor.

To study the passage of electricity through a gas while the pressure is being lowered, connect a vacuum pump and gauge (see chapter 16) to a long glass tube containing two metal plates sealed in with wires. The current from the secondary of an induction coil or transformer passes between the metal plates causing, among other things, the emission of light by the particles of gas left in the tube. When the pressure of the gas has been reduced to a few centimeters of mercury, a wavy streamer of light passes from one electrode to the other. As the pressure is still further reduced, the streamer broadens until it fills the entire cross-section of the tube with a glow of light. The color of the light emitted depends on the gas in the tube, having a greenish color with mercury vapor, red with hydrogen, brilliant red-orange with neon, yellow with helium, and bright red with nitrogen. At approximately one-half millimeter pressure, the conductivity is very good, as may be shown by a spark gap in parallel with the tube. Unless the gap is very short, the electricity chooses the longer path through the discharge tube.

8–7. Starting and Stopping Conditions.—The starting conditions for a glow discharge tube may be crudely described as follows. It is assumed that there are always a few electrically charged particles in the tube at the start. These are accelerated when a potential difference of a few hundred volts is applied between the electrodes and acquire sufficient energy to excite and to ionize the neutral gas atoms or molecules. In turn, the ions created by collision, and the photo-electrons produced by the light given out by the excited atoms, create additional electrical charges until, finally, a complicated array of ionizations, recombinations, drift motions, etc., is established and a measurable current flows through the tube.

There is a certain minimum of voltage, called the *striking potential* V_s, which must be applied across the tube before the discharge will start.   The value of V_s is different for different tubes and gases. Its variation with the pressure of the gas follows a curve of the type shown in figure 8–7.   It may be seen that over a broad pressure range the voltage required to start the discharge is comparatively small.   At higher pressures the ions cannot acquire sufficient energy to ionize because of their frequent collisions with the gas atoms, while at the lower pressure there are so few gas atoms that it is difficult to initiate the discharge.

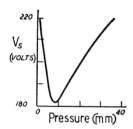

FIG. 8–7. Striking potentials, V_s, for helium at different pressures.

The time for a discharge to start after a suitably high potential has been applied is usually very small, a few micro-seconds, especially if the voltage is well above V_s; but occasionally, when the cathode is contaminated and surface charges exist, the time lag may extend to as much as several minutes.   The time for the discharge to cease after the applied potential has been removed depends on the rate at which the ions recombine with each other or diffuse to the walls and electrodes. This varies from a few micro-seconds to a few milli-seconds.

After a discharge has once started, the applied potential may be lowered below the striking potential, to the *extinction voltage* V_x, before the discharge ceases.   This hysteresis phenomenon is illustrated in figure 8–8, where the current i through the tube is plotted vertically.   This principle has been used in the construction of " relaxation " oscillators, where a battery sends current into a condenser through a resistance, charging it at a rate which depends on the magnitude of the resistance and the capacitance.   A glow lamp, permanently connected in parallel with the condenser, is in the non-conductive state until the voltage across the condenser has risen to the value V_s.   Then the glow discharge suddenly starts, the condenser discharges through the tube until the potential drops below V_x, after which the process is repeated.   The frequency of discharge may be varied over wide limits by changing the resistance or the capacitance.

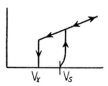

FIG. 8–8. Striking and extinction voltages of a glow discharge tube.

8–8. Probes.[9]—It is possible to obtain a great deal of information as to the potentials, positive ion and electron concentrations and the equivalent temperatures of the electrons and ions at various points in a discharge tube by means of probes or exploring electrodes. For many years the procedure in determinations of the potential and potential gradient in a gas-filled tube was to insert a small wire or probe at the desired point and to measure the potential which it acquired, by means of an electroscope or electrometer. When the discharge is first started, electrons and ions move to the probe. However, the electrons move much faster than the ions, so that more of them reach the probe in a given time and hence give it a potential which is negative with respect to that of the gas in the tube. Thus "floating" probe potentials made in this manner differ from the potential of the discharge at the point under test by an appreciable amount.

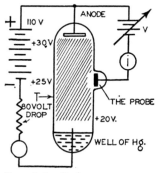

Fig. 8–9. Probe measurements in a mercury arc.

In 1924, Langmuir made an extensive study of probe methods and showed in what manner one may obtain reliable information as to the fundamental phenomena occurring in the tubes. In one method, the probe consists of a filament which is alternately heated and cooled. With the tube in operation, the potential of the filament with respect to the anode, or the cathode, is adjusted to a fixed value. If, at this time, the probe is negative with respect to the surrounding gas, it will repel electrons during the intervals when the filament is capable of emitting them. As the potential of the filament is made less negative and approaches that of the gas, the flow of electrons from it (during the intervals when it is hot) becomes smaller and smaller. When there is no change of current, with the filament hot or cold, the filament is at the same potential as that of the gas.

The *cold probe method* developed by Langmuir will now be described with the aid of figure 8–9. A current of 1–3 amperes flows through the mercury-filled discharge tube (*T*) (the auxiliary mechanism by which this is started is not shown in the diagram) and the shaded area represents the region in which the familiar greenish light appears. The total potential drop across the tube is 30 volts, as shown, and the potential at some point along the discharge is to be measured. Although this potential is the unknown quantity, it is shown in the figure as + 25 volts, for clarity in the following discussion. In this case, the potential (V_s) of the gas near the probe with respect to the anode is 30 minus 25, equals 5 volts.

The probe circuit is shown in the upper right corner of the figure 8–9. A curve of the current (i) and the probe potential (V) with respect to the anode, is shown in figure 8–10. The current

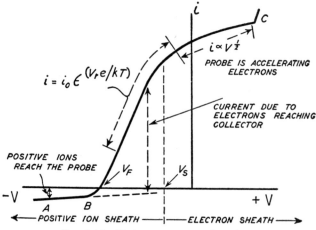

FIG. 8–10.   Probe current *vs.* probe voltage.

is considered as " positive " when electrons flow out of the gas onto the probe.

In the region (A) where the probe is very negative with respect to the anode, electrons are repelled with high velocity from the vicinity of the probe and positive ions are slowly drawn to it. A condition is soon reached in which there is an excess of moving positive ions left in the neighborhood of the probe. The electrostatic lines of force extend from the moving positive ions to the negative probe so that the force of the electric field of the probe no longer extends beyond the *positive ion sheath* into the discharge tube. The thickness of the sheath can be observed as a dark region around the probe, as indicated in figure 8–9. The current to the probe (i_p), under these conditions, is made up of positive ions alone. Further, the only positive ions which are able to reach the probe are those which, due to their random thermal motion in the gas, chance to strike the boundary of the sheath.

As the probe is made less negative, by decreasing voltage (V) in figure 8–9, the positive ion sheath becomes slightly thinner and (i_p) becomes smaller. In addition, at B in figure 8–10, some of the faster electrons in the discharge tube have sufficient energy to force their way against the retarding potential and reach the negative probe. At V_f the number of positive ions which are attracted to the probe is equal to the number of electrons which are able to reach it against the opposing force. This is the voltage (with respect to the anode) which a floating or free probe would assume; it is not the potential of the gas.

At decreasingly negative potentials of the probe, even the slower electrons in the gas are able to force their way to it. At V_s, figure 8–10, the probe has reached the potential of the space (of the gas) at this place in the tube, the positive ion sheath has disappeared, and all electrons which, in their random motion in the gas discharge chance to reach the probe, are collected by it. When the probe is made still less negative (with respect to the anode), it will be more positive than the space and will serve to attract electrons. The curve to the right of V_s rises very slowly since there exists a negative electron sheath, similar but thinner and of opposite sign to the positive ion sheath of the region B. If the probe is made still more positive with respect to the space, the electrons travel toward it with increasing velocities until, at C, they are able to ionize the gas close to the probe and create a current of such large magnitude as frequently to melt the probe.

The next four sections give a more quantitative discussion of the use of probes for the measurement of the phenomena occurring in discharge tubes.

8–9. Maxwellian Distribution of Electron Velocities.[10]—It has been shown that, *if* the electrons in a discharge tube have velocities distributed according to the Maxwellian law, the electron current (i) to the probe is given by the equation

$$i = i_0 \epsilon^{(V_r e/kT)}, \tag{8–2}$$

where i_0 is a constant, $\epsilon = 2.718$, V_r is the retarding potential across the positive ion sheath, e is the electronic charge, k is Boltzmann's constant and T is the equivalent temperature of the electrons in degrees absolute.   If V is the applied potential and V_s the potential of the gas, with respect to the anode, then

$$V_r = V - V_s. \tag{8-3}$$

Whether such a velocity distribution exists or not may be tested by plotting logarithms of the electron current (i) against V, as in figure 8–11.   Substituting equation 8–3 in 8–2 and taking logarithms of both sides, gives

$$\log_\epsilon i = \text{constant} + \frac{e}{kT} V, \tag{8-4}$$

since V_s is constant.   The logarithmic plot will be a straight line if the distribution is Maxwellian. This is often found to be true in practice.

The probe will not disturb the Maxwellian distribution provided its dimensions are small compared with the mean-free-path of the electrons in the gas, for then the electrons which reach it will have come without collision from a comparatively distant region.

At higher gas pressures and also for potentials causing large electron currents; i.e., those potentials in the vicinity of the space potential and more positive, a deviation may be expected.

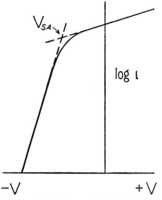

Fig. 8–11.   Logarithmic plot of probe current.

In fact, an approximate method of determining the space potential consists in observing from the logarithmic curve the voltage (V_{sa}) given by the extrapolated straight portions.   See figure 8–11.

8–10.   Quantities Which Can Be Calculated from the Logarithmic Plot.—From equation 8–4, it can be seen that the slope (s) of the straight line at the left of figure 8–11 is equal to e/kT.

In computing s from the line, the current values may be expressed in either amperes, milliamperes or other units, since $\log i_1 - \log i_2 = \log i_1/i_2$ and the ratio i_1/i_2 is not altered by a change of units. Dividing V values by 300 to convert from volts to electro-static units and using $e = 4.8 \times 10^{-10}$ and $k = 1.38 \times 10^{-16}$ gives

$$T = \frac{11,600}{s} \text{, degrees absolute.} \tag{8-5}$$

If common logarithms are used, the constant will be 5040 instead of 11,600; i.e., s in this and in subsequent equations must be multiplied by 2.303. The " partial " or electron temperatures so found, range from tens of thousands to a few hundreds of thousands of degrees absolute.

If the velocities are distributed according to the Maxwellian law, as evidenced by a straight line in the logarithmic plot, then the electrons may be treated as a perfect gas, according to the usual developments of the Kinetic Theory.[11] From this, and from the established relation between electron volts (V_e) and the average kinetic energy ($\mathscr{E}$, in ergs), it can be seen that

$$\mathscr{E} = \tfrac{1}{2}m\overline{v^2} = \tfrac{3}{2}kT = \frac{V_e e}{300}, \tag{8-6}$$

where V_e is the equivalent energy of the electrons in volts, $\overline{v^2}$ is the mean of the squared values of their thermal velocities, e is the electronic charge in e.s.u. and m is the mass of the electron. It is also known that the average velocity $\bar{v} = (8\overline{v^2}/3\pi)^{\frac{1}{2}}$. This, with the known constants and equations 8–5 and 8–6 permits the following quantities to be evaluated:

$$V_e = \frac{3}{2s} = \frac{T}{7733} \text{, volts} \tag{8-7}$$

($V_e = 0.6515/s$, if common logarithms are used), and

$$\bar{v} = \frac{6.7 \times 10^7}{\sqrt{s}} \text{, cm./sec.,} \tag{8-8}$$

as well as

$$\mathscr{E} = \frac{2.4 \times 10^{-12}}{s} \text{ ergs.} \tag{8-9}$$

8–11. Current to a Small Cylindrical Probe.—From the Kinetic Theory, the number of electrons striking unit area each second is $n\bar{v}/4$, where n is the number of electrons per cubic centimeter, of average velocity, $\bar{v}$. This assumes that the electrons have a Maxwellian distribution of velocities. If each electron carries a charge e and the area of the collecting surface is $A \cdot F$, then the current to the probe is

$$i = \frac{n e \bar{v} A F}{4}, \qquad (8\text{–}10)$$

where A is the surface area of the probe and F is a correction factor for the extension of its electrical field into the surrounding space. $A = 2\pi r l$, where r is the radius of the cylindrical probe and l is its length in centimeters. For accelerating fields ($V_a = V - V_s$), between the gas and the probe, and when $V_a e/kT > 2$, as indicated on the right side of V_s in figure 8–10, it can be shown that

$$F = \frac{2}{\sqrt{\pi}} \sqrt{\frac{V_a e}{kT} + 1}. \qquad (8\text{–}11)$$

Substituting in equation 8–10 gives

$$i^2 = a + SV, \qquad (8\text{–}12)$$

where a and S are constants. If, then, values of i^2 are plotted as ordinates and values of V as abscissae, a straight line should be obtained whose slope is S. (See figure 8–12.) These equations do not apply to values of V near the space potential, since here the electron sheath is not large in comparison with the probe, nor do they apply to values of V more positive

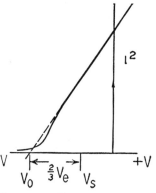

Fig. 8–12. Current squared vs. probe potential.

than V_s by amounts of the order of magnitude of the ionization potential of the gas in the discharge tube, since then the electrons are able to ionize the gas atoms.

8–12. Quantities Which Can Be Calculated from the $i^2 - V$ Curve.—The electron density (n) can be calculated from the slope (S) of the $i^2 - V$ curve and the surface area (A) of the probe. Thus, solving the equations above and evaluating the constants, we find

$$n = 3.32 \times 10^{11} \frac{\sqrt{S}}{A}, \qquad (8\text{–}13)$$

where S is measured in practical units (amperes²/volts) and A is in square centimeters. Densities as high as 10^{11} electrons per cubic centimeter have been observed.

An accurate value of the space potential (V_s) can be determined as follows. The straight portion of the $i^2 - V$ curve is extrapolated to the voltage axis, as indicated at V_o, figure 8–12. Then $i = 0$ and equation 8–12 becomes

$$0 = a + SV_o. \qquad (8\text{–}14)$$

The constants a and S are evaluated from equations 8–10 and 8–11 and the relation $V_e e = 3kT/2$ is introduced. This leads to the equation

$$V_s = V_o + \tfrac{2}{3}V_e, \qquad (8\text{–}15)$$

where V_e is given by equation 8–7.

8–13. The Glow Discharge.—As stated before, at pressures of a few centimeters, a wavy streamer of light is seen in a tube through which electricity is passing. This broadens as the pressure is reduced until it fills the cross-section of the tube. Closer examination will reveal regions along the tube where the intensity of the light is not so great as in other regions. Figure 8–13 shows

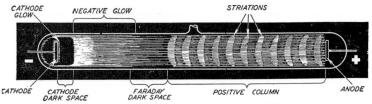

Fig. 8–13. A glow discharge at approximately 0.1 millimeter pressure.

the appearance of a glow or Geissler discharge when the pressure is about 0.1 millimeter, together with the names which have been given to the various regions, while figure 8–14 shows qualitatively the various characteristics of a glow discharge.

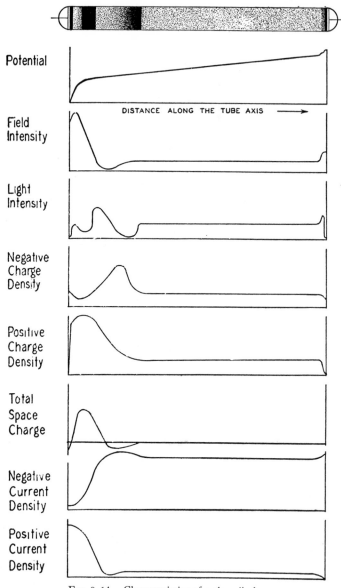

FIG. 8–14.   Characteristics of a glow discharge.

At the higher pressures, the cathode dark space is narrower and the striations in the positive column, if present, are closer together. As the pressure is reduced, the cathode dark space, or, as it is sometimes called, the Crookes' dark space, becomes longer and the striations are farther apart. Experience will soon allow one to estimate the pressure in a tube from these phenomena. As a rough indication, the cathode dark space will be about 1 centimeter long when the pressure is 0.08 millimeters. At a given pressure, the distance from the cathode to the positive column has an approximately fixed value, whereas the positive column fills the remainder of the tube, regardless of its length. In the neon advertising signs, where the pressure is several millimeters, it is the positive column which is seen. If, at a given pressure, the anode is moved toward the cathode, the positive column is reduced in length, but little change occurs in the phenomena near the cathode. When the anode is moved still closer to the cathode, into the negative glow, changes in length occur and the discharge ceases just as the anode passes into the cathode dark space. With two cathodes and two anodes, in connected, parallel tubes with one pair of electrodes far apart and the other one separated by a distance less than the length of the cathode dark space, the discharge prefers the " alternate " longer path. It is obvious, therefore, that the region near the cathode is of great importance in the maintenance of the discharge.

The potential which exists across a discharge tube is largely determined by the pressure of the gas. Consider a tube in series with a protective resistance and a *d.c.* source of potential. If the e.m.f. of the source is increased, the current through the tube will be increased. The larger current causes a larger *ir* drop in the external resistance and in the internal resistance of the battery. Yet the potential difference between the electrodes will remain approximately the same as before (a few hundred volts). One of the outstanding characteristics of a glow discharge is that a large potential drop occurs in the cathode dark space. This is shown in figure 8–14, and again points to the importance of the phenomena in the region near the cathode. Due to the large potential drop in the cathode dark space, it is here that most of the heating in the tube takes place. If cathodes are not to be melted, their areas must be large when large currents are used.

A " *normal* " discharge occurs in a tube when, with small current, the cathode glow covers only a portion of the cathode surface. If the current is increased, this luminous area extends until the entire surface is covered. Beyond this point the discharge is " *abnormal*." For the condition of normal discharge, it has been found that the current density, i_n, is constant; i.e., the area of the cathode covered by the glow is strictly proportional to the total current through the tube. Very approximately, and within restricted ranges of pressure (p), $i_n = kp^2$, where k is a constant. This rule is exceedingly approximate.

Further, with a normal discharge, it has been found that the potential difference between the cathode and a point just in the negative glow is a constant. This is called the *normal cathode fall of potential* (V_n), and has a characteristic value for each combination of gas and electrode material. For platinum and oxygen, its value is 364 volts, for aluminum and nitrogen 179 volts, for iron and helium at pressures from 14 to 0.6 millimeters, it rises from 153 to 158 volts. V_n is least for the inert gases and with electrodes of material having a low work function. Very approximately, $V_n = pd_n$, where d_n is the length of the cathode dark space under normal conditions. This rule is exceedingly rough.

The *cathode dark space* has a sharp boundary at the negative glow, of approximately the same shape as that of the cathode. Positive ions are formed in this dark space and move toward the cathode where, with other possible agencies, they eject electrons. The electrons, which are then repelled from the cathode, suffer many collisions (perhaps 10 to 100) with the gas atoms in the dark space. The cathode dark space is a region of positive space charge, the number of positive ions exceeding the number of electrons. J. J. Thomson has studied the electrical fields in this dark space by observing the deflection of a beam of high-speed electrons shot through this region from an electron gun.

The *negative glow* contains a high concentration of both positive ions and electrons; as many as 10^{11} per cubic centimeter of each have been observed. The concentration falls off in the Faraday dark space so that electrons move into it from the negative glow by diffusion.

The *positive column* will be uniformly illuminated throughout its length if very pure monatomic gases are used. However, viewed in a rotating mirror, striations will be observed moving with considerable velocity. In the case of argon, the striations move from anode to cathode with a velocity between 1,000 and 10,000 centimeters per second. The potential gradient in a uniform positive column is proportional to the pressure and ranges from 0.05 to 150 volts per centimeters for different gases at 1 millimeter pressure. It is less, for a given tube, gas and pressure when the current is greater. Also, for a given gas, pressure and current, it is less when the tube has a larger cross-section. The number of positive ions is equal to the number of electrons at all points in a uniform positive column; this is called a *plasma*. With large currents, relative displacements of the ions and electrons in the plasma have been found to produce electrical oscillations.[12]

When *striations* exist, they are usually concave and diffuse toward the anode. Their separation increases as the pressure is decreased or as the tube diameter is increased and is independent of the current, provided this is large. The potential rises and falls along the positive column whenever striations are present; the potential difference between striations amounting to only a few volts. The number of ions or of electrons per cubic centimeter in the positive column ranges from one-tenth to one one-hundredth of that in the negative glow; with a maximum of approximately 10^{10}.

If one of the electrodes is small and the other is comparatvely large, a *rectifying action* takes place so that the current passes in only one direction. The large electrode acts as the cathode. This phenomenon is due to the fact that a current much greater than the normal current density over the whole cathode cannot be passed through the tube without applying much higher potentials. Thus when the large electrode is negative, its large surface will allow a strong current to flow with normal potentials. However, when the small electrode is negative, a relatively small current will cause its surface to be completely covered with the negative glow. Greater currents require abnormal cathode falls so that the maximum reverse potential applied is only sufficient to cause a relatively small current to flow.*

If the pressure is reduced until the cathode dark space reaches

* The direction of the current as discussed here is that of the electron stream and hence is opposite to that used in practice.

the walls of the containing vessel, a fluorescence occurs, greenish, yellowish or bluish, according to the kind of glass. This fluorescence is due to *x-rays* and begins with pressures of the order of 0.001 mm. of mercury. Whereas current passes easily through the gas at higher pressures, it now becomes difficult for it to get through. Higher potentials are needed, since there is a scarcity of particles to act as carriers, unless a hot filament is used to supply them.

If high potential discharges from a condenser are passed between metal electrodes placed less than a millimeter apart in a vacuum around 10^{-4} mm., a brilliant flash of light is obtained.* This " *hot spark* " is a good source for use in the extreme ultraviolet (100 to 2000 angstroms). The radiations are characteristic of the atoms making up the electrodes and the gases occluded therein. Using the hot spark, various stages in the removal of the valence electrons of the atoms have been studied.

8-14. Gas-filled Triodes.[13]—"Thyratron" and "grid-glow" tubes contain a cathode, a control grid, an anode and a gas whose pressure ranges from a few thousandths to a few tenths of a millimeter. Their action is entirely different from that of the high vacuum triodes, since the grid, which might well be called a trigger grid, serves to initiate an *arc discharge* between the cathode and the plate. Once started, the plate current is no longer affected by the grid voltage and can only be stopped by reducing the plate voltage to zero. The magnitude of the plate current is determined by the external battery voltage and series resistance and can have any value up to the full emission of the cathode. In practice, the upper limit of current is determined by the heating which the tube can stand and ranges from a few milliamperes in the smaller tubes to hundreds and even thousands of amperes in the larger tubes. Since the grid serves only to start the plate current, the tubes are comparable to lock-in relays where a small amount of energy is used to turn on the large currents of a local source of power. The commercial trade name " thyratron " means " door."

Let the grid of a gas-filled tube be made appreciably negative. When the plate voltage is first applied, electrons from the cathode produce positive ions and electrons near the grid. Due to the difference in mobilities of these charged particles, positive ion sheaths

---

* A spark gap in air is used in series with the vacuum spark.

are formed around the grid wires. If the grid is sufficiently negative, the sheaths will be large enough to overlap and prevent the
current flow to the plate. If, now, the grid is made progressively
less negative, the sheaths become thinner until, at a critical value
of the grid potential, they no longer close the largest hole in
the grid. The electric field of the plate is then able to attract
electrons in the region between the cathode and the grid and a
current flows through the tube. When the current has once
started, the sheaths all become much thinner and, although subject to small changes if the grid is made more negative, cannot
again increase in size to the point of stopping the discharge until
the current is practically cut off by a
reduction of the plate voltage to zero.

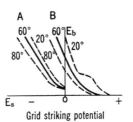

FIG. 8-15. Striking curves of gas-filled triodes.

The critical or *striking potential*, E_s,
of the grid depends on the potential, E_b
of the plate, as shown in figure 8-15.
In this figure, the curves show the
value of the grid potential, for a given
plate potential, which will just start
the current through the tube. Curve
A is for the more usual " negatively
controlled " tubes; B is for a " posi-
tively controlled " tube. In the latter case, negative space
charges on the glass walls add their effects to that of the grid
itself. Tubes filled with a rare gas such as argon are used for
the lower voltages and are not subject to temperature effects.
For tubes operated at the higher voltages (above a few hundred
volts) mercury vapor is used. The pressure of the vapor increases
with temperature and the striking potential becomes more negative, as indicated by the dotted lines in figure 8-15.

The ratio of the plate voltage, E_b, to the grid striking potential,
E_s, is known as the *grid control ratio* ρ. Thus,

$$\rho = \frac{E_b}{E_s}. \qquad (8\text{-}16)$$

This is constant for a given tube over the straight portion of the
striking curve.

In one form of the cold-electrode grid-glow tubes, a cylindrical
metal plate serves as the cathode. The anode consists of a wire

mounted along the axis of the cathode and the grid is located between these electrodes. The rectifying action of a glow discharge with large cathode and small anode has been discussed previously. In the hot-cathode tubes, high efficiency dull emitter cathodes are used. If the positive ions which bombard the filament possess too great an energy, above the *disintegration voltage* (about 30 volts), the emitting surface will be destroyed. If, therefore, the plate voltage is applied before the filament has reached the normal operating temperature, the high voltage across the tube will give the positive ions a destructively high velocity and the filament will be ruined or its life shortened. The filament must be hot before the plate voltage is applied. However, after the filament is heated, and a discharge started, the voltage across the tube falls to a comparatively fixed value (of 10–20 volts) characteristic of the pressure in the tube, as discussed before. It is fortunate that there is a small range of voltage between the disintegration voltage and the ionizing potential needed to create ions in the gas.

After the discharge in a thyratron has ceased, it requires about 10^{-4} second for the positive ions to be collected. If the plate voltage is restored to full value in less than this time then, regardless of the grid voltage, the tube will resume its conducting state. The minimum time is of no consequence in many applications but places a definite limit on the speed with which a thyratron circuit may be made to repeat its operation. Thyratrons, in general, cannot, be turned off in less than the time cited and will not be suitable therefore in circuits requiring operation faster than 10 kilocycles. Indeed, they will generally become unstable at even somewhat lower frequencies and should not be counted on for reliable operation at frequencies in excess of about 1 kilocycle. An example of high-speed operation is encountered in scale circuits that are used to count impulses in nuclear physics. Because of the high statistical probability of close double pulses in a random distribution, thyratron scaling circuits seldom give accurate results when counting at rates in excess of 100 random pulses per second. There is no tube on the market at the present time in which this de-ionization time is lessened by as much as a factor of ten. Since, however, it would be important to have a faster-acting tube, it is to be expected that manufacturers will devote attention to possible designs in the near future.

In modern research laboratories, thyratrons, both small and large, are used for a variety of control operations. The large ones, for example the General Electric type FG27, are used to start and stop heavy currents such as heating currents in thermostating applications or cloud chamber control circuits. The small ones, types 884,885 or the two-grid 2051, are frequently used to drive recording counters, mechanical registers, scaling circuits and a whole variety of other devices. Extinction of the thyratron may readily be accomplished by operating the plate on a.c. instead of d.c. Since the discharge takes place on the half cycle when the plate is positive, it automatically discontinues on the next half cycle following the instant that the grid becomes negative. By this procedure the thyratron may be given the useful property of conducting while the grid is positive and not conducting while the grid is negative, without the need of a relay to interrupt the plate current. If, on the other hand, d.c. is used on the plate, the grid loses control as soon as the discharge starts.

EXPERIMENT 8-1

IONIZATION CURRENT MEASUREMENT WITH A QUADRANT ELECTROMETER

The purpose of this experiment is to observe the current through a gas at atmospheric pressure with various accelerating potentials.

Apparatus.—A quadrant electrometer is well suited to this purpose. A discussion of the adjustment and precautions to be taken is given in chapter 17 and should be read by the student at this time. A deflection of 1000 millimeters per volt increase of potential may readily be obtained on a scale at a distance of one meter and, since the capacity of the quadrant and connection may be as small as 50 electro-static units, a deflection of one centimeter per minute is caused by a current of only 10^{-14} amperes. In other words, the quadrant electrometer readily measures the small currents set up in an ionized gas. In fact, the currents may be so great that the needle moves too rapidly for accurate measurement, in which case it is necessary to add a small capacity in parallel with the ionization chamber.

The ionization chamber may, for simplicity, consist of an electroscope such as that in figure 17-1, without the telescope or the leaf. The metal box serves as one plate of the chamber and the leaf support, which is well insulated with an amber plug, serves as the collecting plate. The latter is to be joined by a short piece of bare copper to one quadrant of the electrometer. For small currents and for accurate measurements the connecting wire should be enclosed in a grounded metal shield.

The ionizing source may consist of a radium D tube wrapped in aluminum about 0.01 centimeter thick. The aluminum cuts off the alpha rays which would ionize the gas in such a manner that large voltages would be required to produce saturation. The beta rays which do pass through the aluminum do not ionize the gas as profusely as do the alpha rays (only about one one-hundredth as much) but saturation occurs at a lower voltage.

Precautions.—For precision work, always time the deflections over the same scale divisions and keep the needle potential constant. Further, it is necessary to place a grounded metal shield around the grounding key and the ionization chamber, which are as close to each other as possible, and to ground the case of the electrometer. Otherwise the readings will be masked by the natural leak of the instrument.

Experiment.—1. Connect as shown in figure 17–13 of chapter 17. Adjust the electrometer in the fashion described in the experiment at the end of that chapter. If a Dolezalek electrometer is used, raise the needle to a potential of 100 volts (V). (If the lighting circuit is 110 volts d.c., this may be used for rough work.)

2. Ionize the air between the metal plates A and B by placing the radioactive substance on A, or by some other convenient means.

3. Make the accelerating potential (v) 2, 4, 6, 12, 20, 40, 60, 80, 100 and 160 volts in succession and raise the key K to measure the relative currents. Do not let the maximum rate of deflection exceed one centimeter in five seconds. Test whether the rate of motion of the needle is uniform. There are usually irregularities at the beginning of the deflection so that comparisons should be made by observing the time for the spot of light to pass over from 2 to 5 centimeters after the needle has begun to move steadily.

4. Plot the rates of deflection as ordinates and the accelerating potentials as abscissae.

5. If the ionization chamber can be evacuated, reduce the pressure to about 2 centimeters of mercury by means of an oil

pump and measure the ionization currents while increasing the potential on the plates until ionization by collision is clearly observed. Plot this data as before.

EXPERIMENT 8-2

MEASUREMENT OF THE ABSOLUTE VALUE OF AN IONIZATION CURRENT AND THE CAPACITY OF AN ELECTROMETER SYSTEM

1. Connect the instrument as in figure 17-13 of chapter 17 and adjust as described in experiment 17-1. Place a small amount of radioactive substance, whose ionization current is to be measured, in the chamber AB.

2. Observe the time t_1 for a deflection of say 10 centimeters.

3. Connect a standard condenser of capacity C_0 in parallel with the ionization chamber and, using the same source of ionization, observe the number of seconds t_2 for a deflection over the same scale divisions.

4. Measure the voltage (Δv) which must be applied directly to the quadrants to give the same deflection.

5. Calculate the capacity of the quadrant system $(Q' KB)$ from equations 17-2 and 17-4. Also calculate the value of the ionization current using equation 17-16. If C_0 and Δv are in electrostatic units and the time in seconds, the current will likewise be in these units.

6. If a condenser standardized for induction coefficients is available, use the method of Harms for determining the capacity of the quadrant system.

EXPERIMENT 8-3

A STUDY OF THE GLOW DISCHARGE

The student should read chapter 16 on Vacuum Technique before starting this experiment.

The purpose of the experiment is (1) to become familiar with the phenomena accompanying the passage of electricity through a gas as the pressure is gradually diminished, (2) to plot a striking potential-pressure curve and (3) to calibrate an ionization gauge by means of a McLeod gauge.

Apparatus.—An oil pump, discharge tube and induction coil will show many of the phenomena, but a more elaborate system, such as that in figure 8–16, is to be preferred. Here *B* is a discharge tube (say one meter long and 5 centimeters in diameter) containing the aluminum electrodes *A* and *C*. A low power transformer (*T*) may be used and is to be controlled by the rheostat (*R*). The alternating current is partially rectified by the use of a pointed anode (*A*) and a large area cathode (*C*). The voltage drop is read on the electro-static voltmeter (*V*); range 200 to 2000 volts.

The discharge tube may be evacuated in steps by use of the stopcocks S_2 and S_3 and the large flask (*F*). S_3 is closed and *F* evacuated by the pump (*P*). Then S_2 is closed and S_3 opened. Air may be admitted to the system through the capillary tube (*t*). It is dried as it enters by the phosphorus pentoxide, P_2O_5. The use of the P_2O_5 tube here, as well as the one near the fore pump, is necessary, especially if the refrigerant in the trap (*D*) is CO_2 (solid pieces of carbon dioxide, slowly added to acetone) since the vapor pressure of ice (frozen in *D*) at the temperature of freezing carbon dioxide is comparatively high. Other gases than air may be introduced at S_4. (This stopcock is shown backwards in figure 8–16 and should be reversed.)

Pressures above one millimeter are determined from the difference between the barometric height and the difference of level of the mercury in the two arms of the open tube manometer (P_1). For lower pressures, the McLeod gauge (P_3) is used. A description will be found in chapter 16. A gauge of this type designed for use at higher pressures, will not be accurate at lower values, and vice versa. Hence, it is suggested that a McLeod gauge be used which covers the range from, say 10^{-2} to 10^{-5} millimeter of mercury, with good accuracy and that the Pirani type (P_2) (see section 16–8) be used in the intermediate region from, say, one to 10^{-2} millimeter. P_4 is the ionization gauge to be calibrated from 0.005 millimeter down. Note that the gauges P_2 and P_4 may be used on the opposite side of the CO_2 or liquid air trap (*D*) from the remainder of the evacuating and pressure measuring equipment.

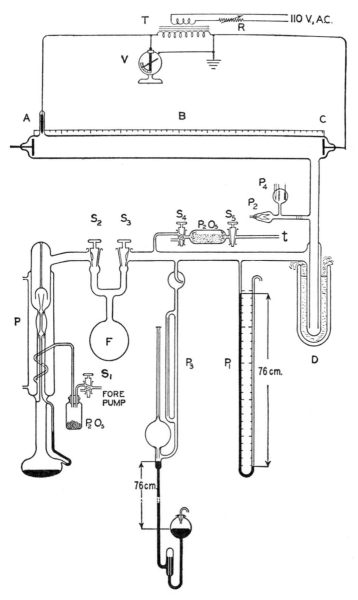

FIG. 8–16. System for studying the passage of electricity through gases as the pressure is reduced.

Precautions.—1. *Turn all stop cocks slowly* so as not to strip the stopcock grease and introduce a leak into the system. 2. Turn the stopcock (S_1) to the outside air *before shutting off the motor of the fore pump*, and especially at the end of the day. Otherwise, oil will be drawn out of the fore pump by the continued suction of the evacuated system and considerable effort will be required to clean and re-assemble the equipment. 3. Raise the mercury in the McLeod gauge (P_3) slowly, particularly as it enters the capillary tube. It may be lowered rapidly. Do not leave the mercury raised above the " cut-off " point at the end of the day. 4. Be sure that *water is running* through the cooling jacket of the pump (P) before turning on its heater. If this has been neglected, do not try to rectify your error by turning on the water until after the pump has had time to cool down. Turn the water off at the end of the day for, if left running and a break occurs in the rubber tubing, the floor of the room will be flooded. Only a small stream of water need run continuously through the pump while it is in use. 5. Let the current run through the discharge tube as long as you wish while studying the phenomena, but turn it off while you proceed with other work. Reason: a hard, colored deposit forms on the inner walls which, after long use of the tube, masks the discharge and requires removal or a new tube.

Experiment.—(1) Tabulate the following characteristics of the glow discharge for, say, ten different pressures from several centimeters down to the point where the tube no longer conducts: length, intensity and color of the positive column, Faraday dark space, negative glow, cathode dark space and cathode glow.

(2) At a given pressure, increase R until the discharge no longer occurs. Slowly decrease R and note the voltage V_s on the electrostatic voltmeter V at which the discharge may just be seen to start in the tube. Repeat at different pressures. This work may be carried out simultaneously with (1), at the same pressures. Plot values of V_s as ordinates and of pressure as abscissae. A logarithmic scale may be used for the latter, if desired, in order to spread out the lower pressures.

(3) At a given pressure and with constant electron current in the ionization gauge (P_4) (section 16–11) record the positive ion current in P_4 and the McLeod gauge pressure reading. Repeat for, say, ten values of pressure below the point where P_4 lights up

all over with a strong blue glow. The refrigerant should be used in the trap (D) during this work because P_4 registers vapor pressures, as well as gas pressures, while P_3 does not. Without the refrigerant, the readings of P_4 will not go below the vapor pressure of mercury (about 10^{-3} millimeter, at room temperatures), even though P_3 registers much lower values. Plot a curve for the ionization gauge which shows pressures vertically and positive ion currents horizontally.

EXPERIMENT 8-4

A STUDY WITH PROBES

Apparatus.—In figure 8-17, a large glass tube (B), say 70 centimeters long and 4 centimeters in diameter, is used as the discharge tube. The aluminum anode (A) and cathode (C) are

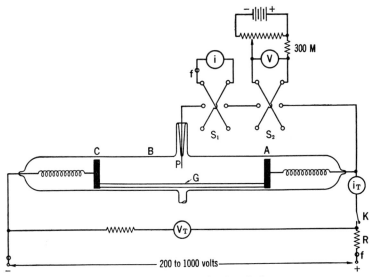

FIG. 8-17. Probe study of a glow discharge.

rigidly supported about 30 centimeters from each other by two glass rods. The lead-out wires are coiled so that, by tipping the tube, it is possible to locate the probe (P) at a desired position in the discharge. The probe may consist of a 7 mil (0.0178 centimeter diameter) tungsten wire whose exposed end is 1.3 centimeters long.

The high voltage is supplied by a motor-generator or by a rectifier-filter system capable of delivering 100 milliamperes. It should be possible to vary the potential from approximately 200 to 1000 volts. Fuses (f,f) are provided in both sides of the line and a protective resistance (R) of, say, 20,000 ohms is included in the anode lead. The voltmeter (V_t) should be of the high resistance type (1000 ohms per volt). The switch (K) should have a long insulation handle and be so mounted as to drop open, rather than closed. The milliammeter which measures the tube current (i_t) should have a range up to 50 or 100 milliamperes.

The probe voltage (V) is supplied by batteries or a well-filtered rectifier-filter unit capable of supplying 50 milliamperes, and is varied by means of a slide wire rheostat. The voltmeter (V) should be of the high-resistance type with ranges from 0 to 15 and 0 to 150 volts. The milliammeter, which measures the probe current (i) should have ranges from 0 to 1 and 0 to 15 milliamperes. A fuse (f) and two reversing switches (S_1) and (S_2) are included in the probe circuit.

A complete pumping and pressure measuring system may be used but it is possible to obtain excellent results with the following simple equipment: a mechanical oil pump, an acid bottle with P_2O_5 in the bottom to stabilize the pressure and dry the air, and a Pirani gauge (see section 16–8). All parts are joined with pressure tubing, the pump is kept in operation and the pressure in the discharge tube is varied by means of a pinch cock on the tubing near the pump.

Precautions.—1. The high potential is exceedingly dangerous, particularly if the supply is capable of delivering considerable power. 2. Watch the probe so that it does not overheat. 3. By means of a stopcock, connect the pump to the outside air before shutting off its motor, particularly at the end of the day, for the vacuum can suck the oil out of the pump into the system.

Procedure.—1. Adjust the pumping system until the pressure is 0.1–0.2 millimeter and remains constant. Stability of both pressure and tube current is important. Readjust the pressure every few readings by noting i_e for e(probe) = 0. To raise the pressure slightly, run high current density through the tube so as to drive some gas out of the electrodes. 2. Locate the probe somewhere in the range from 7 to 17 centimeters from the anode. 3. With the probe circuit disconnected (S_1 and S_2 open) turn on the high voltage, close K and raise the voltage until the discharge begins. Then, lower the voltage a little. If the probe is in a striation, change its position, opening K before handling the tube. 4. Adjust V to a large value and close S_2 in such a direction as will make the probe negative with respect to the anode. Then close S_1. The positive ion current will probably be too small to be observed with the meters specified above. 5. Slowly increase V and observe the probe currents (i) up to a point where, after a slow rise, they start to increase rapidly. Care must be used here. It is impossible to give general figures for this upper limit since it depends on the gas pressure, the tube current and the distance between the probe and the anode.

Experiments.—1. With constant gas pressure, tube current and probe position, plot a volt-ampere characteristic curve, as in figure 8–10. Test for a Maxwellian distribution of velocities, as in section 8–9. Queer kinks are sometimes found in the logarithmic plot, usually at the higher pressures. If there are two or more straight lines in this plot, there are a corresponding number of groups of electrons in the discharge, each with a Maxwellian distribution, but differing in their average velocity. The percentage of electrons in each group can be determined as the ratio of the current ranges of the separate straight lines. When several groups are found to exist, the value of V_e should be taken as the weighted mean of the values given by the respective groups. Measure the slope (s) of a straight line and compute T, V_e, $\bar{v}$ and $\mathscr{E}$, using equations 8–5, 7, 8 and 9.

Next, plot an $i^2 - V$ curve, as in figure 8–12, measure its slope (S) and compute n and V_s from equations 8–13 and 8–15. In drawing the straight line in the $i^2 - V$ curve, choose only those voltages which are in the range from 2 to 17, approximately, above the space potential (whose value is known approximately from the logarithmic plot), since it is only in this region that the equations are applicable.

2. Measure the potential gradient in the positive column and Faraday dark space by determining the space potential at various

points along the tube axis.   The tube current and the gas pressure
are kept constant.   To shorten the experiment, it is suggested that
only the logarithmic plots (Fig. 8–11) for each point be made and
the approximate space potentials V_{sa} be determined.   Plot values
of V_{sa} vertically and distances of the probe from the anode horizontally.

3. In experiment 8–3 a curve is plotted of the voltage required
to start a glow discharge for various pressures of the gas.   With the
apparatus of figure 8–17, it is possible to determine the striking
voltage for various distances between the electrodes, using the
probe as the anode and either of the other electrodes as the cathode.
The probe circuit is not required.   It is suggested that the voltage
supply have a range from 200 to 1000, that the pressure be maintained constant at approximately 0.1 millimeter and that the distance between the electrodes be varied from 20 centimeters to as
short a value as possible.   The striking potentials at the smaller
distances are of particular interest in the design of x-ray tubes.
Data on striking potentials are frequently presented in terms of
the product of the electrode separation and the pressure.

EXPERIMENT 8–5

STRIKING POTENTIALS OF A GAS-FILLED TRIODE

Connect the apparatus as in figure 8–18.   Either an 884 or an
885 tube may be used.   They differ only in their heater voltages.
Have the circuit checked by the instructor before turning on any
of the voltages.   Turn on the cathode heater at least one minute
before the grid voltage E_c or the plate voltage E_b is turned on.
The cathode heater will be the very last to be turned off.   With
E_c at its maximum negative value (greater than 15 volts, say),
turn on the full value of plate voltage (E_b, say 110 volts) by closing
the switch S.   Now reduce E_c, making the grid less negative, and
note its value when the plate current just starts.   Again make E_c
more negative and note that the plate current continues to flow and
is uninfluenced by the grid voltage.   Shut off the plate current
by opening the switch S.   Repeat several times.   Record E_b
and the value of E_c *just before* the plate current starts to flow.
This value of E_c is the striking (or " starting " or " firing ") voltage

E_s. Repeat for about ten values of the plate voltage from 110 volts down to as low a value as will yield consistent results. *Plot* values of E_b vertically on the right-hand side of the graph and E_g values horizontally, with zero at the right and increasingly negative values to the left. Compare your curve with that of the manufacturer. *Compute* the grid control ratio and record its value on the graph.

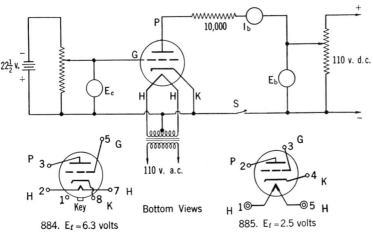

884. $E_f = 6.3$ volts   Bottom Views   885. $E_f = 2.5$ volts

Fig. 8–18. Striking potentials of a gas-filled triode.

REFERENCES

1. L. B. Loeb, Rev. Mod. Phys., **8**, 267 (1936).
   Table 3 at the end of this book.
   General Reference B, Chapter 5.
2. General Reference B, pages 33–36.
3. L. C. Marshall, Phys. Rev., **34**, 618 (1929).
   O. Luhr, Phys. Rev., **35**, 1394 (1930); **36**, 24 (1930).
   O. Luhr and N. E. Bradbury, Phys. Rev., **37**, 998 (1931).
4. General Reference B, pages 14–32.
   General Reference C, pages 543–637.
5. H. A. Erickson, Phys. Rev., **24**, 502, 622 (1924).
6. N. E. Bradbury, Phys. Rev., **40**, 508 (1932).
7. C. F. Powell and L. Brata, Proc. Roy. Soc. **A138**, 117 (1932).
8. From a letter to the author by L. B. Loeb.
9. I. Langmuir and H. Mott-Smith, G. E. Rev., **27**, 449, 539, 616, 762, 810 (1924).

10. Reference 9, page 450.
11. General Reference C.
12. L. Tonks and I. Langmuir, Phys. Rev., **33**, 195 (1929).
    I. Penning, Nature, **118**, 301 (1926).
13. A. W. Hull, G. E. Rev., **32**, 213, 390 (1929).
    D. D. Knowles and S. P. Sashoff, Electronics, **1**, 183 (1930).

GENERAL REFERENCES

A.—K. G. Emeléus, *The Conduction of Electricity Through Gases*
   Dutton & Co. (1928).
B.—J. A Crowther, *Ions, Electrons and Ionizing Radiations*, Sixth
   Edition, Chapters 1, 2, 3, 5, and 6. Longmans, Green &
   Co. (1934).
C.—L. B. Loeb, *Kinetic Theory of Gases*, Second Edition. Mc-
   Graw-Hill Book Co. (1934).
D.—K. K. Darrow, *Electrical Phenomena in Gases*. Williams and
   Wilkins Co. (1932).
E.—J. J. and G. P. Thomson, *Conduction of Electricity Through
   Gases*, Third Edition, Vol. I (1928); Vol. 2 (1933). Cam-
   bridge University Press.
F.—J. S. Towsend, *Electricity in Gases*. Oxford, Clarendon Press
   (1915).
G.—R. Bär, *Handbuch der Physik* (Geiger and Scheel), Vol. XIV.
   Springer (1927).
H.—Wien and Harms, *Handbuch der Experimentalphysik*, Vol.
   XIII, Third Part. University Press, Leipzig (1929).
I.—R. Seeliger, *Physik der Gasentladungen*. Second Edition,
   Barth (1934).
J.—J. D. Stranathan, *The Particles of Modern Physics*. The
   Blakiston Co. (1942).
K.—L. B. Loeb, *Fundamental Processes of Electrical Discharge in
   Gases*. John Wiley & Sons (1939).

CHAPTER 9

X-RAYS

9-1. Introduction.—In 1893, Lenard announced his discovery of an invisible radiation produced in a discharge tube and capable of passing through a thin aluminum window opaque to ordinary light; a radiation now called Lenard rays, or electrons. This was followed by a systematic search by Roentgen for penetrating radiations in the vicinity of " Crookes " tubes. He prepared a platino-barium-cyanide or fluorescent screen, covered his discharge tube with black paper to avoid the light from the trace of gas in the tube and was making preliminary adjustments of the interrupter on the induction coil used to excite the tube when he noticed that the screen was occasionally emitting light. In the sense that he succeeded before he expected to, his discovery was an " accident." He found that the radiation which was produced by the tube and which caused the screen to fluoresce could not be deflected by magnetic fields as was the case with Lenard rays and that it was exceedingly penetrating. He announced the discovery of these unknown or " X " rays in 1895.[1]

He soon found that x-rays were capable not only of causing certain materials to fluoresce but also of ionizing gases and affecting photographic plates. They could not be reflected or refracted but were scattered in various directions and were more or less absorbed by all kinds of matter. Their absorption was found to be much greater in elements of high than in those of low atomic weight.

Whenever an electron beam strikes a solid target, x-rays are produced. The x-rays may be likened to the sound waves produced at a target bombarded by bullets (electrons) from a machine gun.

There are two distinguishing characteristics of x-rays. The first, the intensity, is the number of ergs per second of a beam of one square centimeter cross-section. The second is their hardness, penetrating power or wave-length. The latter also determines the energy content in each quantum. X-rays are of the same nature as light rays except that their wave-lengths are much less, of the order of one angstrom (10^{-8} centimeter), as compared with 5000 for light rays, and the energy in each of their quanta is much greater.

Figure 9–1A shows the intensity at different wave-lenghts of the " white," " general " or *continuous* x-radiation from a tungsten target bombarded by electrons which have been accelerated by various voltages. The maximum of the intensity wave-length curve shifts toward shorter wave-lengths as the voltage of the tube is increased, as shown by the dotted line. Also, it is to be

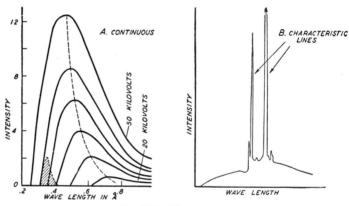

Fig. 9–1. X-ray spectra.

noted that there is a sharp short-wave-length limit for each voltage. The use of this limit in the determination of Planck's constant is described in the chapter on photo-electricity. The general radiation contains the majority of the energy emitted by an x-ray tube and is used in fluoroscopic and photographic work.

In addition to the continuous x-rays, there are *characteristic* x-rays indicated by the sharp peak in figure 9–1B. These are characteristic of the particular element used as a target, just as the spectral lines in optics are characteristic of the emitting material. If the energy of the bombarding electrons is sufficiently high, the characteristic x-rays will be produced and will have fixed wave-lengths, independent of the speed of the electrons.

A third type known as *fluorescent* x-rays may be produced by matter through which primary x-rays are passing. They will be discussed in the section on Absorption Processes.

9–2. Gas-filled X-ray Tubes.—Early in the studies of x-rays it was found that greater intensities could be obtained by the use of materials of high atomic weight as the target upon which the electrons impinged. A simple gas-filled tube is shown in figure 9–2

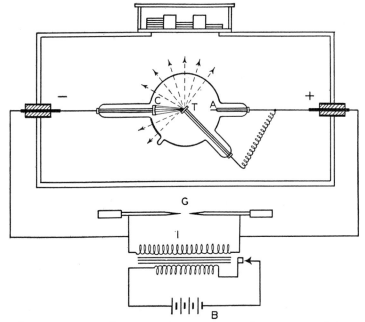

Fig. 9–2. A gas-filled x-ray tube arrangement for the study of the absorption of x-rays.

where A is the anode and C is the cathode which, due to its curved surface, focusses electrons upon the target or anti-cathode T. The dotted lines indicate the emitted x-rays. The target is commonly made of tungsten since this material has a comparatively high atomic weight and also has a high melting point. It, then, serves to give good x-ray intensity and yet can withstand the heat produced by the sudden stoppage of the electrons.

When the pressure of the gas in the x-ray tube is of the order of 0.001 millimeter, the x-rays given out are easily absorbed,

scarcely passing through the human hand. They are then said
to be *soft* and are found to have a comparatively long wave-length,
perhaps one or more angstroms. At a gas pressure of approximately 0.0003 millimeter, exceedingly high voltages are needed
to operate the discharge, the x-rays are exceedingly penetrating,
and are able to pass through the bones of the hand with very little
absorption. These rays are of comparatively short wave-length,
say 0.1 angstrom and are called *hard* x-rays. Gas-filled tubes are
normally evacuated to approximately 0.0005 millimeter pressure
and are frequently provided with a device whereby the pressure
may be altered. As a tube is operated, it tends to harden because
of the clean-up action of the electrode materials.

As we have seen in a previous chapter, the voltage across a
discharge tube depends to a large extent upon the pressure of the
gas in the tube. An increase in the battery B, operating the induction coil I of figure 9-2, will cause an increase in the intensity of
the emitted x-rays but will not affect to any great extent the
voltage drop across the tube. At the lower gas pressures, however, the emitted x-rays are not only more penetrating but also
of greater intensity. The intensity rises very rapidly as the
voltage across the tube increases; it is very nearly proportional
to the square of the voltage, if the current is constant.

9-3. Hot-cathode X-ray Tubes.—In order to avoid the
changes due to variations in gas pressure and the " wandering "
of the focal spot in the earlier tubes, Coolidge,[2] in 1913, replaced
the gaseous source of electrons by a hot filament. A later form
of such a hot-cathode high-vacuum tube is shown in figure 9-3.
The cathode C consists of a spiral of tungsten wire surrounded by
a metal cylinder which serves to focus the electrons upon a definite
area, the focal spot, of the anode A. The anode is constructed of
copper into which a tungsten plug has been imbedded. It is
cooled in a variety of ways; by means of the radiating fins B or,
upon the removal of the rod carrying the fins, by a stream of water
circulated inside the anode by either convection or pressure.
The bulb, which is evacuated to 0.000,05 millimeter or less, is
sometimes made of thick, lead impregnated glass except in the
region of the small, thin, lime glass window W where the rays may
emerge in appreciable intensity. Demountable tubes, constructed
mostly of metal, are usually used in research work where rapid

change of target material and filament replacement are important. Tubes are also designed in such a manner that the focal spot is rectangular instead of circular. This permits larger x-ray intensity without destruction of the target.

In figure 9–3, the high voltage is supplied by the transformer T_2 (20 to 2000 kv.) and is often rectified by a diode R in order to produce a steadier and more homogeneous beam of x-rays. The insulation between the primary and secondary of the diode transformer T_3 must be sufficient to withstand the peak voltage

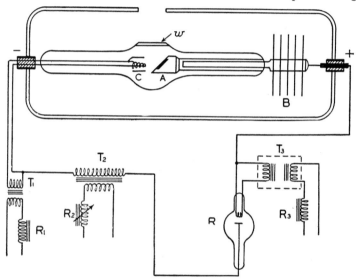

Fig. 9–3. A hot-cathode x-ray tube arrangement.

of the transformer T_2. The intensity of the emitted x-rays is varied by changing the temperature of the filament C by means of the auto-transformer of variable impedance R_1. Since the current flow through the tube is very sensitive to changes in filament temperature, current regulators are often used in research work to maintain constant x-ray intensity output. The voltage is varied by means of the impedance R_2. The control of the intensity and hardness of the emitted rays is therefore much better than with gaseous tubes. For a given current through the tubes, the intensity of the x-rays is proportional to the square of the voltage across the tube.

For rapid photographic (diagnostic) work in clinics, 50 to 140 kilovolts are used. Usually this is 80 kilovolts, the upper limit being set by scattering phenomena. Then, with a broad focal spot of say 3 square millimeters, a usual value of the current would be 50 to 100 milliamperes and the power consumption around 4 to 8 kilowatts. With a focal spot 4 square millimeters and a slightly higher power consumption, 150 to 250 milliamperes would be used. For slow exposures and a 1.5 to 3 kilowatt tube, using a fine focal spot of say 1 square millimeter, in order to obtain good detail in the photograph, 10 to 30 milliamperes would be used. For therapeutic work, a fixed voltage of 200 kilovolts is common although much higher values have been used.

9–4. Intensity Measurements.—The intensity of an x-ray beam may be roughly estimated by the brightness of the illumination which it produces on a fluorescent screen. The screens usually consist of a thin layer of calcium tungstate supported on paper.

The photographic films used to record x-rays are coated on both sides with the sensitive emulsion. A series of correct exposure times for various thicknesses of absorbing material may be plotted as in figure 9–4 for various operating conditions. With a given

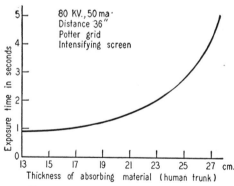

FIG. 9–4. An exposure-thickness curve.

frequency or wave-length, the product of the intensity of the rays and the time of exposure is a reliable measure of the blackening of the film. A comparison of the intensity of an x-ray beam may be made in terms of a second beam by varying the latter until it produces the same blackening as the former. The beams are then of equal intensity. This procedure is used in experiment 9–1.

When x-rays pass through a gas, photo-electrons are ejected from the molecules in the same manner as photo-electrons are ejected from a gas by ultra-violet light. The total number of ions which the photo-electrons in turn produce in the gas is far greater than their own number. Thus, the ionization of a gas by x-rays is, to a great extent, an indirect process.

Drop-tracks,[3] formed in an expansion chamber upon the ions created by the photo-electrons, may be observed by means of the apparatus shown in figure 9–5. As the piston P is pulled down, the shutter S permits a narrow beam of x-rays to pass through the water-saturated gas in the chamber C. The droplets of water which form on the ions may then be seen and are represented by the crooked lines. The total number of ions produced

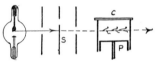

FIG. 9–5. A drop-track apparatus used with x-rays.

is a direct measure of the strength or intensity of the x-ray beam.

Since the ions are electrically charged particles, they may be drawn over to charged metal collecting plates. The current which then flows between the plates is observed and may be used as a direct measure of the intensity of the x-rays. This is the most common method of measuring the intensity of x-rays. It is, of course, necessary that sufficient voltage be applied to the ionization chamber plates to draw over all ions, before any of them have recombined, if a reliable comparison of intensities is to be made. Since the photo-electrons are ejected with considerable energy from the gas molecules, the ions are found to be distributed throughout a considerable volume of the gas. The chance of recombination of the ions is small so that saturation currents may be obtained with comparatively low potentials, say 100 volts, with the usual type of chamber. In figure 9–6, I is the ionization chamber. The brass walls of the cylinder serve as one electrode and a stiff wire C supported off the center of the chamber by an insulating plug serves as the other. The x-rays enter through a thin cellophane or aluminum window in one end. The gas in the chamber may be dry air or argon at atmospheric pressure. The latter offers higher absorption of the x-rays and hence is preferable except above 3.86 angstroms where it is as transparent as air. Below 0.86 angstroms, krypton is very efficient.

If the intensities of x-ray beams of different wave-lengths are to be compared, correction must be made, among other factors, for their respective absorption in the gas of the chamber.

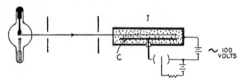

FIG. 9–6.   An ionization chamber used with x-rays.

In 1931, the International Congress of Radiology defined the "Roentgen" (r), as that quantity of (monochromatic) x-radiation which, when the secondary electrons are fully utilized and the wall effect of the chamber is avoided, produces in one cubic centimeter of standard air one electro-static unit of ions. Before 1928,

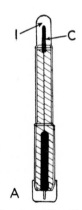

"standard air" implied a pressure of 760 millimeters and a temperature of 18° Centigrade; but today the temperature is taken as 0° Centigrade. The intensity of an x-ray beam is expressed as the number of roentgens per second. A hot cathode x-ray tube at 100 kv. and 10 milliamperes gives out approximately 0.34 roentgens per second, at a distance of one meter from its target.

The thimble type of ionization chamber shown in figure 9–7 is about the size of a large fountain pen and contains an ionization chamber I. The collecting rod C is supported by a solid dielectric, represented by the shaded area, and has a fixed capacity with respect to the surrounding metal container. The collector is charged to a definite potential by means of the mechanism at A, and as tested with an electroscope. After exposure to the x-rays for a specified time, the ionization chamber is returned to the electroscope and the extent to which the charge on the chamber has been reduced is then indicated by the position of the fibers of the

FIG. 9–7. The thimble type ionization chamber.

electroscope and is a measure of the intensity of the x-ray beam. In a particular instrument, 25 roentgens are required to completely discharge the collector. An accuracy of one or two per cent may be expected.

9-5. Protection from X-rays.—As specified by the Third International Congress on X-ray and Radium Protection in 1931, the following thickness of lead should always exist between the source and the observer. Thus, for a gas-filled tube operated by

Peak kilovolts across the tube	Minimum thickness of lead in mm.
75	1.0
100	1.5
125	2.0
150	2.5
175	3.0
200	4.0
250	6.0
300	9.0
350	12.0
400	15.0
500	22.0
600	34.0

a small induction coil, 1 mm. of lead is ample. With the apparatus of figure 9-2, a continued, direct exposure of 5 minutes is exceedingly dangerous. The student should use a fluoroscope tilted at an angle so as to protect the eyes from the direct rays and should not expose his hand for more than 15 seconds at a time nor oftener than 10 times in a month. The danger may be greatly reduced without large loss of x-ray intensity by the addition of a half millimeter of aluminum over the hole; or a fluorescent screen may be used which has, as an integral part of its construction, a sheet of lead glass ($\frac{3}{8}$ inch thick), between the source and the observer.

Comparatively large doses of x-rays can be applied in safety for very short time intervals spaced far apart. The effect of x-rays on the skin depends on *the rate* at which they are applied.

9-6. Absorption Coefficients.—The intensity of the rays emitted by an x-ray tube is less at a great distance than near the tube for two reasons; first, the spreading out in all directions, which follows the inverse square law, and second, the absorption by the material through which the rays are passing. The decrease of energy, which follows the inverse square law, need not be considered here. We shall consider only the loss of energy from a parallel beam, or, in practice, one which is nearly parallel.

The intensity of an x-ray beam whose rays are parallel and of but one wave-length or hardness is reduced as the beam passes through an absorbing medium according to the exponential law,

$$I = I_0 \epsilon^{-\mu d}, \tag{9--1}$$

in which I is the intensity of the beam after passing through d centimeters of the material, I_0 is the intensity of the original or incident beam, $\epsilon = 2.718$ and μ is the *linear absorption coefficient* or fractional decrease in intensity of the beam per centimeter through the absorbing material. The linear absorption coefficient, which will be a larger number when the beam is more rapidly absorbed, may also be considered as the fraction of energy absorbed by each cubic centimeter of the matter from a beam of x-rays of one square centimeter cross section. Since the amount of material in a unit volume, say of steam, is less than that for water, it is obvious that this absorption coefficient depends on the physical state of the material. On the other hand, the *mass absorption coefficient* μ_m or fraction of energy absorbed from a beam of unit cross section by one gram of the material, is a characteristic of the material and is independent of its density ρ. It is obvious that

$$\mu_m = \frac{\mu}{\rho}. \tag{9--2}$$

Now, if n is the number of atoms per cubic centimeter in the absorbing material, and μ (as above) is the absorption due to each cubic centimeter, then the *atomic absorption coefficient*, μ_a, is

$$\mu_a = \frac{\mu}{n} = \frac{\mu}{\rho} \cdot \frac{M}{N}, \tag{9--3}$$

where M is the atomic weight and N is Avogadro's number. This represents the fractional energy absorbed from a beam of unit cross section by each atom. For ordinary light rays, carbon is transparent when in the form of diamond and opaque when in the form of graphite. For x-rays, however, both μ_a and μ_m are the same for the two forms of carbon.

If the x-ray beam contains more than one wave-length, the softer rays will be absorbed by the first portions of the material, leaving the harder components to penetrate to greater depths. This is true for the emulsion of a photographic plate as well as for intermediate absorbing screens. The *effective absorption coefficient*, as computed from equation 9-1, is, therefore, greater for the rays which have just entered the absorber than for those which have penetrated to a greater depth. For a satisfactory study of the absorption of different materials, it is necessary to use a monochromatic or one wave-length beam of x-rays. Such a monochromatic beam may be obtained by the use of an x-ray spectrometer, just as a monochromatic beam of light is obtained by the use of a spectroscope. As a crude but simpler method, one may use a filter consisting of a sheet of copper of such thickness as to reduce the original intensity of the beam to ten per cent or less of its unfiltered value. For the less penetrating rays from the lower voltage tubes, a copper filter one-half millimeter in thickness is commonly used and for the higher voltage tubes this is increased to one or two millimeters. It is customary to place beyond these filters, a one millimeter sheet of aluminum, in order to reduce the effects of the rays scattered by the copper.

9-7. Absorption Processes.—The term "absorption" is customarily used in two senses. In the first, a constant fraction of the energy in the parallel beam, per centimeter of path, is transferred to the absorbing material, ejecting electrons from its atoms, giving them kinetic energy and also, perhaps, adding potential energy to electrons which remain in the atoms. In the second process, "absorption" is the result of scattering or deviation of part of the x-rays from their direct path, with consequent reduction of the intensity along the parallel beam. The former, *photo-electric or true absorption*, may be expressed by means of an absorption coefficient τ and the latter, or *scattering* process, by means of a coefficient σ, such that

$$\mu = \tau + \sigma \qquad (9\text{-}4)$$

X-rays whose wave-lengths are greater than approximately ten angstroms are readily absorbed, even by a fraction of a millimeter of air and can only be studied with apparatus placed in an evacuated chamber.   Shorter and shorter x-rays are increasingly penetrating.   In the wave-length range from, roughly 3 to 0.3 angstroms, the photoelectric type of absorption greatly exceeds that due to scattering.   Very approximately, one may then say

$$\mu = \tau = c\lambda^3 \qquad (9\text{-}5)$$

where c is a constant $(=c'Z^4$, c' is another constant, Z is the atomic number of the absorbing element) and λ is the wave-length of the x-rays.   This is known as Owen's law.   Typical values are as follows: between 0.4 and 2.3 angstroms, for a certain specimen of mica, $\mu = 36.56\lambda^{2.76}$ and for cellophane $\mu = 3.52\lambda^{2.66}$.

A graph of the mass absorption coefficients of argon at different wave-lengths is given in figure 9–8.   Here, it is seen that the gas becomes more and more transparent as the wavelength decreases (in approximate agreement with Owen's law) until a critical wavelength, marked K in the figure, is reached.   For silver, this occurs at a wave-length of 0.484 angstrom and for bromine at 0.918 angstrom. At this *critical absorption limit* the material suddenly becomes comparatively

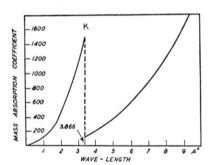

Fig. 9–8.   Mass absorption coefficients of argon for different wave-length x-rays.

opaque to the x-rays.   In other words, just below K, large amounts of energy are extracted from the beam by the atoms.   It can be shown that this energy is used to raise electrons from the innermost or K shell inside the atoms to higher energy levels.   Upon the subsequent return of these atomic electrons to their normal energy levels, a part of the absorbed energy is re-radiated in the form of *fluorescent x-rays* whose wave-length is characteristic of the atoms of the absorbing material and independent of that of the incident x-rays.   The shortest fluorescent wave-length which can be excited is always of longer wave-length than that of the primary rays, corresponding to Stokes' law in optics.

A discussion of the photo-electrons ejected from atoms will be found in the chapter on photo-electricity.

As the wave-length of the x-ray decreases, below about 0.2 angstroms,* the second absorption process, scattering, becomes the predominating factor. Thus, σ becomes increasingly great in comparison with τ. The scattered x-rays have nearly the same wave-length as the incident x-rays. As a first approximation,

$$\sigma = \sigma_o/(1 + 2h/mc\lambda), \tag{9-6}$$

where σ_o is a constant, h is Planck's constant, m the mass of an electron, c the velocity and λ the wave-length of the ray. A more accurate but complicated equation relating the absorption coefficient σ and the wave-length has been given by Klein and Nishina.[4]

When the wave-length of the rays is exceedingly short, below 0.012 angstroms, an additional type of absorption process becomes important. Pairs of positive and negative electrons are ejected from the atoms. This *pair production* will be discussed in a later chapter.

9-8. The Compton Effect.—In the preceding section it has been pointed out that the x-rays which are scattered possess nearly the same wave-length as the incident rays. However, most of the energy of these deflected rays are found to have a small but definitely longer wave-length. In 1922, A. H. Compton [5] first demonstrated clearly that this modification of the wave-length took place and offered the following important interpretation. The x-ray beam is considered as made up of quanta or photons, each of which possesses an energy $h\nu$ and a momentum $h\nu/c$, as in the case of light rays in the photoelectric effect. When a photon collides with a free electron, it gives up part of its energy, causing the electron to recoil. The energy given to the recoil electron comes from the original x-ray photon, decreases the value of $h\nu$, i.e., decreases ν, since h is a constant. Thus, the wave-length ($\lambda = c/\nu$) of the *modified " line "* is greater than that of the incident ray. From the laws of conservation of energy and

---

* This wave-length can only be stated roughly, for it depends upon the absorbing material.

momentum, Compton predicted that the increase in wave length should be

$$\Delta\lambda = \frac{h}{mc}\,(1 - \cos\phi)$$

$$= 0.024\,(1 - \cos\phi),\ \text{angstroms},\qquad(9\text{–}7)$$

where h = Planck's constant, m the mass of the electron, c the velocity of the rays and ϕ the angle between the forward direction of the incident ray and the scattered ray, as in figure 9–9.

The wave-length of the modified ray was carefully measured and found to agree within a fraction of one per cent with that predicted. The recoil electrons have also been observed in the drop-track apparatus. This leads to the conclusion that, for this phenomenon, x-rays must be treated as though quantized. For other experiments, the wave picture is required, so that, as in the case of the electron, a dualistic particle-wave picture must be adopted for x-rays. In addition, in view of the photo-electric effect with light rays and the Raman effect with infra-red rays, it is concluded that all electro-magnetic rays possess this dualistic nature.

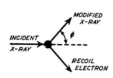

Fig. 9–9. The increase of wave-length of an x-ray scattered by a free electron. (Compton effect)

9–9. Wave Properties of X-rays.—It is now known that x-rays exhibit all of the phenomena associated with electro-magnetic waves, i.e., they may be reflected, refracted and polarized and are capable of producing diffraction and interference patterns. Plane *polarized x-rays* were first obtained by Barkla [6] in 1906 by scattering them from blocks of carbon oriented like the mirrors in the familiar polariscopes used with light rays. The *refraction* of x-rays was first accomplished in 1924 by Larsson, Siegbahn and Waller,[7] by allowing soft x-rays to pass through the corner of a glass prism after striking its surface at a small angle. The *reflection* of x-rays was first successfully carried out by A. H. Compton in 1923,[8] who allowed them to glance at a sufficiently small angle along a metal surface. The index of refraction of metals is slightly less than unity for x-rays so that this is a case of "total internal reflection." When the metal surface is ruled with parallel grooves, as for optical gratings, the reflected components of the x-ray beam combine or interfere with each other to produce maxima and minima of intensity. This grating method was used by Compton and Doan [9] to obtain the first direct measurements of the wave-length of x-rays (see the first chapter in this book).

The first reliable *diffraction* experiments with x-rays were carried out with fine slits as early as 1909 by Walter and Pohl and interpreted by Sommerfeld in 1911. The next two sections will give a discussion of the diffraction of x-rays by means of crystals.

9-10. The Bragg X-ray Spectrometer.—In figure 9–10, an x-ray beam, collimated by narrow slits A and B, strikes the surface of a crystal C, is diffracted and passes through a slit D into an ionization chamber I and is recorded by the electrometer E. The

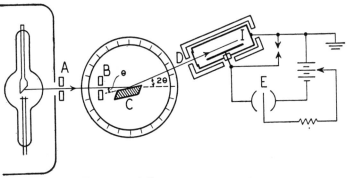

Fig. 9–10. A Bragg x-ray spectrometer.

chamber, as well as the crystal, may be rotated about the center of the spectrometer circle. With this Bragg spectrometer a number of interesting experiments may be performed; for example, the absorption coefficient of screens placed in front of D may be determined, the wave-length of the x-rays and the structure of the crystal may be measured, the intensities of the x-rays at various wave-lengths and under various operating conditions, such as voltage and current in the tube, may be observed.

In 1912, von Laue assumed that a crystal, such as rock salt, which has a symmetrical shape, must be made up of units of atomic or molecular size regularily spaced in the same geometrical figure as that of the crystal itself. When he calculated the average distance between the atoms in the crystal he found that it was of the same order of magnitude as the wave-length of x-rays. A crystal, composed of reflecting centers regularly spaced in planes at suitable distances apart should serve as a three dimensional grating for x-rays. His idea was tested by Friedrich and Knipping [15] and found to be correct. This work will be discussed in the next section (9–11).

Bragg devised his spectrograph shortly after the work of Friedrich and Knipping and gave the following simple interpretation of its operation. When the x-ray beam reached the crystal, it encountered an array of atoms such as that in figure 9–11. Although the atoms are large enough to "fill" the space, they are depicted by small circles, except in the lower right hand corner

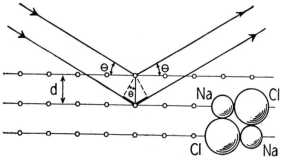

Fig. 9–11. X-rays diffracted from crystal planes.

where the comparative sizes of the sodium and chlorine atoms of a rock salt crystal are shown. That portion of the x-rays which is reflected from the second crystal plane must travel a greater distance than that reflected from the upper plane. Unless this distance, the heavy line in the figure, is equal to an integral multiple of the wave-length of the x-rays, the emerging rays will destroy each other. From the geometry of the figure it may be seen that the path difference is equal to $2d \sin \theta$, where d is the distance between the planes and θ is the angle of incidence or emergence. If, then, the rays are to aid each other it is necessary that

$$n\lambda = 2d \sin \theta \qquad (9\text{–}8)$$

where λ is the wave-length of the x-rays and n is a whole number, called the "order." This is known as Bragg's law. The smallest value of d is called the crystal grating constant. See, also, Section 3-4.

An x-ray spectrum, such as that in figure 9–12A, is obtained with the apparatus of figure 9–10 by varying the angle θ, keeping the chamber at an angle 2θ. It is seen in this case, where tungsten was used as the target and calcite was used as the crystal, that the x-rays consisted of three " lines " or wave-lengths. The distance d was calculated from equation 1–25 and found to be 2.814 angstroms. The wave-lengths of the tungsten lines were calculated from the Bragg law, using both the first and second orders ($n = 1$ and 2). The same values were found when the beam was reflected

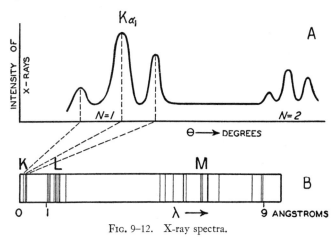

Fig. 9–12. X-ray spectra.

from other planes in the same crystal or from other kinds of crystals, each with its own spacing d. The wave-lengths are characteristic of the target from which they are emitted. A nickel target will give characteristic lines differing in intensity, number and wave-length from those of tungsten. Figure 9–12B shows the tungsten K, L and M lines on a wave-length scale.

9–11. Laue Spots and Crystal Analysis.[10]—The apparatus suggested by Von Laue for the study of the passage of the general radiation from an x-ray tube through crystals may be arranged as in figure 9–13. The x-ray tube is enclosed in a lead box so that the rays can only pass through two small holes A and B in thick lead screens. They then pass through the crystal C onto a photographic plate *P*. Upon suitable exposure and development of the plate a series of spots will be found around the central region where the direct beam reached the plate. For the case of x-rays passing through a rock salt crystal, normal to its cleavage plane or cube face, the photograph will appear as in figure 9–13, at the right. The Laue spots lie on ellipses, all of which pass through the center

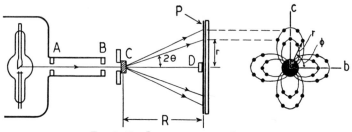

FIG. 9–13.   Laue apparatus and spots.

of the pattern and whose major and minor axes are the axes *b* and *c* of the crystal; the plane of the photographic plate is parallel to the *bc* plane of the crystal.

The planes in a crystal are customarily identified by means of three numbers, called the Miller indices, *h*, *k*, and *l*. Let three axes be drawn in the crystal, along rows of atoms, as in figure 9–14

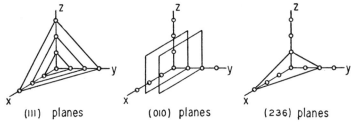

(111) planes   (010) planes   (236) planes

FIG. 9–14.   Miller indices (*hkl*) are used to designate the crystal planes.

and let *a*, *b* and *c* be the grating constants or distances between the atoms along the *x*, *y* and *z* axes, respectively. The Miller indices are the smallest integers proportional to the reciprocals of the intercepts of the planes on the axes. Thus, if the intercepts of a plane with the axes are 3*a*, 2*b* and 1*c*, as in the right hand figure of 9–14, their reciprocals are $1/3a$, $1/2b$ and $1/1c$ or **2**/6*a*,

3/6b and 6/6c. The Miller indices of this plane are then said to be $h = 2$, $k = 3$ and $l = 6$.

The perpendicular distance d between those Bragg planes which have the same Miller indices is given by

$$d = 1\bigg/ \sqrt{\frac{h^2}{a^2} + \frac{k^2}{b^2} + \frac{l^2}{c^2}} \quad * \tag{9-9}$$

This reduces to

$$d = a\bigg/\sqrt{h^2 + k^2 + l^2} \tag{9-10}$$

for a crystal such as rock salt which has a cubic lattice; i.e., where $a = b = c$. If the last equation is substituted in Bragg's law and $nh = H$, $nk = K$ and $nl = L$, we arrive at equation 3–12 used in the electron diffraction experiments.

For the case of x-rays incident along one of the three major axes of a cubic crystal, it is comparatively easy to associate each Laue spot with its reflection plane. It can be seen from figure 9–13, that

$$\tan 2\theta = r/R. \tag{9-11}$$

It can also be shown that

$$\tan \phi = \frac{k}{l} \tag{9-12}$$

and

$$\sin \theta = h\bigg/\sqrt{h^2 + k^2 + l^2}. \tag{9-13}$$

The polar coordinates r and ϕ of each spot in one quadrant are measured, as well as the distance R from the center of the crystal to the emulsion of the photographic plate. Values of $\tan \phi$ and $\sin \theta$ are then calculated for each spot. The values of h, k and l, as determined by trial and error, which numerically satisfy equations 9–12 and 9–13, are the Miller indices of the plane which reflected the x-rays to the given spot.

For more general cases than cubic crystals, a gnomonic projection method is used.[11] In practice, Laue photographs are usually taken as the first step in the analysis of a crystal, since their interpretation makes it possible to reduce the number of

---

* This equation is true only for orthorhombic crystals; i.e., for those in which the three axes are all at right angles to each other.

forms which the crystal might have. They show, in a beautiful manner, the symmetry of crystalline formations.

9–12.   Other Forms of X-ray Spectrometers.[12]—The *powder method* of Debye and Sherrer has been discussed briefly in the chapter dealing with the wave-length of electrons.

The *rotating or oscillating crystal method* is of great practical importance in the analysis of crystals. The crystal is oscillated or rotated slowly about one of its axes, perpendicular to the x-ray beam. At certain positions of the crystal, a given set of planes will make the correct Bragg angle for the reflection of x-rays of a given wave-length. Each spot on a photographic plate, located as in the Laue apparatus, will correspond to the reflection of a given wave-length from a given plane, or one of the higher orders.

X-rays are reflected in succession from two crystals in the *double crystal spectrometer*. This instrument is used for precision measurements of wave-length or of the distribution of energy around any one wave-length.

A *curved* sheet of *crystal* (mica for example) may be used instead of a plane crystal in such a manner as to focus a given x-ray line and decrease the required exposure time.

9–13.   Moseley's Law.—In 1913–14, Moseley[13] made the first systematic study of the x-ray spectra (see figure 9–12) of different elements used as targets in x-ray tubes. He found two distinct series of lines, identical with the K and L fluorescent lines of Barkla and Sadler. Moseley also discovered an important relationship between the frequency ν of the x-rays and the atomic number Z of the emitting element. Moseley's law states that

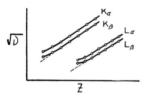

FIG. 9–15. A Moseley diagram.

$$\sqrt{\nu} = C(Z - \sigma), \qquad (9\text{–}14)$$

where C and σ are constants. The value of C differs for the K and L series but is the same for lines in the same series for all elements. The value of σ, the " screening constant," also differs between the series but is nearly constant for different elements in any one series. Figure 9–15 expresses Moseley's law in graphical form. The existence of a " fine structure " in the x-ray spectra is indicated by the K_{α}, K_{β} lines in the K series as well as by

L_α, L_β in the L series.   This multiplicity of lines is accounted for in the equation by slight changes in the value of σ.   Moseley's law is not exact, particularly for the lighter elements as may be seen by the deviations from straight lines for smaller values of Z. The K series lines are of shortest wave-length as may be seen in the diagram.   Two other series, M and N are known but are so soft as to require a vacuum spectrograph for their study.

9-14.   Electron Energy Levels Near the Nucleus.—In chapter 7 we have seen that an atom contains a massive, positively charged nucleus around which negative electrons are confined in a number of known energy levels and that light is radiated whenever the outer electrons move from exterior levels toward inner levels in the atom.   Figure 9-16 shows an energy diagram which may

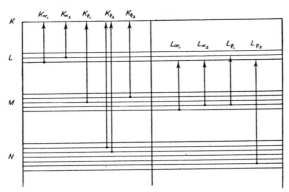

FIG. 9-16.   Part of an x-ray energy diagram.

be used to account for the emission of characteristic x-ray lines. The inner electrons, in the K, L, M, etc., levels in the atoms of the target material are given additional energy by bombardment by the electrons from the filament of the x-ray tube.   It is assumed that the outer electrons are undisturbed in this process.   As the excited inner electrons return to their normal levels they give up amounts of energy equal to the difference $(\mathscr{E}_1 - \mathscr{E}_n)$ between the levels.   Thus, as for light emission,

$$h\nu = \mathscr{E}_1 - \mathscr{E}_n. \qquad (7\text{-}9)$$

However, the energy differences in the case of x-ray emission are much greater, so that $h\nu$ and hence ν is much greater; in other words, x-rays are of appreciably shorter wave-length than light rays. The elementary theory of Bohr may be modified by assuming that the effect of the charge on the nucleus, Ze, is reduced by the outer electrons by an amount σe. Thus, $(Z - \sigma)e$ is the effective nuclear charge.

In figure 9–16, no attempt has been made to show the actual energies but only to indicate that the K, L, M, etc., levels are more or less separate from each other and also to show the further, complicating feature that each of these, except K, consists of several adjacent levels of roughly the same energy. The transition of an electron between the upper L and the K level gives an x-ray whose wave-length in the case of tungsten is 0.208 angstrom and is called the $K_{\alpha 1}$ line. The transition from middle L to K is of smaller energy and hence longer wave-length (=0.213 angstrom, called $K_{\alpha 2}$). The wave-lengths of $K_{\beta 1}$ and $K_{\beta 2}$ are 0.184 and 0.179 angstrom, respectively. Transitions are not possible between all levels: certain " selection rules," similar to those in optical spectra, must be followed. The relative intensities of the lines in the K series are independent of the voltage on the tube; for tungsten $K_{\alpha 1}$, $K_{\alpha 2}$, $K_{\beta 1}$ and $K_{\beta 2}$, they are approximately 100, 50, 35 and 15, respectively. The ratios for the L series depend on the voltage.

9–15. The Number of Extra-nuclear Electrons.—From the studies of alpha particle scattering, it was established that the charge on the nucleus of an atom was numerically equal to its atomic number. In order, therefore, that the complete atom should be electrically neutral, the number of extra-nuclear electrons must be equal to the atomic number. Measurements on the *scattering* of x-rays at various angles from different materials has given direct proof that this is true. For elements of low atomic number and for x-rays of moderate wave-lengths, the classical theory of Thomson[14] may be used with confidence. In this theory, the electric vector of the x-ray wave causes an acceleration of the electrons in the scattering material and, due to the acceleration, a new x-ray wave is radiated. The integrated effect of many electrons is calculated to obtain the total intensity of the x-rays scattered at various angles; from which the mass scattering coefficient can be computed. This quantity, the logarithmic fraction of the incident x-rays scattered by each gram of matter traversed by the rays is 0.20 for carbon; using a ray of $\lambda = 0.71A$. This quantity, multiplied by $3m^2c^4/8\pi e^4$, is equal to the number of electrons in each gram, according to the theory. For carbon, then, there are 3.0×10^{23} electrons in each gram. Also, the number of carbon atoms per gram is $N/M = 6.06 \times 10^{23}/12 = 0.505 \times 10^{23}$. Hence, there are 6.0 electrons in each atom of carbon, a number equal to its atomic number.

The index of refraction of materials for x-rays is less than unity. The deviation from unity, which is called the *unit decrement*, δ, of the index of refraction, can be measured[15] and is related to the number, n, of electrons per cubic centimeter by a simple equation ($\delta = ne^2\lambda^2/2\pi mc^2$) when the wave-lengths (λ) are much shorter than any critical absorption wave-lengths. From n, the number of electrons per atom can be calculated with ease and is found to be equal to the atomic number in the large number of cases tested.

9–16. The Distribution of Electrons in Atoms.—As indicated in figure 9–11, the atoms fill much of the space between the lattice planes. Hence, x-rays are not diffracted from mathematically thin planes but from the myriad of electrons arranged in layers of finite thickness. In these layers there is a distribution of the atomic electrons which affects the intensity of the diffraction patterns in a manner analogous to, but more complicated than, the effect of the finite width of each individual slit of a diffraction grating used for visible rays. From extensive studies of the intensities of diffracted x-rays,[16] it has been found possible to deduce the distribution of the electrons in many atoms.

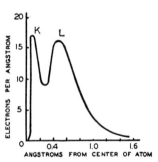

Fig. 9–17. Radial distribution of electrons in the neon atom.

Measured values of the intensities of x-rays scattered at various angles from the atoms of gases have been used [17] with the quantum mechanics to calculate the number of electrons (per angstrom) at various distances away from the nucleus. The results of Wollan for the neon atom are indicated in figure 9–17. It is to be noted that there are more electrons in two regions, the K and L levels and also that there is no precise meaning to be attached to " the radius of the atom." It is this diffuseness, this probability of electron position, which is emphasized in wave mechanics. The electron may exist at a certain distance out from the nucleus, but it may also, with lessening probability, be found at other positions on either side of the most probable location.

EXPERIMENT 9–1

THE ABSORPTION AND WAVE-LENGTH OF X-RAYS

(Read section 9–5 about " Protection from X-rays ")

The purpose of this experiment is to determine the mass absorption coefficients of aluminum, iron and copper and the wave-lengths of the x-rays which have passed through these materials. A method of successive approximations is to be used, starting with the known coefficients of carbon for x-rays of different wave-lengths.

The absorptions screens and filter of figure 9–18 are placed over

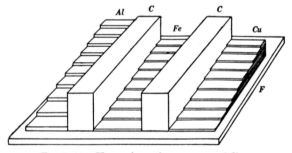

FIG. 9–18.   X-ray absorption screens and filter.

the hole in the top of the lead box of figure 9–2. The filter F consists of a sheet of copper which, for x-rays whose mean wavelength is around 0.3 angstrom, should be 0.05 centimeter thick. The effect of the filter on the continuous x-radiation is indicated by the shaded area in figure 9–1A. Thus, at a sacrifice of intensity, the beam is rendered more nearly mono-chromatic. The approximately homogeneous rays which pass through this filter travel upward through the various absorbing materials (*Al, Fe, Cu,* and *C* of figure 9–18) to a photographic plate. The plate should be supported parallel to and 6 to 7 centimeters above the filter in order to reduce scattered radiations. A drawing of the photographic record is shown in figure 9–19. The graphite blocks *C* are about 1.27 centimeters thick. Each of the aluminum, iron and copper steps is approximately 0.082, 0.005 and 0.005 centimeter thick, respectively.

With proper exposure time (trial and error, 2 minutes to 2 hours, using Eastman duplitized x-ray films) and development, the blackening back of the graphite lies between the extremes of light and dark for the other substances. A certain step may possibly be found by eye for which the blackening is the same as that back of the graphite. The illusion that a given step is lighter in the region near the next darker step may be avoided by masking off the adjacent steps with sheets of paper. If a step of the same blackness as

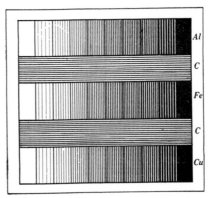

Fig. 9–19. The photographic record.

that back of the graphite cannot be found, the thickness which would give equal blackening may be estimated by eye with surprising accuracy or may be determined by photometer measurements.

The intensities of the x-rays reaching the plate then being equal, we may write, from equations 9–1 and 9–2

$$I = I_0 \epsilon^{-\mu_m \rho_m d_m} = I_0 \epsilon^{-\mu_c \rho_c d_c} \tag{9–15}$$

from which

$$\mu_m = \mu_c \frac{\rho_c}{\rho_m} \frac{d_c}{d_m} \tag{9–16}$$

where d_m is the thickness in centimeters of the aluminum, iron or copper, as the case may be, which allows the same intensity of x-ray beam to pass through as does d_c centimeters of graphite. ρ_m is the density of the aluminum, iron or copper, and ρ_c is that of graphite. The μ's are mass absorption coefficients.

The mass absorption coefficient μ_c for graphite (which is the same for any form of carbon) is to be taken as the standard. This is chosen since its value does not change with wave-length as much as other substances. (See table 14 at the end of the book.) Inasmuch as the wave-length emitted by the tube is unknown, the correct value of μ_c cannot be obtained at first. Let us assume that the wave-length is around 0.5 angstrom. Then, from the table, the value of μ_c is about 0.32. Substituting this and the other quantities in equation 9–16 gives an approximate value of μ_m. Say μ_m for copper was thus found to be 7.00. This corresponds to a wave-length of 0.350 angstrom as seen from the table or, better, from a graph plotted from this data. The process is now to be repeated, i.e., μ_c at 0.350 angstrom is equal to 0.224. Using 0.224 instead of 0.32 in equation 9–16 gives the mass absorption coefficient of copper as 3.63 which, from the table, corresponds to a wave-length of 0.269 angstrom. The process is then repeated again. If, for the average gas-filled tube, the value of μ_c is taken as 0.20, the steps need be repeated but once.

This method of successive approximations is to be repeated for the other absorbing materials. It is not to be expected that the wave-lengths so determined will all be exactly the same since the x-ray beam is not strictly monochromatic but the values should be less for those substances having greater absorption coefficients.

EXPERIMENT 9–2

LAUE PHOTOGRAPHS *

(Read section 9–5 about " Protection from X-rays ")

The purpose of this experiment is to take a photograph of the Laue spots from a rock salt crystal, using the general radiation from an x-ray tube, and to identify each spot with the crystal planes from which it was reflected.

The arrangement of the apparatus is shown in figure 9–13,

* The author is indebted to Dr. E. Dershem for the details of this experiment.

where the x-ray tube may be either a gas-filled tube operated by an induction coil or a hot-cathode tube operated at low voltage, say 50 to 80 kilovolts. The lead plates A and B each should be 3 to 4 millimeters thick and should be pierced with holes of approximately 1 millimeter diameter. They should be separated from each other by approximately 10 centimeters. Adjustment for maximum intensity of the rays which pass through A and B may be made with the aid of a fluorescent screen. The crystal C is supported on a brass or lead-alloy shield whose hole is slightly larger than the width of the x-ray beam at this point. The rock salt crystal is prepared by tapping a large piece with the sharp edge of a knife so as to break it along its natural cleavage planes. It should be about 0.05 centimeter thick and may be mounted over the hole with wax or cement or, if small, supported on a thin piece of glass or celluloid over the hole. The photographic plate is enclosed in a light tight paper cover and is supported as shown, 4 to 6 centimeters from the crystal. A lead disc D, 2 to 3 millimeters thick and 1 centimeter in diameter may be supported by fine threads over the central part of the plate in order to avoid the halation from the intense direct beam. A fluoroscope may be used for this adjustment.

The exposure time should be about one-half hour for each 20 milliamperes in the lower voltage tubes and the same with approximately 10 milliamperes in the higher voltage tubes.

Measure the distance R from the center of the crystal to the photographic plate.

After a properly exposed Laue photograph has been obtained and a positive print made, draw in the axes b and c. Then, follow the procedure outlined in section 9–11. Lack of symmetry of the spots may be corrected for by measuring the distance between diametrically opposite spots and dividing by 2 to get r. As an example, let $R = 5.9$ centimeters. For a selected spot, measurements give $r = 3.53$ centimeters and $\phi = 33.5°$. Then, $\tan \phi = 0.662$, $\tan 2\theta = 0.598$ (equation 9–11), $2\theta = 30° 53'$ and $\sin \theta = 0.266$. Now, 0.662 is nearly equal to $\frac{2}{3}$, so that, from equation 9–12, we choose $k = 2$ and $l = 3$. If, then, $h = 1$, we find that the right hand side of equation 9–13 is equal to 0.267, in essential agreement with 0.266. In similar manner, identify all of the more intense spots, recording their indices near them on the photograph.

STUDIES WITH A BRAGG SPECTROMETER *

(Read section 9–5, about " Protection from X-rays ")

1. An x-ray spectrum and the wave-lengths of the characteristic lines of a given target material may be measured by means of
the apparatus shown in figure 9–10.

Apparatus.—The x-ray tube should preferably be of the hot-
cathode type. If the target is made of molybdenum, the voltage
applied to the tube should exceed 30 kilovolts, a value of 50 to
60 kilovolts proving satisfactory. In any case, the voltage
should be well above the value needed to excite the characteristic
lines to be studied, as calculated from the relation $Ve = h\nu$. A
typical voltage supply is shown in figure 9–3 while other circuits
are given in chapter 13 and a filament transformer is described in
chapter 19.

In figure 9–10, the anticathode of the x-ray tube should be as
close to the slit A as the electrical insulation will permit. Slits A
and B should be about 0.3 to 0.4 millimeter wide and 1.5 centimeters long in lead sheets 3 to 4 millimeters thick, with the longer
dimension parallel to the crystal face (perpendicular to the paper).
They should be about 20 centimeters apart. Slit D, likewise parallel to the crystal face, should be about 0.3 centimeter wide and
1.5 centimeters long in a similar lead sheet.

The spectrometer table, upon which the crystal C is mounted,
should be capable of giving angles to at least 2 minutes of arc.
The crystal C may be calcite. The alignment of the slits and
crystal is made with the aid of a fluorescent screen.

The ionization chamber I, which is mounted on an extension
arm so as to rotate about the center of the table, is surrounded
with a lead sheath about 3 millimeters thick and is located as
close as possible to the crystal, just outside the circle. The
x-ray beam must not strike the collecting rod or the walls; only
the ends of I. The chamber consists of a brass tube about 20
centimeters long and 5 centimeters in diameter. The brass disc

* The author is indebted to Dr. E. Dershem for the details of these experiments.

which covers the front end contains a slot 0.2 centimeter wide and 2 centimeters long over which a thin aluminum window about 0.025 centimeter thick or a cellophane window 0.008 centimeter thick is sealed with Duco cement or held firmly by a compressed rubber gasket. The collecting rod is supported by means of an amber plug as indicated about 0.5 centimeter from the inner wall; its lead may come out the side or the end. The chamber is filled with argon at a pressure of 2 to 3 atmospheres.

The electrometer should have a sensitivity of 10 millimeters per volt or better. The entire electrometer circuit should be carefully shielded in a grounded metal case. The voltage on the ionization chamber may be 50 to 200 volts.

Experiment.—Place the crystal and chamber as shown in figure 9–10 and start the tube. With the chamber fixed in position, slowly rotate the crystal until a maximum rate of deflection of the electrometer is observed. Now rotate the crystal in steps of 15 minutes, simultaneously moving the chamber by twice this value. Great care must be taken that the chamber movement is just twice the crystal movement. Observe the rate of deflection of the electrometer, which is proportional to the intensity of the x-rays, at each position of the crystal. As a characteristic x-ray line is approached, the intensity will increase very rapidly, perhaps to such a value as to make accurate readings of the electrometer difficult. Then, a sheet of aluminum is placed across the beam near D; one-half millimeter of aluminum will reduce molybdenum radiation to about one-half its unscreened value. The ratio of intensities with and without this absorbing screen is determined in the lower regions of a line and used to adjust values at the higher points to the unscreened scale. Near the lines, the steps should be taken very much closer together.

After moving the crystal over a total of, say 15°, from the direct beam, the crystal and chamber should be rotated to the opposite side of the direct beam and an accurate setting made on the peak of at least one of the lines. One-half of the angle between the two crystal positions (for a given line) is equal to the angle in the Bragg equation (9–8).

Plot the curve of the intensities of the x-rays as ordinates and the angular positions of the crystal as abscissae and compute the wave-lengths of the lines, using equation 9–8. The constant (d)

for calcite is 3.029 angstroms. Compare your values with accepted values.

Additional Experiments.—2. Set the crystal and chamber for any one wave-length, say 0.5 angstrom, in the more intense portion of the continuous radiation. The wave-length is determined as in (1) above, and the corresponding frequency calculated; call it ν_{max}. Plot a curve of the intensity of this x-ray for various voltages up to 60 kilovolts across the tube. The voltages are peak values and may be measured with a spark gap. (See chapter 19.) Full wave rectification must be used in the supply in order that the spark gap voltmeter will read correctly. The plot will show a straight line, called an *isochromat*, whose intercept (at V) on the voltage axis may be used with ν_{max} in the Duane-Hunt law (equation 4–22) to compute h/e.

3. Plot the intensity of the $K_{\alpha 1}$ line of molybdenum (the one of shorter wave-length, for which θ is smaller) for various voltages up to 60 kilovolts across the tube. Note the difference between this curve and the isochromat. The intercept on the voltage axis corresponds to the frequency of the absorption limit of the K series of molybdenum (0.618 angstrom, *not* that of the line $K_{\alpha 1}$ whose wave-length is 0.707 angstrom). Although not so satisfactory a method as (2), it can be used to compute h/e (equation 4–22).

4. Measure the K absorption limit of tin by inserting a sheet of thickness 0.08 millimeter in the path of the x-rays and plotting the spectrum curve as described in (1) above. Only that region near the critical limit need be plotted. The correct value is 0.424 angstrom.

REFERENCES

1. See translation by Stanton. Science, **3**, 227 and 726 (1896).
2. W. D. Coolidge, Phys. Rev., **2**, 409 (1913).
3. General reference A, page 16.
4. General reference A, page 237.
5. A. H. Compton, Phys. Rev., **21**, 207, 483, and **22**, 409 (1923).
6. C. G. Barkla, Proc. Roy. Soc., **A77**, 247 (1906).
7. See Phys. Rev., **25**, 235 (1925).
8. A. H. Compton, Phil. Mag., **45**, 1121 (1923).
9. A. H. Compton and R. L. Doan, Proc. Nat. Acad. Sci., **II**, 598 (1925).
10. W. H. Bragg. *The Crystalline State.* Volume I, Macmillan (1934).

10. (*cont.*) R. W. G. Wyckoff. *The Structure of Crystals*. The Chemical Catalog Co. (1931).
 P. P. Ewald. *Handbuch der Physik* (Geiger and Scheel), XXIII/2, p. 207, Springer (1933).
 P. P. Ewald, et al., *Strukturbericht* (Zeit. f. Kristallographie) (1931) (1936).
 W. P. Davey. *A Study of Crystal Structure and Its Applications.* McGraw-Hill Book Co. (1934).
11. Reference 10 above and general reference B, page 339.
12. Reference 10 and the general references.
13. H. G. J. Moseley, Phil. Mag., **27**, 703 (1914).
14. Reference A, page 116.
15. Reference A, page 280.
16. Reference A, chapter VI.
17. Reference A, page 134.

GENERAL REFERENCES

A.—A. H. Compton and S. K. Allison, *X-rays in Theory and Experiment.* D. Van Nostrand Co. (1935).

B.—G. P. Harnwell and J. J. Livingood, *Experimental Atomic Physics*, Chapter IX. McGraw-Hill (1933).

C.—J. D. Stranathan, *The Particles of Modern Physics.* The Blakiston Co. (1942).

CHAPTER 10

POSITIVE RAYS AND ISOTOPES

10-1. Introduction.—In preceding chapters of this book we have seen that the atom contains a massive, positively charged nucleus around which negative electrons are confined in a number of known energy levels. The electrons in the outer or valence shell are of importance in the chemical combination of various elements, in metallic and heat conduction and in the emission of light. The electrons in the inner shells, near the nucleus, are responsible for the radiation of the characteristic x-rays. It has also been pointed out that the nucleus contains most of the mass of the atom and determines whether the atom is one element or another. In this chapter we shall delve into the properties of the nucleus.

Early measurements of the atomic weights of various elements, in terms of oxygen as 16, yielded very nearly whole number values. Thus Prout was led to the belief that all substances are made up of hydrogen, whose atomic weight is nearly equal to unity. The hydrogen atom was considered as the unit block out of which the heavier atoms were built. More accurate atomic weight determinations, however, showed that they were not exact multiples of a unit amount. Still later, by methods to be presented in this chapter, it was shown that for those cases in which the atomic number was not a whole number, the actual chemical substances consisted of a mixture of groups of atoms, each of which had the same chemical property as the other but a different atomic weight. These *isotopes* of an element were found to have atomic weights which were exceedingly close to whole numbers. In view of the smallness of these latter deviations, one is tempted to accept Prout's hypothesis and to consider the heavier elements to be made up, perhaps not of hydrogen atoms but at least of a small number of elementary units or of stable combinations of these entities.

A streak of light may be seen back of a small hole in the cathode of a discharge tube evacuated to approximately 0.01 mm. This is caused by the positively charged and neutral particles which have passed through the hole and are colliding with molecules of the residual gas. The moving particles are called *positive* (*or canal*) *rays*.* The charged particles or positive ions readily lose their charge as they move through the gas so that they are usually studied in a very good vacuum (0.001 mm. of mercury or less) by means of a willemite screen, photographic plate, thermocouple or Faraday chamber.

The velocity of the positive rays can be measured by making use of Doppler's principle. As the positive ions move away from the cathode, they undergo energy changes which result in the emission of light. This light will show the usual spectrum of the element making up the gas in the tube. Wave-length measurements of one of these lines can be obtained from the side of the beam and from directly in front of it. Viewed end on, the wave-length from the moving particle is shifted toward the blue end of the spectrum as compared to that observed from the side. Say the end-on wave-length is λ', that from the side is λ, then the Doppler shift is $\lambda - \lambda'$, and the velocity of the emitting source is

$$v = c\,\frac{\lambda - \lambda'}{\lambda} \tag{10–1}$$

where c is the velocity of light. The shift in wave-length in the case of the blue line of hydrogen (H_β) may be as great as five angstrom units. The velocity of the particles is thus found to be around 10^7 centimeters per second, a value which is small compared with that of the electrons in the discharge tube.

If the region back of the cathode is maintained at a very low pressure by the continued action of a fast pump, it will be found that the beam of light decreases in intensity according to an exponential law. With hydrogen gas in the discharge tube, its intensity is practically zero, four centimeters behind the cathode. From this and the velocity of the ions, the maximum time duration

---

* The name " canal rays " comes from the German " Kanalstrahlen," meaning rays that have passed through small openings. They were discovered in 1886 by Goldstein.

of light emission from hydrogen ions has been computed [1] as about 10^{-7} seconds.

10–2. Positive Ray Parabolas.—In 1907, J. J. Thomson [2] studied the nature of positive rays by means of electric and magnetic fields.   As indicated in figure 10–1, a positive ray is passed through a region in which electric and magnetic fields act simultaneously to deflect the ray in two directions at right angles to each other.   If the ray is made up of positively charged par-ticles, all of which have the same velocity and the same ratio of charge to mass, they will be equally deflected to the same point on the screen where they will produce a spot of light.   If, however, the positive ions are produced in a cold electrode discharge tube,

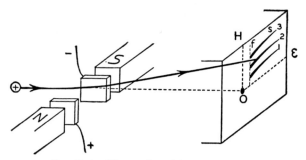

Fɪɢ. 10–1.   Thomson's positive ray parabolas.

they will have a range of velocities from zero up to a definite maximum.   The slower ions are deflected more than the faster ones by both the electric and magnetic fields so that a line of light instead of a spot will appear on the screen, as indicated in figure 10–1.   It can be shown [3*] that the deflections produced by the electric field $\mathscr{E}$ alone are inversely proportional to the square of the velocity of the particles whereas the deflections due to the magnetic field H are inversely proportional to their velocity. Hence the line of light on the screen increases in the $\mathscr{E}$ direction more rapidly than in the H direction.   The actual shape of the

* $x = \mathscr{E}(E/M)ld/v^2$, $y = H(E/M)l'd'/v$, where $\mathscr{E}$ = electric field intensity, d = distance from center of deflecting plates to the screen, l = length of a deflect-ing plate, v = velocity of particle whose ratio of charge to mass is E/M, and H = magnetic field intensity; d' = distance from center of magnetic field to the screen and l' = axial extent of the magnetic field.

line is that of a parabola whose vertex is at the origin. Each parabola is due to particles of the same ratio of charge to mass (E/M) but of different velocities. In figure 10–1, the faster particles were deflected to f and the slower ones to s.

It is found that several parabolas appear simultaneously. Each is due to particles of a given charge to mass ratio. If the charges are the same, the different parabolas are due to particles of different masses. Thus the parabola 3 in figure 10–1 was caused by a group of particles whose mass was small compared with those in the groups which produced parabolas 2 or 1. The greater the mass of a particle, the less easily is it deflected.

Occasionally *higher order* parabolas are observed. These lines are due to particles of differing charge but identical mass. The greater the charge, the greater the deflection. For example, a line near the $\mathscr{E}$ axis in figure 10–1 might be due to singly ionized mercury atoms, Hg^+, i.e., atoms from which one electron has been removed. The second order parabola is displaced farther from the $\mathscr{E}$ axis and would be due to doubly ionized mercury atoms, Hg^{++}, while the third order line would be due to trebly ionized mercury atoms Hg^{+++}.

At very low pressures, the lines are sharp, but at higher pressures, when some of the positive ions lose their charge over a portion of their path, it is found that a general fogging of the screen is produced or the parabola extends down to the origin (O in figure 10–1). Also, at the higher pressures, the positive ion on rare

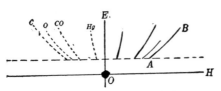

Fig. 10–2.   Positive ray parabolas.

occasions captures more electrons than needed to neutralize its charge. Faint *negative parabolas* are then found, reversed and inverted with respect to the usual ones.

In addition to the parabolas formed by atomic ions, others are observed which are due to molecular ions. Thus in figure 10–2, the CO parabola is due to molecules of carbon monoxide.

Inasmuch as the $\mathscr{E}$ and H axes do not appear on the screen, nor upon a photographic plate placed in the same position, the location of the lines is determined by reversing the magnetic field during the exposure. A record such as that in figure 10–2 is then obtained. It is, however, customary to obtain parabolas of the unknown and of a substance of standard mass on the same plate. Measurements of the distances between the parabolas then permits a determination of the mass of the unknown in terms of the standard. The higher order lines may be used to advantage to compare two masses which differ widely from each other.

10–3. Aston's Mass Spectrograph.—Aston[4] has improved the Thomson parabola method so that ions of different velocities but identical E/M are brought to the same focus. This *velocity focus method* increased the resolving power so that it was possible to distinguish between ions whose masses differ by only *1* part in *600*, as contrasted with *1* in *20* of Thomson's method. The accuracy of the Aston method of determining the ratio of two masses is *1* in *10,000*. This method of mass analysis has proved to be more accurate than the chemical methods of determining atomic weights.

An extensive and detailed study of the different atomic masses of the elements was made. A simplified diagram of the apparatus is shown in figure 10–3; it is enclosed in an evacuated chamber,

Fig. 10–3. Aston's positive ray apparatus.

not shown. When a discharge is maintained between the anode A and the cathode C, positive ions are formed in the rarefied gas and pass through the hole in the cathode. They are confined to a narrow beam by the slits S and pass through the electric field $\mathscr{E}$. The faster particles follow the line f and the slower ones move along s. They are then deflected by the magnetic field H so as to come to a focus on the photographic plate P. The apparatus is so arranged that rays of the same ratio of charge to mass but differing velocities are all brought to the same focal point, thus reducing the exposure times and assuring fine lines. Rays with different values of charge to mass ratio come to different focal lines.

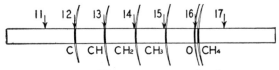

Fig. 10–4.   The mass spectrum of methane.

The photographic records [5] show sections of the lines, as indicated in figure 10–4.

10–4. Isotopes.—In 1913, Thomson studied the parabolas produced by the lighter gases. He observed a line at mass 22 which could not be identified with any known substance in the discharge tube. At first he thought the line might be a second order line of carbon dioxide (CO_2^{++}) but soon found that it persisted after eliminating this gas and its strong first order line. However, he found that the line always appeared when neon was present in the discharge. The atomic weight of neon, as determined by chemical means is 20.183. It was, nevertheless, thought that the line at 22 was caused by neon.

With greater dispersion of the lines, Aston was able to announce [6] in 1919 that there were two kinds of neon, one of atomic weight 20 and the other of 22. The chemical and physical properties of these *isotopes* are the same as for ordinary neon. They differ only in their atomic weights. Neon gas is a mixture of the two isotopes. They are to be grouped together at the same place in the periodic table. Iso means *same* and topos means *place*.

Isotopes were known to exist among the radioactive substances in 1905, before the work with positive rays. Details of radioactive isotopes will be presented in chapter 11. After the discovery of the neon isotopes, many others were quickly found among the common elements.

10–5. Dempster's Direction Focus.[7]—Electrons from the filament F in the evacuated chamber of figure 10–5 are used to ionize gases or vapors produced by heating a solid in the small electrical oven O. The positive ions which are thus produced are drawn to a cathode and pass through the slit S_1. They are then given their major acceleration by a large potential on the second cathode (S_2). By this means, the positive ions all have approximately the same velocity, as contrasted with the wide range of velocities in

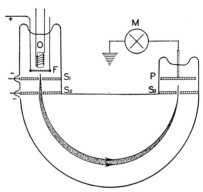

the case of a cold discharge tube. However, because of the comparatively wide slits used, they travel in slightly different directions as they pass through the second slit S_2. Under the action of a magnetic field perpendicular to the paper, the various ions which have the same value of E/M are brought to a focus at the slit S_3. They are collected on the plate P and recorded by means of the electrometer M. Equations

FIG. 10–5. Dempster's early mass spectrograph.

2–1 and 2–6 are applicable to this apparatus.

Ions of different E/M values are focussed on the slit S_3 either by a change in the magnetic field strength or by a change in the velocity of the particles by an alteration in the accelerating potential between S_1 and S_2. Figure 10–6 shows the observed number of ions (proportional to the electrometer readings) of different atomic weights (proportional to the accelerating potential) for the case when magnesium was placed in the oven. It is seen that there are three isotopes of magnesium of atomic weights 24, 25, and 26. The " lines " are not sharp because, first, the direction focussing is not perfect and second, the ions do not all have exactly the same velocity.

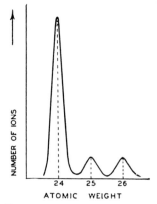

FIG. 10–6. Magnesium isotopes.

The *abundance* of the isotopes of an element can, in certain cases, be measured by means of Dempster's apparatus. For example, the relative amounts of magnesium 24, 25 and 26 are

77.4, 11.5 and 11.1, respectively. The mean atomic weight, when 24, 25 and 26 are taken in these proportions is 24.34. This is in good agreement with the chemical atomic weight of magnesium, 24.32. It is of interest that the isotopes of a given element are so mixed together in nature that samples from widely different regions of the earth have the same atomic weight.

10–6. Velocity Selection.[8]—Positive rays, collimated by the slits S_1 and S_2 of figure 10–7, pass through a velocity selector S where they are subjected to the action of electric and magnetic fields arranged perpendicularly to each other as in the case of the beta rays in figure 2–9. The ions which can then pass through the slit S_3 are all of nearly the same velocity. Actually. there is an exceedingly small range of velocities. The ions are deflected by a second magnetic field, also perpendicular to the paper, and come to a focus on the photographic plate P.

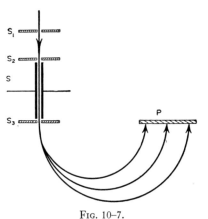

FIG. 10–7.
Bainbridge's early mass spectrograph.

10–7. Simultaneous Velocity and Direction Focus.—In order to increase still more the resolving power and hence the accuracy in mass determinations, the sharpness of the images on the photographic plate has been improved by more elaborate combinations of electric and magnetic fields which give simultaneous velocity and direction focus. Here, a radial electrostatic field,[9–14] produced by curved condenser plates, is followed by a uniform magnetic field.[12–15] A diagram of the apparatus of Dempster is shown in figure 10–8. Positive ions from the source (S) are accelerated by a potential of 3,000 to 20,000 volts applied between the slits, S_1 and S_2. The mixture of ions of various E/M values and of slightly differing velocities emerges from the slit (S_3), which is only a fraction of a millimeter in width. The beam, now a slightly divergent bundle of rays, enters the electrostatic field of the cylindrical condenser and is deflected through 90° to the wide slit (S_4) (several millimeters wide) in such a manner that all those of a given velocity come to a common focus; the faster ones on the left, at A; the slower ones on the right, at B, with all gradations between, thus forming a velocity spectrum across the slit. They then enter the magnetic field, whose strength is so adjusted with respect to the electrostatic field and the distance, d, that all ions of the same E/M ratio, irrespective (within limits) of the velocity and direction with which they left S_3, are brought

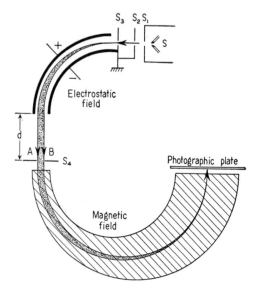

Fig. 10–8. Dempster's apparatus, which provides for both velocity and direction focus.

to a common focus on the photographic plate. Ions which differ in mass by only 1 part in 4000 mass units can be resolved.

As a source of positive ions, Dempster has used a high frequency spark (600 kc), operated from a Tesla circuit, between electrodes made of the material to be studied. This form of source has proven useful in that it has been possible, for the first time, to study such metals as palladium, platinum and gold. In addition, the high frequency source is rich in multiple charged ions so that accurate mass measurements using higher order lines are possible. In this way, it was found that the atomic weight of actino-uranium was 235 and not 234, in agreement with a suggestion by Ruther-ford. Together with the chemical determination of the atomic weight of proto-actinium as 231, by v. Grosse, it is now established that the elements of the actinium series (see section 11–4) have odd, rather than even, atomic weights.

Bainbridge [15] has used a different arrangement of the radial electrostatic and uniform magnetic fields, as in figure 10–9, in order to obtain simultaneous velocity and direction focus. His electrical field extends over an angle of 127° so that the ions of one velocity, selected by a slit, approach the magnetic field in an essentially parallel bundle. The lines are found to be in focus over the en-tire length of the photographic plate and the mass scale is linear. With this apparatus, a number of accurate mass analyses have been made, par-ticularly among the lighter elements.

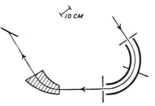

Fig. 10–9. Bainbridge's mass spectrograph.

10–8. Atomic, Isotopic and Nuclear Weights.—From studies of band spectra it has been shown [16] that there are three isotopes of oxygen, namely oxygen 16, 17 and 18. The abundance of the latter two isotopes is not great. The international atomic weight is that of the mixture and is taken as exactly equal to 16. In the mass spectrograph, however, the lighter and more abundant isotope has been assigned an atomic weight exactly equal to 16. There exists, therefore, a small difference between the chemical and physical atomic weights. The *isotopic weight* (M) of an element is its comparative weight in terms of O^{16} as 16.0000 and the *international atomic weight* $(\mathscr{M})$ of an element is its comparative weight in terms of the mixture of O^{16}, O^{17} and O^{18} as 16.0000. The relation [17] between these two systems is

$$\mathscr{M} = 1.00027\,M. \qquad (10\text{–}2)$$

The weight of one electron is 0.00055 mass units; i.e., the weight of one electron is to that of one oxygen sixteen atom as 0.00055 is to 16.

A table (15) of isotopic weights is given in the back of the book. The values are for neutral atoms and include the extranuclear

electrons. The weight of these electrons in mass units is equal
to 0.00055 multiplied by Z, the atomic number. Thus, the *nuclear
weight* of the oxygen sixteen isotope is $16.0000 - 8 \times 0.00055$
$= 15.9956$ mass units.

10–9. The Case of Hydrogen.—In 1927, Aston found the
atomic weight of hydrogen to be 1.00778, in good agreement with
the international value 1.00777. But, in 1929, the 0^{18} isotope
was discovered. With 0^{18} as a standard, the mass spectrum
value for hydrogen would have been 1.00756, which is too small.
On the other hand, if the international atomic weight of oxygen
had been taken as slightly greater than 16, in order to allow for the
heavier isotope, then the hydrogen value would have been too
large to agree with that of Aston. In 1931, Birge and Menzel
pointed out that the discrepancy might be due to the existence of
heavier isotopes of hydrogen.

In 1932, Urey [18] sought for and established the existence of
an isotope of hydrogen whose mass was nearly twice that of
ordinary hydrogen. This isotope has been named *deuterium* and
its symbol is H^2 or D. The nucleus of the deuterium atom is
called the *deuteron*. It has about twice the mass of the proton but
carries the same electrical charge. H^1 is about five thousand times
as abundant as D^2. The atomic weight of H^1 was remeasured by
Bainbridge and by Aston and found to be 1.00813.

"Heavy water" or deuterium oxide (D_2O) may be prepared in
a very nearly pure form by extended electrolysis of water.[19,20]
The density of the heavy water is 1.1079 times that of ordinary
water. The number of possible chemical combinations has been
greatly extended by the discovery of deuterium.

10–10.   The Mass Defect.—The *mass number*, A, of an atom
is the nearest whole number to its isotopic weight, M. The *mass
defect* (Δ) is the difference between the isotopic weight and the
mass number. The defect is very small, never exceeding 0.1 mass
units, but is a real difference and not an experimental error.

$$\Delta = M - A. \tag{10–3}$$

The measured masses (M) are greater than the mass numbers (A)
for the very light and for the very heavy elements, as indicated in
figure 10–10. For a majority of the isotopes the reverse is true.

This small difference may also be expressed in relation to the total weight of the atom. Aston has defined the *packing fraction*, f, in the following manner,

$$f = 10^4 \frac{\Delta}{A}. \tag{10-4}$$

The factor of 10^4 is included in order that f shall be a number of convenient size. Values range from 0 to 80, and are positive for

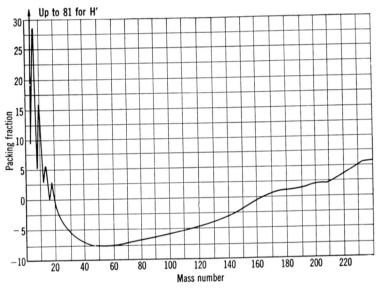

FIG. 10-10.   Packing fraction curve.

the light and heavy atoms and are negative for those of intermediate mass. The mass defects for elements lighter than neon (20) are all positive but scatter widely (e.g., $H^3 = 0.017$ and $He^4 = 0.003$).

10-11. The Neutron-Proton Theory.[21]—The weights of the atoms, on the basis of O^{16} as 16.0000, are found to be very nearly, although not exactly, equal to whole numbers. The nuclear charges (Z) are found to be exact integers. These two facts can be explained if it is assumed that the nuclei of various atoms are composed of particles of unit atomic weight, some of which are charged positively with one electron unit (protons or hydrogen nuclei) while the others are neutral (and hence are called *neutrons*). (See chapter 14.)   For example, the helium nucleus is known to have a mass of (nearly) four and a charge of $+ 2e$.   In order to have this mass the nucleus must be composed of four of the elementary particles and in order to have this charge it is necessary that two of these be protons.   On this theory, the mass number, A, is equal to the total number of protons and neutrons in the nucleus, while the nuclear charge or atomic number, Z, is equal to the number of protons in the nucleus.*   If the number of neutrons is N, then

$$A = N + Z. \qquad (10\text{--}5)$$

The small differences between the nuclear masses and the integers will be considered in the next section.

10–12.   The Binding Energy.   Stability of Nuclei.—The *binding energy* of the nucleus of an atom is the difference between its nuclear weight and the sum of the weights of the lighter particles of which it is supposed to be formed.   Consider the isotope Li^6; i.e., a lithium atom whose nucleus has a mass number of 6 and a charge of $+3$.   Assume that its nucleus consists of three protons and three neutrons, whose free masses are $3 \times 1.0076 = 3.0228$ and $3 \times 1.0089 = 3.0267$, making a total of 6.0495 mass units. But this is 0.0328 mass units greater than the observed nuclear weight of 6.0167.   If the theory is correct, it must be concluded that the elementary particles have less mass, when bound together in a nucleus, than the sum of their masses when they are free. Now, the relativity theory states that mass and energy are interchangeable.   Thus, using equation 2–27, we may say that the binding energy of the lithium atom is 0.0328 mass units, 48.6 microergs or 30.6 Mev, compared with free protons and neutrons.   This is a measure of the *stability* of the lithium nucleus, or, in other words, a measure of the difficulty of breaking down a lithium nucleus into free neutrons and protons.   The greater the binding energy, the more stable the nucleus.

It has been suggested by astro-physicists that the energy radiated from the sun and the stars consists of that which is lost when

---

* The excess number of neutrons over the number of protons is called the " isotopic number," I, and is given by $I = N - Z = A - 2Z$.

Isobars have nuclei of the same weight but differ in their atomic numbers.

heavier atoms are formed from lighter particles. Only a small mass is needed to give a comparatively large amount of radiant energy.

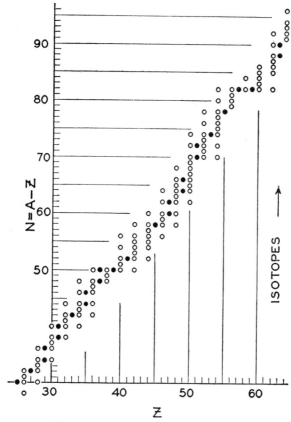

FIG. 10–11. Some of the stable isotopes.

The dots and circles in figure 10–11 represent the known isotopes from $Z = 25$ to 65 which exist in *stable form* in Nature. Z and N are, according to theory, the respective numbers of protons and neutrons in the nuclei. It is to be noted that the isotopes all lie within more or less clearly defined boundaries. This means that for a given element, with constant Z value, N has a limited range; any excess of N forms an unstable atom which does not exist in natural state.   Similarly, for a given N value, Z is restricted within rather definite limits.

Isotopes of the elements with *odd atomic number* are represented by solid dots in figure 10–11.   For these, there are never more than two stable isotopes, except in the case of hydrogen. A and N always differ by two units and A is odd when Z is odd, except for the very light elements.

For the elements of *even atomic number*, the mass number, A, of the lightest stable isotope is never less than twice the atomic number, Z, of the element, except for hydrogen.   For example, the atomic number of neon is 10 and the mass number of its lightest isotope is 20.

10–13.   The Separation of Isotopes.[22]—When several isotopes are mixed together, they cannot be separated by the usual chemical or physical methods.   In several cases, however, methods based on the small mass differences between the various isotopes in the mixture have been used with success.

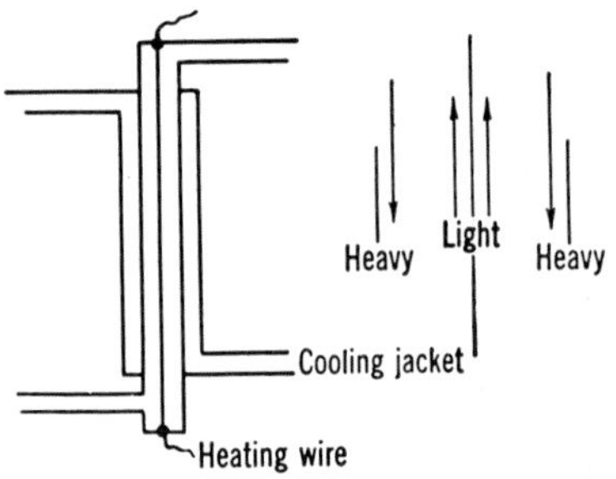

For example, the *rate of evaporation* of a liquid depends inversely on the square root of the weight of the molecules. This means that the number of light molecules evaporating each second from a liquid mixture will be greater than the number of heavy molecules. If the vapor is continuously removed from above a liquid containing isotopes, the concentration of the heavier isotope in the liquid will gradually increase.

Fig. 10–11A.   Schematic diagram of thermal diffusion method of separating isotopes.   The heavy isotopes are withdrawn from the cooled periphery while the light ones tend to diffuse toward the hot central wire.

This method amounts to fractional distillation. The boiling points of the heavier constituents are slightly higher than those containing the lighter isotopes.   Careful temperature control is necessary to achieve successful separation.

In the *electrolytic method*, pointed out in section 10–9, the mobility of the deuterium ions is less than that of the lighter hydrogen ions.   With continued passage of the current, the residual electrolyte becomes richer in deuterium.   It is to be noted that the ratio of the masses of deuterium to " hydrogen one " is as two is to one, or one hundred per cent.   In the case of neon, for example, the masses are twenty and twenty-two; the difference is only ten per cent.

The rate at which a gas *diffuses* through a porous material varies inversely as the square root of the mass of the molecules. By repeated, " regenerative " circulation of neon for twenty hours through the walls of clay pipes of special design, G. Hertz[23] was able to obtain a light fraction containing only one per cent of neon twenty-two and a heavy fraction containing only about three per cent of the lighter gas.   Normal neon gas contains approximately nine parts of neon twenty to one part of neon twenty-two.

The *mass spectrograph* offers a method for the complete separation of isotopes but is handicapped by the small amount of material which can be isolated even with large positive ion currents and long time of operation.   However, sufficient quantities of the lithium isotopes have been isolated for use in nuclear distintegration experiments.[24]   (See chapter 14.)

The *centrifuge* has been used successfully in separating isotopes. As in the case of separating cream from milk, the heavier components experience greater forces and concentrate at the periphery, whereas the lighter fraction may be drawn off at the center.   Since the mass differences are small, the highest centrifugal speeds possible are necessary.

Finally, *the chemical exchange* method has been used.   Simple chemical exchange reactions show a slight dependence on atomic weight, and this method has been used to separate isotopes among the lighter elements.

10–14.   Review of Definitions.

Atomic number, Z, is the number assigned to the elements when arranged in order from the lightest to the heaviest.   Examples: Hydrogen = 1; Helium = 2; Lithium = 3; Oxygen = 8; Uranium = 92. Z has also been proven to be equal to the number of electronic charges on the nucleus of an atom.   (This is also equal to the number of extra-nuclear electrons.)   (It is also equal to the number of protons in the nucleus.)

Atomic weight, $\mathcal{M}$ (international or " chemical "), is the relative mass of an atom of an element in comparison with that of an " atom " of the *chemical mixture* of O^{16}, O^{17} and O^{18} taken as

16.0000 . . . . Examples: Hydrogen 1.00800; Lithium 6.940; Oxygen 16.000

Isotopic weight, M ("physical"), is the relative mass of an atom of an element in comparison with that of an atom of *oxygen-sixteen* (O^{16}) taken as 16.0000. . . . Examples: Hydrogen 1.0081; Deuterium (H^2) 2.0147; Lithium-six 6.0167; Lithium-seven 7.0178; Oxygen-sixteen 16.0000; Oxygen-eighteen 18.0049

Nuclear weight is the relative mass of the *nucleus* of an atom of an element in comparison with O^{16} as 16.0000. . . . Example: Hydrogen nucleus = proton = 1.00745; Heavy hydrogen (deuterium) nucleus = deuteron = 2.0142; Helium nucleus = alpha particle = 4.0019; Oxygen-sixteen nucleus = 15.9956.

Mass number, A $(= N + Z)$, of an atom is the nearest whole number to its isotopic weight. Examples: Hydrogen (H^1) = 1; Deuterium (H^2) = 2; Lithium (6.0167) = 6; Lithium (7.0178) = 7; Oxygen (18.0049) = 18.

Mass defect, Δ $(= M - A)$, is the difference between the isotopic weight and the mass number. It is very small. Examples: Hydrogen (1.008 − 1) = +0.0080; Oxygen 18 (18.0049 − 18) = +0.0031; Neon 22 (21.9985 − 22) = −0.0015.

Packing fraction, f $(= 10^4 \Delta/A)$, is 10^4 times the mass defect divided by the mass number. Examples: Hydrogen (+0.0081/1) 10^4 = +81; Helium^4 (+0.0039/4)10^4 = +9.7; Argon 40 (−0.0246/40)10^4 = −6.15.

Binding energy is the difference between the nuclear weight and the sum of the weights of the separated particles which, if combined, would form the atom. Example: Helium 4, assumed to be formed from two protons ($2 \times 1.00758 = 2.01516$) plus two neutrons ($2 \times 1.00893 = 2.01786$), a total of 4.03302, as compared with 4.00390 mass units for helium. Hence the binding energy is 4.03302 − 4.00390 = 0.02912 mass units, which is 0.02912 × 0.00149 = 4.339×10^{-5} ergs; or 0.02912 × 931 = 27.1 Mev.

EXPERIMENT 10–1

POSITIVE RAY PARABOLAS

Apparatus.—Figure 10–12 shows one form of apparatus which may be used to study positive ray parabolas. It is drawn to scale. The anode (A) consists of a hollow cone made of molybdenum or

tungsten to withstand the heat developed by electron bombardment at this point. The pyrex discharge tube (B) is 5 centimeters
in diameter and about 50 centimeters long. The cathode (C) is
made of steel and has a circular groove into which the discharge
tube is waxed. The edges of this groove must be rounded to
prevent electrical breakdown of the glass. Water cooling is provided by a single turn of copper tubing OO soldered around the
anode. The canal (K) consists of a hole 1.4 millimeters in diameter and 5 to 7 centimeters long. The cathode is soldered to a

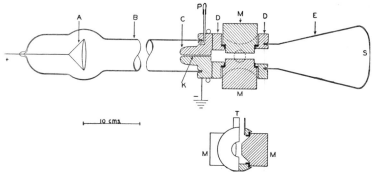

Fig. 10–12. To study positive ray parabolas.

brass cylinder (DD) which is drilled axially for the passage of the
positive ions and transversely for the tapered pole pieces (MM) of
an electromagnet. The faces of the pole pieces are 2 centimeters
high, 5 centimeters long and 1 centimeter apart. The poles are insulated from the brass cylinder by circular hard rubber washers and
are waxed in place. A sheet of mica in the magnetic circuit serves
to insulate the pole pieces from each other electrically. Then, the
poles can also serve as the plates of an electrical condenser. The
110 volt dc line, varied with a slide wire potentiometer, is used to
produce the electrostatic field.

The scintillation screen (S) can be obtained from a burned out
cathode ray oscillograph tube or prepared by coating a glass plate
with a thin layer of phosphorescent zinc sulphide or with willemite.
A trace of saliva or gelatin is used as a binder. The tube (E) may
be of glass or metal.

Procedure.—The apparatus is evacuated to as low a pressure as
possible through the large tube (T), which should be at least 2.5

centimeters in diameter. It should be impossible to pass a discharge through the tube when 40 to 60 kilovolts are applied between A and C. The high voltage may be obtained by the use of a transformer and rectifier tube as in experiment 3–1. A static machine may be used but does not give good intensity. A Bunsen burner with a small blue flame is now used to warm the palladium thimble (P). Then, hydrogen flows through P into the discharge tube. Adjust the heating until, with the vacuum pumps in operation, a faint blue discharge is just visible in the tube. A spot of light should be seen at the center of the screen (S). Apply both the magnetic and electric deflecting fields and observe the positive ray parabola with varying field strengths. If conditions are sufficiently steady, measurements can be made and e/m and v of the positive ions calculated; or the parabola may be photographed.

Precautions.—1. Ground the cathode. *Keep away from the anode.* 2. Be sure the cathode is water cooled before starting the discharge. 3. Do not heat the palladium tube beyond a very dull red.

If there is breakdown of the glass near the cathode, slip a snugly fitting iron tube over its end. Let the iron tube extend beyond C, toward A, about 5 centimeters.

REFERENCES

1. A. J. Dempster, Phys. Rev., **15**, 138 (1920).
2. J. J. Thomson, Phil. Mag., **13**, 561 (1907).
3. See Harnwell and Livingood, *Experimental Atomic Physics*, McGraw-Hill Book Co. (1933), page 136.
4. General Reference A, page 73.
5. General Reference A, pages 82 and 86.
6. General Reference A, Chapter IV.
7. A. J. Dempster, Phys. Rev., **11**, 316 (1918); **20**, 631 (1922).
8. K. T. Bainbridge, Jr. Frank. Inst., **215**, 509 (1933).
9. W. Bartky and A. J. Dempster, Phys. Rev., **33**, 1019 (1929).
10. A. L. Hughes and V. Rojansky, Phys. Rev., **34**, 284 (1929).
11. R. Herzog and J. Mattauch, Ann. der Phys., **19**, 345 (1934).
12. R. Herzog, Zeits. f. Physik, **89**, 447 (1934).
13. J. Mattauch and R. Herzog, Zeits. f. Physik, **89**, 786 (1934).
14. A. J. Dempster, Proc. Amer. Phil. Soc., **75**, 755 (1935).
15. K. T. Bainbridge and E. B. Jordan, Phys. Rev., **50**, 282 (1936).
16. Giauque and Johnston, Nature, **123**, 318 (1929).
17. From estimates of the relative abundance of the oxygen isotopes. Mecke and Childs, Zeits. f. Physik, **68**, 362 (1931).

18. Urey, Brickwedde and Murphy, Phys. Rev., **39**, 164 (1932); **40**, 1 (1932).
    Urey and Teal, Rev. Mod. Phys., **7**, 34 (1935).
19. G. N. Lewis, Jr. Amer. Chem. Soc., **55**, 1297 (1933).
20. C. M. Slack and L. F. Ehrke, Rev. Sci. Inst., **8**, 39 (1937).
21. W. Heisenberg, Zeits. f. Physik, **77**, 1 (1932), §1, 6, 7, 8, 11.
22. General Reference A, Chapter XVII.
23. G. Hertz, Zeits. f. Physik, **79**, 108 (1932); **82**, 589 (1933).
    D. E. Wooldridge and W. R. Smythe, Phys. Rev., **50**, 233 (1936).
24. Oliphant, Shire and Crowther, Proc. Roy. Soc. **A146**, 922 (1934).
    Rumbaugh, Phys. Rev., **49**, 882 (1936).

GENERAL REFERENCES

A.—F. W. Aston, *Mass-Spectra and Isotopes*, Longmans, Green & Co. (1933).
B.—*International Committee on Isotopes*, Rev. Sci. Inst., **7**, 334 (1936).
C.—G. T. Seaborg, *Table of Isotopes*, Rev. Mod. Phys., **16**, 1 (1944).
D.—J. D. Stranathan, *The Particles of Modern Physics*. The Blakiston Co. (1942).

CHAPTER 11

SPONTANEOUS DISINTEGRATION

11-1. Introduction.—In 1896, Becquerel discovered that uranium salts emitted radiations capable of blackening a photographic plate even after passing through bodies which were opaque to light rays. It has been found, since then, that all of the heavier elements from $Z = 84$ to 92, at the end of the Periodic Table, spontaneously emit radiations which are capable not only of blackening a photographic plate but also of ionizing a gas through which

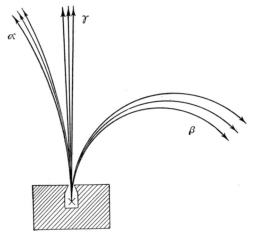

Fig. 11-1. Magnetic deflection of alpha, beta and gamma rays.

they pass, making it a conductor of electricity, and of producing scintillations or small flashes of light when they strike a suitable material. The action of the radiations make it possible not only to detect the presence but also to measure the amount of radioactive substance at hand, even though only a small quantity is scattered through tons of ore.

11-2. The Nature of the Radiations.—The radiations which are emitted by radioactive substances are of three kinds, as may be shown by allowing them to pass through a magnetic field. In figure 11–1, the field is perpendicular to the paper and the active material is located at x. The deflection of the alpha ray is greatly exaggerated in comparison with that of the beta ray. From the direction of the deflections and of the field it is found that the alpha rays are positively charged and the beta rays are negatively charged whereas the gamma rays are uncharged.

It will be shown in the next chapter that the alpha rays are made up of a stream of alpha *particles* each of which has a positive charge, numerically equal to twice that of the electron, and an atomic weight nearly equal to 4. It will also be shown that beta *particles* are high speed electrons and that gamma rays are electromagnetic radiations similar in nature to x-rays.

11–3. Units of Radioactivity.[1]—In order to specify the amount of a substance at hand, one may state its mass. The unit, for radioactive substances, consists of a certain number of grams of a gas called radium emanation or radon. This mass unit, called the *curie*, after the Curies, was defined by the Radiology Congress in Brussels in 1910 as " The amount of emanation in equilibrium with one gram of pure radium." It has a mass of 6.51×10^{-6} grams and occupies 0.66 cubic millimeters at 76 centimeters pressure and 0° C. The international radium standard consists of the radon in equilibrium with 21.99 milligrams of specially purified radium chloride prepared by Madame Curie and preserved at the Bureau Internationale des Poids et Measures at Sévres near Paris, France. Secondary standards have been prepared and distributed throughout the various countries.

When alpha, beta or gamma rays are emitted from the atoms of a radioactive substance, it is obvious that the atoms must undergo a change. They are said to " disintegrate." It is, therefore, possible to specify the amount of a radioactive substance in terms of the number of atoms which disintegrate each second; called the activity. A substance has an activity of *one curie* when **3.71×10^{10}** atoms disintegrate each second; which *is the activity of one gram of radium*. A unit one thousand times smaller, called the *millicurie*, is more often used in practice.

The Mache unit of radon concentration is that amount of radon gas per liter which will produce a saturation current of 10^{-3} e.s.u. when all the radiation is absorbed. The alpha rays from one curie of radon will produce a saturation current of 0.92 milli-amperes.   Hence, one Mache unit is the equivalent of 3.64×10^{-10} curies per liter.

In order to determine the activity of a given substance it is only necessary to compare the rates of fall of the leaf of an electro-scope in which the unknown and a standard have been placed in succession.   Certain necessary precautions are discussed in chapter 17.

11–4.   Radioactive   Series.—Rutherford   and   Soddy   have shown that when a radiactive substance, the *parent*, emits an alpha or a beta ray, an entirely new substance, the *product*, is left which

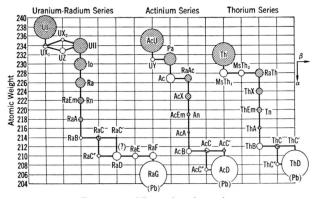

Fig. 11–2.   The radioactive series.

has different chemical and physical properties from the parent. Thus, radioactivity is a nuclear phenomenon.

Starting with uranium and thorium, the radioactive substances change from one material into another, branch along three distinct paths and end in three isotopic forms of lead, as given in table 16 at the end of the book and as shown in figure 11–2.   Potassium (K^{40}), rubidium and samarium are also radioactive, but only to an exceeding small degree.

The rate at which these transformations take place is different for each substance in the series.   Some radioactive substances have a life of many hundreds of years, as represented by the large circles of figure 11–2, while others last only a fraction of a second. In other words, the probability that the nuclei of certain atoms will remain unchanged over a period of time is greater than that for other nuclei.

The rate at which a *given* substance spontaneously disintegrates cannot be altered by any agency known to man at the present time. It is not affected by chemical reactions, pressure changes from a good vacuum to twenty thousand atmospheres, from liquid air temperatures up to three thousand degrees centigrade nor by electric, magnetic or gravitational fields.

11-5. A Simple Radioactive Transformation.—To illustrate the transformation of one radioactive substance into another, a particular case will be given where uranium I changes into uranium X_1. Uranium I, with an atomic weight of 238 and an atomic

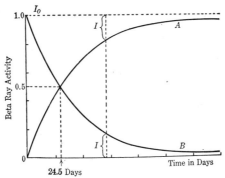

Fig. 11-3. Formation and decay of uranium X_1.

number of 92 is found at the end of the Periodic Table. As it emits alpha rays, it slowly changes into uranium X_1 so that the two are always found together. Uranium X_1 is continually emitting beta and gamma rays, changing into another substance. Hence, if the mixture is placed in a beta ray electroscope,* a constant activity is shown, the uranium X_1 decaying at the same rate as it is being formed. This is known as *stable* or *secular equilibrium* of the product with the parent. The two may be separated from each other by chemical means † and placed in

* For the distinction between alpha, beta and gamma ray electroscopes, see chapter 17.
† An aqueous solution of uranium nitrate in ammonium carbonate yields a precipitate which may be redissolved. A new precipitate is formed which is uranium X_1 alone.

different beta ray electroscopes.   Their activity curves are shown in figure 11–3.   Curve A shows the beta ray activity in the uranium I sample and hence shows the formation of uranium X_1 (since uranium I does not emit beta rays).   Curve B shows the decay of the isolated uranium X_1.   In order to show that this is the decay curve of uranium X_1 and not of its disintegration products, the following series is given.

$$\text{UI} \xrightarrow{\alpha} \text{UX}_1 \xrightarrow{\beta, \gamma} \text{UX}_2 \xrightarrow{\beta, \gamma} \text{UII} \xrightarrow{\alpha}$$
$$4.4 \times 10^9 \text{ years} \quad 24.5 \text{ days} \quad 1.14 \text{ minutes} \quad 3 \times 10^5 \text{ years}$$

The numbers which are given are the times for half of the substance to decay.   It is to be noted that neither uranium I or II contribute to the activity as they emit only alpha particles, and a beta ray electroscope is used.   The beta rays of uranium X_2 constitute the major activity of the curve B of figure 11–3 but, since this substance decays quickly, it is its continual replenishment by uranium X_1 which determines the shape of the curve, i.e., the shape of B is determined by uranium X_1, although it is actually due to uranium X_2.   The fact that a decay curve follows the activity of a long-life substance in spite of the presence of its short-lived products is a general principle in this subject.

11–6.   Rutherford-Soddy Theory of Transformations.   Isolated Substances.—It is assumed that the number of atoms which break up each second is a constant fraction of those present at any given instant.   For example, if there are 10,000 atoms at the start and 200 (2%) break up during the first second, sending out an alpha or beta and gamma ray, then during the next second 2 per cent (196) of the remaining 9800 atoms will break up and during the third second 2 per cent of the remaining atoms break up, i.e., 192 of the 9604 will disintegrate, etc.   The ratio of the number which break up each second to the total number is called the *transformation or disintegration constant* and is designated by λ. Then

$$n = \lambda N \tag{11–1}$$

where N is the total number present at a certain time and n is the number which break up at that time during one second.   We then have

$$\frac{dN}{dt} = -\lambda N \tag{11–2}$$

the negative sign indicating a decrease in the number of unchanged atoms. From this

$$\int \frac{dN}{N} = \int - \lambda dt \qquad (11\text{–}3)$$

$$\log_\epsilon N = - \lambda t + C \qquad (11\text{–}4)$$

and when $t = 0$

$$\log N_0 = C \qquad (11\text{–}5)$$

giving

$$\log \frac{N}{N_0} = - \lambda t \qquad (11\text{–}6)$$

$$N = N_0 \epsilon^{-\lambda t} \qquad (11\text{–}7)$$

where ϵ is the base of the Naperian system of logarithms. This exponential equation gives the number of atoms N existing after a time t when there were N_0 atoms at the start. Substituting this equation in 11–1 gives

$$n = (\lambda N_0) \epsilon^{-\lambda t} = n_o \epsilon^{-\lambda t} \qquad (11\text{–}8)$$

which is the number of atoms breaking up each second (n) after a time t seconds, while n_o is the number disintegrating each second at the start. It is now assumed that the number of particles emitted each second is the same as the number of atoms breaking up. It has been shown that saturation ionization currents are proportional to the number of particles emitted. Hence equation 11–8 may be written

$$I = I_0 \epsilon^{-\lambda t} \qquad (11\text{–}9)$$

where I is the intensity of a radioactive substance t seconds after it had an intensity I_0 and λ is the transformation constant. This is the equation of curve B, figure 11–3, as has been tested experimentally many times. Curves A and B being similar, but inverted, the equation of the former is

$$I' = I_0 - I = I_0(1 - \epsilon^{-\lambda t}) \qquad (11\text{–}10)$$

which has also been verified experimentally.

11–7. Radioactive Constants.—The transformation constant of a given substance may be determined by plotting the data used for curve B of figure 11–3 in a different manner. If the ordinates are $\log_\epsilon I$ and the abscissae the time, a straight curve will result whose negative slope is λ, the transformation constant.

The *mean or average life* (L) of a radioactive substance is given by the relation,*

$$L = \frac{1}{\lambda}. \qquad (11–11)$$

Substituting this time for t in the transformation law gives $N/N_0 = 1/\epsilon$. In other words, during the average life of a substance $1 - 1/2.718+$ of it will disintegrate.

The third constant is the one most widely used and is called the half life period or *half life* (T). It is the number of seconds for the activity to fall to half its original value, i.e., for half the atoms to break up. Then $N/N_0 = \frac{1}{2} = \epsilon^{-\lambda t}$; $-\log_\epsilon 2 = -\lambda T$, whence

$$T = \frac{0.693}{\lambda} = 0.693L. \qquad (11–12)$$

As an example, the transformation constant λ of radium is 1.39×10^{-11} seconds^{-1}. This means that approximately one atom in every 10^{11} atoms breaks up each second. From equation 11–12, the half period T is equal to 1590 years. If one had a gram of radium today, he would have only one-half a gram at the end of 1590 years, one-quarter of a gram at the end of 3180 years, one-eighth of a gram at the end of the next 1590 years, etc.

The radioactive constants are characteristic of a given substance and allow its identification equally as well as chemical analysis. They may be measured directly if the substance can be isolated from its parent and products or they may be deduced from the activity curves. The constants may also be computed from measurements on the range of alpha particles together with the Geiger-Nuttall relation discussed in the next chapter although the results are not of high accuracy.

The transformation constant is obtained if the number of alpha particles emitted per gram each second, observed with a fluorescent screen or Geiger counter, is divided by the number of atoms per gram of the substance. The number of atoms per gram

* $L = (1/N_0) \int_0^\infty t(\lambda N dt) = 1/\lambda.$

is given by dividing Avogadro's number (6.02×10^{23}) by the molecular weight.

Several methods have been used for short-lived products, one of which is illustrated in figure 11–4. Air is drawn through a metal tube and carries the emanation (a gas) from the active sub-stance (XX), say actinium X, along the negatively charged wire where it leaves an active deposit. During the time the gas is passing the length of the wire, it has practically all decayed. Hence the amount of active deposit (having comparatively long life) at the front end of the wire is greater than that near the end

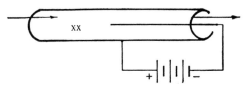

FIG. 11–4. Decay rate of short-lived substances.

of the tube. The wire is removed and cut into pieces, each of which is tested with an electroscope. From these activities and the rate of flow of the gas, the rate of decay is obtained. In this way the half period of actinium emanation was found to be 3.92 seconds.

For weak substances having very long periods, the transforma-tion constant may be obtained by measuring the intensity of it and its product combined when a stable condition of equilibrium exists between them, i.e., the number of atoms of the parent which break up each second (also equal to the number of atoms of the product formed each second) is equal to the number of atoms of the product which break up each second. Then

$$\lambda_1 P = \lambda_2 Q \quad \text{or} \quad \lambda_1 = \lambda_2 \frac{Q}{P}. \tag{11-13}$$

The transformation constant λ_2 of the product and the equilib-rium ratio Q/P of product to parent (grams/grams) must be known from previous determinations.

11–8. The Parent Substance Transforms Rapidly. Active Deposits.—In the case of a slowly changing parent, the rate of pro-duction of its first product is essentially a constant but, when the parent transforms rapidly, the new substance is formed in smaller and smaller amounts as time goes on. This is illustrated by the alpha ray activity of the thorium active deposit.   Upon disintegration,

$$\text{Th A}\xrightarrow{\alpha}\text{Th B}\xrightarrow{\beta,\gamma}\text{Th C}\xrightarrow{\beta}\text{Th C}'$$

$$3\times 10^{-7}\text{ sec.}$$

Th A $\xrightarrow{\alpha}$ Th B $\xrightarrow{\beta,\gamma}$ Th C $\xrightarrow{\beta}$ Th C′

0.158 sec.   10.6 hr.   60.5 min. α α

$$\searrow \text{Th C}''\xrightarrow{} \text{Th D (Lead)}$$

Isolate   3.1 min. β ∞

thorium emanation or thoron (a gas) becomes a solid called thorium A and may be collected on a negatively charged metal plate nearby.   When the metal plate is first placed in an alpha ray electroscope,* the activity is practically zero.   If the rate at which the electroscope leaf collapses is observed at regular time intervals, a curve like that in figure 11–5 will be obtained.   This

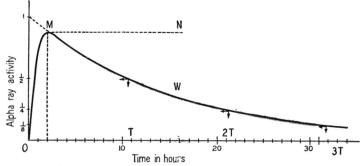

FIG. 11–5.   Activity curve of a substance having a comparatively short-lived parent.

alpha ray activity curve is a result of the combined formation and decay of thorium C from thorium B.   From the active deposit series of thorium (above), it may be seen that the thorium A quickly disappears, leaving thorium B whose life is much longer. The beta and gamma rays from thorium B, however, do not appreciably affect the alpha ray electroscope so that the observed activity must result from the alpha rays from thorium C and C′. The alpha rays from the latter produce the major activity but the life of this substance is so short that it does not mask the shape of the activity curve of thorium C.

* For the distinction between alpha, beta and gamma ray electroscopes, see chapter 17.

With a parent of very long life, the curve of figure 11–5 would rise to a maximum and remain constant, as *OMN*. In the present case, however, the thorium B is decaying at a moderate rate, so the activity drops to *W* as time goes on. The curve *MW* decreases to half value in 10.6 hours, which is the half-life of thorium *B*. The rapid rise *OM* is due to the fact that thorium C is being formed at a greater rate than it is decaying. These two rates are equal at the maximum *M* where a condition of *transient equilibrium* exists.

As a second illustration of the case where the parent transforms very rapidly, we may take the active deposit of radium. On decaying, radium produces a gas called radium emanation or radon. This, in turn, decays into radium A, as a solid deposit on the walls of the containing vessel. This, in turn, changes into radium B, then C, C' and C''. A, B, C, C' and C'' form the *short life active deposit*. They are followed by D, E and F (Polonium), which constitute the *long life active deposit*. F changes into lead which undergoes no further changes as far as we can tell.

The alpha ray activity of actinium C, which was produced from actinium B in the series

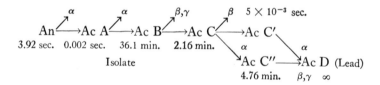

is similar to that for thorium C, as shown in figure 11–5, except that the maximum is reached in 9 minutes.

11–9. Transformation Theory. Parent and Product Together. —Let P and Q be the amounts of the parent and of its product at any time t and let λ_1 and λ_2 be their respective transformation constants. The exponential decay of the parent may be expressed in the form

$$dP/dt = -\lambda_1 P \cdot \qquad (11–14)$$

Now, since $\lambda_1 P$ is the rate of production of the product and $\lambda_2 Q$ is its rate of decay,

$$dQ/dt = \lambda_1 P - \lambda_2 Q. \qquad (11–15)$$

The solution of these two equations gives

$$P = P_o \epsilon^{-\lambda_1 t} \tag{11-16}$$

$$Q = \left(\frac{\lambda_1}{\lambda_2 - \lambda_1} P_o\right) \epsilon^{-\lambda_1 t} + \left(Q_o - \frac{\lambda_1}{\lambda_2 - \lambda_1} P_o\right) \epsilon^{-\lambda_2 t} \tag{11-17}$$

where P_o and Q_o represent the amounts of the substances at the start, when $t = 0$. The activity of the two substances together is directly proportional to $P + Q$.

When only the parent is present at the start, $Q_o = 0$ and equation 11–17 becomes

$$Q = \frac{\lambda_1}{\lambda_2 - \lambda_1} P_o(\epsilon^{-\lambda_1 t} - \epsilon^{-\lambda_2 t}). \tag{11-18}$$

This is the equation for the curve OMW in figure 11–5. By equating the first derivative of this expression to zero, the equation for the time to reach transient equilibrium may be obtained.

When the parent has a very long life in comparison with that of its product, $\lambda_2 \gg \lambda_1$, and if $Q_o = 0$, the formation of the product is expressed by

$$Q = \frac{\lambda_1}{\lambda_2} P_o(1 - \epsilon^{-\lambda_2 t}). \tag{11-19}$$

After an appreciable time, the product is formed at the same rate as that at which it decays and secular equilibrium is established. Equation 11–13 is then applicable.

11–10. General Theory of Transformations.—For those cases where more than two radioactive substances are together and are simultaneously emitting particles, the reader is referred to Chapter I of " Radiations from Radioactive Substances " by Rutherford, Chadwick and Ellis.

11–11. Statistical Fluctuations.—Consider a radioactive substance which has a long life. When measurements are made over a *very* long time interval, the activity or number of atoms which disintegrate each second $(\bar{n})$ is found to be a constant. But, when measurements are made over a comparatively *short time*, it will be found that the activity (n) is sometimes greater and sometimes smaller than the average $(\bar{n})$. The fluctuations around the average value will be brought out clearly by using a feeble radioactive source and a sensitive detector. Then, the emission of single alpha particles and the disintegration of individual atoms may be noted. It will be found, for example, that during the first ten minutes 100 atoms disintegrated, that during the next ten minutes 101 atoms ejected alpha particles, during the third interval, 98, etc. The distribution of the observed number around the average can be determined from probability considerations [2] and is represented by the Gaussian error curve when $\bar{n}$ is large.

An electroscope or a counter tube (see chapters 17 and 18) has a " natural leak," " residual count " or background of activity $\bar{b}$ (average) due to contaminations, cosmic rays, etc., which is likewise subject to statistical fluctuations. It can be shown [3] that

$$bT = \bar{b}T \pm 0.67 \sqrt{\bar{b}T} \qquad (11\text{–}20)$$

where b is the background count, measured over a comparatively short time interval T. If, now, a radioactive source is brought near the instrument, the activities will be increased to $\bar{a}$ (average) and a (over time T). These include the background. Then,

$$aT = \bar{a}T \pm 0.67 \sqrt{\bar{a}T}. \qquad (11\text{–}21)$$

The activity of the source (n) is then given by

$$nT = (\bar{a} - \bar{b})T \pm 0.67 \sqrt{(\bar{a} + \bar{b})T} \qquad (11\text{–}22)$$

from the theory of propagation of errors. The first term on the right side of equation 11–22 gives the average activity

$$\bar{n} = (\bar{a} - \bar{b}) \qquad (11\text{–}23)$$

and the second term gives the probable error which will be made in a single observation. Since the latter involves the square root of $\bar{a}$ and T, it will be comparatively small in comparison with the first term and may be neglected when the activity ($\bar{a}$) is large or the measurements are carried out over a sufficiently long time interval (T). The *limit of observation* is given when

$$\bar{a}T \gtrless 0.67 \sqrt{\bar{b}T}. \qquad (11\text{–}24)$$

When expressed in percentage, the *probable error* is

$$r = \frac{67 \sqrt{a + b}}{(a - b) \sqrt{T}} = \frac{67}{S \sqrt{T}}, \qquad (11\text{–}25)$$

where

$$S = \frac{a - b}{\sqrt{a + b}}. \qquad (11\text{–}26)$$

S is called [4] the *relative sensitivity* of the instrument.

11–12. Radioactive Displacement Laws and Isotopes.—Radium, of atomic weight 226, emits an alpha particle of atomic weight 4 and becomes radium emanation of atomic weight 222. With the emission of an alpha particle, the nuclear charge and its equivalent, the atomic number, decrease by two, changing from 88 to 86.   That is to say, the chemical properties of radium and its emanation are different.   Radon, in turn, emits an alpha particle and becomes radium A with atomic weight 218 (less by 4) and atomic number 84 (less by 2).   In general: *For any alpha ray transformation, the new element has an atomic weight less by four units and an atomic number less by two units than its parent.*

Radium B emits a beta particle and becomes radium C.   The beta particles are electrons having a mass negligible in comparison to the nuclear mass.   Hence, no essential difference exists between the atomic weights (214) of radium B and C.   But the chemical and physical properties of these two are different since the nuclear charge has increased positively by an amount equal to one electron.   Thus, the atomic number of radium B is 82 while that of radium C is 83.   In general: *For any beta ray transformation, the new element has the same atomic weight as its parent but an atomic number greater by one.*

Following these *displacement laws*, the location of any radioactive element in the periodic table can be determined.   The accompanying table of radioactive elements shows such an arrangement (figure 11–6).

Those elements in the same vertical column have the same atomic number although their atomic weights differ, which means that they have the same chemical and physical properties except atomic weight.   They are thus grouped together at the same place in the periodic table.   In other words, all elements in a vertical

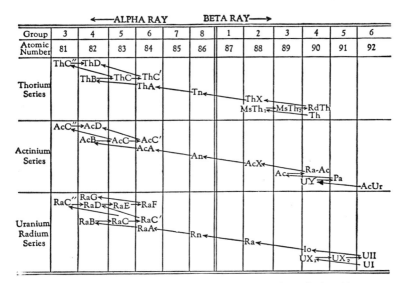

FIG. 11-6. Positions of radioactive substances in the periodic table.

column of the table are isotopes and, when once mixed together, cannot be completely separated by any chemical or physical means known today. (See, however, the mass spectrograph, chapter 10.)

11-13. The Separation of Radioactive Substances.—Substances may be isolated chemically by precipitation, electrochemical deposition or by fractional crystallization. They may also be separated by volatilization, since different substances have different volatilization points, or by electrolysis. The method of *recoil* makes use of the fact that as an alpha particle leaves its atom the remainder of the substance recoils backwards. Thus, if thorium C, radium A or actinium C be placed between positive and negative metal plates, the recoil thorium D, radium B or actinium D will collect on the negative plate. From considerations of the momenta involved, the velocity of the alpha particle may be computed. From radium A, this amounts to 3.16×10^7 cm. per second. Gases may be freed from their parents by bubbling air through a solution containing them, or by boiling the solution. In the ignition method for radium emanation from radium, the radium salt is mixed with an appropriate flux, such as sodium acid phosphate, and sealed in a glass tube. Within 7.7 days, 75 per cent of the total equilibrium amount of gas will be formed and in 3 weeks there will be 99 per cent. The tube is then connected to an emanation electroscope and heated to drive out the emanation.

Experiment 11–1

THE INTENSITY OF RADIOACTIVE SUBSTANCES

Read the discussion of electroscopes given in chapter 17.

The active material, in a shallow metal tray, is placed in the electroscope. Since the alpha rays are easily absorbed, only the surface layers contribute to the activity and the thickness of the material in the pan is unimportant unless the layer is very thin. However, some of the activity is due to beta rays which are not so easily absorbed in passing through the material itself. Therefore, use equal weights, or roughly, use equal thicknesses (1 mm.) of the various materials (spread evenly in shallow metal pans about 6 cm. in diameter).

Experiment.—Compare the intensities of at least three substances such as uranium oxide, pitchblende, thorium nitrate, etc., taking the average of four determinations for each. If a *standard* is available, express the activities in milligrams of radium; if not, express in terms of one of them, say the pitchblende.

Measure the capacity of the leaf system and compute the ionization current in amperes produced by the standard substance. Also compute the number of ions which it produces per second per square centimeter.

Experiment 11–2

RATE OF FORMATION OF THORIUM C

Apparatus.—Read the discussion on electroscopes, in chapter 17.

In figure 11–7, a metal cup contains approximately 0.6 milligrams of radio-thorium. The radio-thorium is continuously disintegrating and becomes thorium emanation or thoron, a gas, which is confined to the cup by a tight fitting bakelite cover. The thoron, in turn becomes thorium A, a solid, whose particles are positively charged and may be collected on a negatively charged metal plate *P*. 110 volts may be used.

Precautions.—(1) The active material should not be left in the cup for extended periods of time (weeks or months), as it is usually prepared in slightly acid form. Store the material in a

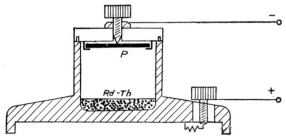

Fig. 11–7.   Thorium C apparatus.

glass tube. (2) It is *imperative* that the instrument be kept away from electroscopes, electrometers, etc., since the thoron will distribute itself throughout the room and add greatly to their natural leak. Do not store the active material with these instruments and do not use it in the same room.

Experiment.—1. Prepare an alpha ray electroscope and measure its natural leak. 2. Thoroughly clean the lid of the apparatus of figure 11–7; unscrew the binding post and use a fine grade of sandpaper on the post, the clips and the under side of the lid. Clean with alcohol or ether and wipe with a clean cloth. This is to prevent contamination of the plate *P* and is very important. 3. Place a freshly sandpapered copper plate (*P*) in the electroscope and observe that it is free from radioactive contaminations. 4. Moisten *gently* the radio-thorium with two or three drops of distilled, non-radioactive water. This will increase the strength of the deposit on *P* by assisting in freeing thoron from the radiothorium. Sufficient gas can be obtained from one sample that the apparatus may be used about twice a week. 5. Place the copper plate at *P*, connect the 110 volt d.c. line through a protective resistance of, perhaps, 10,000 ohms (unless such a unit has been mounted in the base of the apparatus). Record the time when the voltage is applied. This is the "zero time." 6. At the end of 3 to 10 minutes, remove the copper plate, without touching its lower surface. Put the lid back in place. 7. Promptly, but without haste take the plate to the electroscope and record the activity every five minutes for two hours. The natural leak should be measured at hourly intervals, at least. 8. Correct the observed rate of fall of the leaf of the electroscope for the natural leak (average value) and plot the corrected activities as ordinates and the times, at the center of each activity reading, as abscissae. 9. If desired, the curve may be continued. Activities may be measured every half hour from the two to the five hour point and every hour or so from then on. Determine the half period of thorium B.

EXPERIMENT 11–3

RATE OF DECAY OF THORIUM C

The apparatus and procedure are the same as in the preceding experiment, through the sixth step, except that a platinum or a tantalum plate should be used and the plate should be left at P (figure 11-7) for at least one hour and preferably two hours. While this is going on, place 3 cubic centimeters of concentrated hydrochloric acid in a watch glass over a small beaker containing 25 or more cubic centimeters of distilled water. Heat carefully, just to boiling, with a gentle flame. Keep hot but do not continue the boiling.

7. After the plate has been exposed for one or two hours place it in the hot HCl for three minutes (one to five minutes). Remove with tweezers and wash with approximately 25 cubic centimeters of hot water, allowing the water to drain off the disc into the acid so as to dilute the acid to approximately 1.0 normal. 8. Put an uncontaminated *copper* plate into the solution. Move the plate slowly about in the hot solution for three minutes.

From now on, the work must be carried on *as quickly as possible*. 9. Remove the copper plate and record the time. This is the " zero time." Wash the plate *very* gently in very hot water, then with a few drops of alcohol. Quickly transfer the plate to the electroscope (in a different room), placing it on a piece of uncontaminated paper. 10. Record the time of fall of the leaf over, say ten small divisions, repeating as rapidly as possible for fifteen minutes. Be sure to record the total time from " zero " to the center of the activity time at each point. 11. Measure the natural leak. 12. Continue readings every five minutes for two hours. The activity will be found to be more nearly that of the natural leak than in the formation curve of experiment 11–2. 13. Correct all activities for the natural leak, using the value measured at the end of fifteen minutes. This leak will probably be large, due to contaminations (perhaps a trace of thoron gas). Plot activities as ordinates and times as abscissae. Also plot on semi-logarithmic paper, with activities on the logarithmic scale and times on the linear scale. 14. Note and record on this graph the half life of thorium C and compare with the accepted value. 15. If desired, or if necessary, the experiment may be repeated, using the solution of step 7. The solution will be sufficiently active for a second trial for about one day.

EXPERIMENT 11–4

DECAY OF THORIUM EMANATION

Charge an emanation electroscope, figure 17–7, and observe the natural leak. If it is too large, the chamber must be opened, sand-papered and cleaned with alcohol or ether to remove active deposits. Partially evacuate the chamber, charge the leaf and then introduce a small amount of thorium emanation, stopping as soon as the leaf begins to fall rapidly. Since the half life of thorium emanation is comparatively short, observations of the activity must be made quickly. Observe the time of fall over a small number of divisions, allowing the leaf to continue for a second observation at a different part of the scale. The relative current changes for the various parts of the scale may be found by observing the time required to pass over the specified divisions with a constant source of ionization.

Plot a curve showing the decay of the emanation with time and deduce the half period of the thorium emanation.

EXPERIMENT 11-5

DECAY OF RADON

An emanation electroscope is used as in the preceding experiment but the decay rate of radon (radium emanation) is slower than that for thorium emanation so that the activities at various times may be determined more leisurely.

Seal some uranium ore, such as carnotite, with an equal amount of sodium acid phosphate, in a long glass tube. Glass wool plugs are used to keep the material in place. The ends of the tube are drawn down to points when sealing off. The radon is allowed to accumulate for about two weeks. A rubber tube is then slipped over one end of the tube and connected to the partially evacuated electroscope chamber. When ready to take the readings, heat the tube, starting at its middle and working the flame both ways. While this is being done, break the end of the tube inside the rubber tubing and open the stop cock to the chamber. Then break the far end of the glass tube so that air will sweep through the tube. Finally close the stop cock. The chamber then contains the radon.

Plot the activity curve from observations made at intervals of several hours and deduce the half period of radon.

REFERENCES
1. Reference A, page 246.
2. H. Bateman, Phil. Mag., **20**, 704 (1910). Also, General reference B, page 32.
3. R. D. Evans and H. V. Neher, Phys. Rev., **45**, 144 (1934).
4. R. D. Evans and R. A. Mugele, Rev. Sci. Inst., **7**, 441 (1936).

GENERAL REFERENCES

A.—Geiger and Scheel, *Handbuch der Physik.* Springer (1933).

B.—F. Rasetti, *Elements of Nuclear Physics.* Prentice Hall (1936).

C.—Rutherford, Chadwick and Ellis, *Radiations from Radioactive Substances.* Macmillan (1930), Chapter I.

D.—J. Chadwick, *Radioactivity and Radioactive Substances.* Pitman and Sons (1923). Chapters I, VI to IX.

E.—W. Makower and H. Geiger, *Practical Measurements in Radioactivity*. Longmans, Green and Co. (1912), pp. 80 to 88, 121 and 127.

F.—Hevesy and Paneth, *Lehrbuch der Radioaktivität*. Barth (1931).

G.—E. Rutherford, *Radioactive Substances and Their Radiations*. Chapters VIII, and XI.

H.—J. D. Stranathan, *The Particles of Modern Physics*. The Blakiston Co. (1942).

CHAPTER 12

ALPHA, BETA AND GAMMA RAYS

12-1. The Nature of Alpha Particles.—The charge of an alpha particle is determined by measuring the total charge carried by a measured number of particles. In the apparatus of figure 12–1, alpha particles are emitted in all directions from the radioactive material (X). The entire apparatus is evacuated, except the interior of G, in order to eliminate the ionization which would be produced by the alpha particles. A magnetic field is applied perpendicularly to the plane of the paper and over the area indicated by the circle, so as to eliminate all secondary electrons

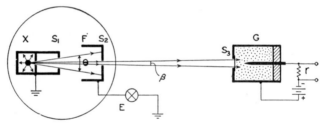

Fig. 12–1. Apparatus used to determine the charge of the alpha particle.

(delta rays). All alpha particles which leave the source in the solid angle θ are caught in the Faraday chamber (F). The charge collected in F each second is measured by means of the electrometer (E). This current, multiplied by the ratio of the solid angle of a sphere around X $(= 4\pi)$ to the solid angle θ, is equal to the total charge which leaves the source each second.

In the absence of a magnetic field, some of the alpha particles pass through the holes $S_1 S_2$ and S_3 into the Geiger counter tube (G). This counter consists of a sharply pointed wire, such as platinum, supported, in a gas at atmospheric pressure, along the axis of a metal tube by means of an insulating plug. The wire is raised to a negative potential of from one to two thousand volts with respect to the cylindrical tube, so that a discharge of elec-

270

tricity just does not take place. A single alpha particle, in passing through the tube, is able to create sufficient ions to cause a discharge to occur. The potential across the tube then falls to a few volts because of the ir drop in the resistance r and the discharge ceases. The potential drop across r may be used to operate a loud speaker or a mechanical counter. (See chapter 18 for further details.)

The average number of particles which enter the tube each second is obtained from a long series of readings and multiplied by the ratio of 4π to the solid angle β to obtain the total number of particles which leave the source in all directions each second. In this manner it has been found that one gram of radium, free from its products, emits 3.71×10^{10} alpha particles each second.

Another method for directly counting the number of particles is to observe the scintillations which they produce on a piece of diamond. At first, it was not known whether every alpha particle produced a scintillation, but comparison with the Geiger counter has shown this to be true.

It has been found that a small percentage, perhaps one-quarter of one per cent, of the alpha particles are neutralized as they pass through the apparatus of figure 12-1. After making this correction, it was found that a total charge of 32.9 e.s.u. was carried by the 3.71×10^{10} alpha particles emitted by one gram of radium in one second and that a total charge of 3.77×10^{-4} e.s.u. accompanied the 393,500 particles ejected by a given sample of radium F each second. When averaged with determinations made with other sources, it was shown that the *positive charge* (E_α) of the alpha particle is accurately *twice that of an electron*. Thus, $E_\alpha = + 2e = + 2 \times 4.80 \times 10^{-10}$ e.s.u. $= 9.60 \times 10^{-10}$ e.s.u.

That the alpha particle consists of a helium atom less two electrons, i.e., of a *helium nucleus*, has been verified by the following experiment. Radium emanation is collected in a tube A, figure 12-2, whose glass walls are only 0.01 mm. in thickness. The walls are then sufficiently thin so that the alpha particles from the emanation and its decay products can escape into the highly evacuated bulb B, which is made of glass sufficiently thick to stop them. When the emanation has first been introduced into A, no electrical discharge can pass from the mercury C to the electrode D. At the end of a few days, the mercury is raised to compress any gas in B into the capillary tube at the top. Then a discharge can be passed through the capillary, which on examination with a spectroscope shows the complete helium spectrum.

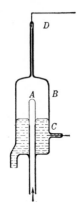

Thus when an alpha particle has slowed down it picks up two electrons and becomes an atom of helium. That the helium collected in B is not due to a trace of this gas in the emanation is shown by filling A with pure helium. Although left for a long time, no trace is found to leak through the thin walls into B.

By a method similar to that used in determining the charge to mass ratio of cathode rays, i.e., by magnetic and electric deflection, E_α/M_α for alpha particles has been found to be 4823 e.m.u. per gram while their velocities vary between

FIG. 12–2. The 1.37 × 10^9 and 2.06 × 10^9 cm. per second. There
alpha particle is is a *characteristic velocity* for each of the radio-
the nucleus of a active substances as shown in Table 4. We shall
helium atom. return to a discussion of their velocities in the next
section. The energy of an alpha particle is of the order of 10^{-6} ergs or 10^6 electron volts. Now, for the alpha particle

$$\frac{E_\alpha}{M_\alpha} = \frac{2e}{M_\alpha} = 4823 \text{ e.m.u./g.} \qquad (12\text{--}1)$$

whereas for the hydrogen ion we have $e/M_H = 9574$. It follows that the *mass* of the alpha particle is

$$M_\alpha = 3.970 \, M_H = 6.6 \times 10^{-24} \text{ grams.} \qquad (12\text{--}2)$$

The ratio of the atomic weights of helium and hydrogen is also equal to 3.970.

12–2. Alpha Ray Spectra. Nuclear Levels.—It has just been stated that the alpha particles from a given radioactive substance all have the same velocity. This is so nearly true that it was not until 1930 that Rosenblum[1] was able to detect and measure a number of velocities grouped very closely around the previously known value. He used the magnet constructed as a memorial to Pasteur and located at Bellevue, France; which has pole pieces 75 centimeters in diameter and is able to produce a uniform field of 23,200 gausses over a diameter of 35 centimeters when the gap is

6 centimeters. The alpha particles from a given radioactive substance were collimated with slits, and, after deflection through 180 degrees with the strong magnetic field, formed fine lines on a photographic plate. From the sharpness of the lines in this so-called *fine structure spectrum*, it is seen that among the alpha particles which leave a given substance, all with approximately the same velocity, there are distinct sub-groups, each containing particles of but one velocity.

Later, Rutherford and his associates [2] used a shallow ionization chamber (see chapter 18) to detect the alpha particles, rather than a photographic plate, thereby making possible the study of extremely weak groups. The field of their " annular " magnet is confined to a narrow ring of mean diameter 80 centimeters and amounts to approximately 10,000 gausses.

It has been found that certain substances such as Rn, RaA and Po have but one line, while others, such as ThC, An, AcC, AcX and RdAc, have two or more lines. That the velocities of the particles from any one substance are all of nearly the same velocity may be seen from the typical case of ThC, where the particles in one of the lines (α_1) have a velocity only 1.0034 times that of the average of the group. The short-lived substances, RaC' and ThC', emit a few alpha particles of much higher velocity, in addition to the main group of lines. Tables of alpha ray spectra will be found in the literature.[3]

In the preceding chapter we have seen that alpha particles are emitted from the nucleus of the atom. The fact that they are emitted in definite energy (velocity) groups suggests that there are energy levels in the nuclei of these atoms. When an alpha particle is ejected from a nucleus, it might be expected that a readjustment would take place whereby transitions of the alpha particles remaining in the product nucleus should be accompanied by the radiation of a gamma ray, just as electronic transitions in the outer parts of the atom give rise to light and x-rays. It has been found that the energies ($h\nu$) of the various gamma rays emitted by certain radioactive substances are equal to the differences of energy ($E_2 - E_1$) of the fine structure components of the alpha ray spectrum of that substance.

12-3. The Range of Alpha Particles.—If a gas, saturated with water vapor, is suddenly expanded, its temperature falls below the dew point. Small drops of water then form on condensation centers, such as dust particles or ions. C. T. R. Wilson has used this principle to make visible the paths traversed by *single* ionizing radiations such as alpha, beta, gamma and x-rays. (See chapter 18 for details of the *expansion chambers*.) The type of *drop tracks* produced by alpha particles is shown in figure 12–3.

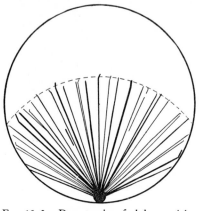

One of the most striking features of figure .12–3 is that the drop tracks are all of essentially the same length. Thus, the alpha particles from a given substance all have a definite *range*, characteristic of that substance. Therefore, a measurement of the range may be used to identify an unknown radioactive substance.

FIG. 12–3. Drop tracks of alpha particles.

The range in air (at 15° C. and 76 cm.) for various substances varies from 2.7 to 8.5 centimeters. (See Table 4 at the end of the book.)

Consider a stream of alpha particles emanating from a radioactive source and collimated into a narrow pencil by suitable tubes or slits. Let measurements be made of the number of particles which reach various distances from the source, by means of the scintillations which they produce on a fluorescent screen. A curve such as *I* in figure 12–4 will be obtained. The long

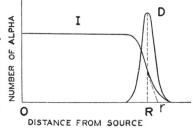

FIG. 12–4. Integral (*I*) and differential (*D*) distribution-in-range curves for alpha particles.

horizontal portion shows that none of the particles are lost from the beam until the very end, where, within a comparatively short distance, they are all absorbed. This behavior is in striking contrast to the passage of light rays, x-rays and gamma rays through a gas, where the intensity falls off (exponentially) as the distance from the source is increased. One must conclude that the process by which alpha particles lose energy in their passage through a gas is essentially different from that for the other cases just mentioned. We shall return to this later, in the discussion of the Ionization by Alpha Particles.

The alpha particles from a given radioactive substance do not all penetrate a gas exactly the same distance. This so-called *straggling* may be seen in the drop tracks of figure 12–3 and by the rounded drop at the end of curve I in figure 12–4. If the slope of the latter is calculated, the differential distribution in range (curve D) is obtained. This gives the number of particles with ranges between R and $R + dR$ and is approximately a Gaussian curve, indicating a statistical or random fluctuation in those processes which operate to stop the alpha particles. The *average range* of alpha particles is located by the peak of the curve and is indicated at R in figure 12–4. The range straggling parameter is the half-width of the distribution curve at $1/e$ of the maximum. It amounts to 0.084 cm. for a collimated group of polonium alpha particles.[7] The *practical or extrapolated range* is shown at r. The methods described below give values of r.

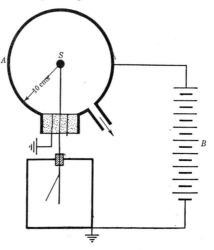

One of the best methods for measuring the range of alpha particles is to use a shallow ionization chamber to detect the ionization at

FIG. 12–5. An electrical method for measuring the range of alpha particles from weak sources.

various points along the path. This is discussed in detail in section 12–6 (see Specific Ionization) and in Experiment 12–2.

A simple method is to place a fluorescent screen in the path of the rays and observe the distance from the source at which the scintillations just disappear, or just appear.

The range varies directly as the absolute temperature and inversely as the pressure of the gas through which the rays pass;

i.e., inversely as the number of gas molecules passed through. By observing the range of the alpha particles at different pressures and temperatures with a shallow chamber or with a fluorescent screen, one may then compute the range under standard conditions; i.e., 76 centimeters of mercury and 15° C. (0° C. is also used). Another method, due to Geiger and Nuttall, for measuring the range of alpha particles from weak sources uses the apparatus illustrated in figure 12–5. The source of alpha particles is located at S in the center of a charged metal sphere A whose radius is greater than the maximum range at atmospheric pressure. The battery B has sufficient potential, say 700 volts, to draw over to the ball all ions produced. As the pressure in the ball is reduced, the alpha particles are able to reach its walls and at still lower pressures would go beyond, were it not for the walls. The ionization current as measured by the electroscope is fairly constant as the pressure is decreased, until after the particles have begun hitting the walls. It then falls off markedly since the particles are not producing as many ions as they are capable of doing. In figure 12–6, the kinks in the curves indicate the pressures at which the alpha particles have a range equal to the radius of the ball. Two kinks in the curve indicate two sets of alpha particles of different ranges coming from two radioactive substances.

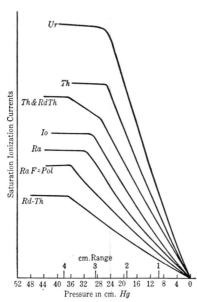

FIG. 12–6.   Results from the apparatus of figure 12–5.

The range of alpha particles in various gases and liquids has been measured by the scintillation method. (See table 5.) For solids, a fluorescent screen and an active source are placed on opposite sides of a thin wedge of the material. The scintillations are seen to cease abruptly over that thickness of material which is equal to the range of the alpha particles. The values in table 5 give the minimum thicknesses of material required to stop the particles from radium C' and from polonium. Due to the straggling, slightly thicker materials must be used in practice to cut off all the particles.

12–4. Range-Velocity-Energy-Life Relations.—Tables 4 and 7 at the end of this book gives values of the mean range R for alpha particles of various initial velocities v_0 and energies $\mathscr{E}_0$ (relativity values).[7] For ranges in standard air, between three and seven centimeters, the approximate *Geiger law* may be used. Thus,

$$r \doteq a v_0^3 \doteq b \mathscr{E}_0^{3/2}, \tag{12–4}$$

where v_0 is in cms./sec., r is the (extrapolated) range in centimeters and $a = 9.25 \times 10^{-28}$. For the lower velocities, the exponent of v_0 drops to 1.5 and for the higher velocities it increases to 4.

An unstable atom has a short life and sends out long range, high velocity, high energy alpha particles. If λ is the fractional number of atoms breaking up each second ($= 0.693$ divided by the time T for one-half of a given amount of radioactive substance to change into its next element), then,

$$\log \lambda = A + B \log R, \tag{12–5}$$

where A and B are constants. This is known as the *Geiger-Nuttall relation* and was discovered empirically in 1911. This law has proved useful in determining the transformation constant λ of newly discovered substances. It is not of high accuracy and a bad exception occurs in the case of actinium X, as may be seen in figure 12–7. A in equation 12–5 is different for the different series, while the slope of the lines (B) is very approximately a constant.

This relation between the probability of a transformation and the energy of the emitted alpha particle suggests that there is a property of the nucleus which is held in common by the different members of a given radioactive series. In the application of quantum mechanics to the study of the probability of escape of an alpha particle from the nucleus, Condon and Morse and also Gamow have shown that only one form of the potential barrier (discussed in the next paragraph) and only one radius (approximately) of the nucleus need be assumed in order to arrive at a theoretical derivation of the Geiger-Nuttall relation.

If we assume that the force near the nucleus of an atom is inversely proportional to the square of the distance from its center, then, in order that an alpha particle can approach head-on to

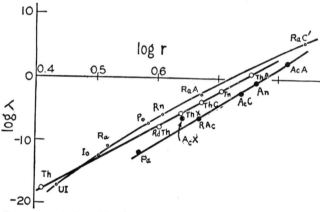

FIG. 12–7. A short life substance sends out long range alpha particles.

within a distance d of the center of the nucleus of an atom, it must have an energy equal to

$$\mathscr{E} = 2Ze^2/d, \qquad (12-6)$$

where Z is the atomic number and e is the electronic charge. The nucleus may be said to have a potential energy ($\mathscr{E}$) at the distance d. This is represented by the solid line in figure 12–8, where the center of the nucleus is at O. The scattering experiments described in section 7–3 have shown that the inverse square law is only satisfactory to within approximately 10^{-12} centimeter of the center. We may then define the radius of the nucleus as that distance from the center at which the inverse square law begins to break down. For lesser distances, there is a potential " hole," indicated by the dotted lines of figure 12–8, which usually retains the nuclear parts and keeps the atom stable. The probability that an alpha particle can escape from the nucleus depends both on the shape and the height of the potential barrier. This shape is not yet known, depending as it does on the forces between the component parts of the nucleus, but the Geiger-Nuttall law can be derived with the assumption of only one simple form, a square hole, as indicated in the figure and with only one radius ($\sim 8 \times 10^{-13}$ cm.) for the nuclei of different radioactive substances. The exact shape of the potential well is not particularly important as long as its diameter and depth are known.

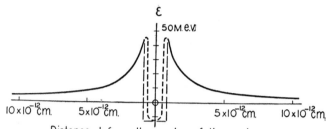

Distance d from the center of the nucleus

FIG. 12–8. The potential barrier of a nucleus.

12–5. Air Equivalent and Stopping Power.—The *air equivalent* (t_a) is defined as that thickness of air under standard conditions which produces the same loss of energy of the alpha particles as does a given thickness (t) of material placed in their path. If the energy loss is sufficiently small, such as occurs when a very thin foil of the material is used, it will be directly proportional to the corresponding reduction in range of the particles.

In order to measure t_a, determine the range (d) of the alpha particles emitted by a given radioactive substance, say by the scintillation method. Then, insert the thin foil in the path of the rays and re-determine the distance (d') from the source to the screen at which scintillations just disappear. The reduction in range ($d - d'$) is then adjusted to standard conditions (usually taken as 15° C. and 76 centimeters pressure). Thus,

$$t_a = (d - d') \frac{T_o}{T} \frac{p}{p_o}, \qquad (12\text{–}7)$$

where $T_o = 288°$ K., $p_o = 76$ centimeters, and $T = 273 + °$ C.; p, of course, is the pressure of the air in centimeters of mercury, at which the experiment was carried out.

The air equivalent is a characteristic constant of the absorbing screen material, but it increases a little as the screen is moved toward the end of the range of the alpha particles. It may be expressed in a slightly different manner. Thus, the *equivalent stopping power* is that thickness t_e of the material which will produce the same energy loss as one centimeter of air. Then, for small energy loss,

$$t_e = t/t_a. \qquad (12\text{--}8)$$

Near the end of the range of the alpha particles from polonium, one centimeter of air is the equivalent of approximately 0.006 millimeter or 1.6 mg./cm.^{2} of aluminum and of 0.002 millimeter or 4 mg./cm.^{2} of gold.

The energy lost by an alpha particle in travelling unit distance in a substance is called *the stopping power* of that substance. It varies with the velocity of the particle. On the other hand, the *relative stopping power* (S); i.e., the ratio of the energies lost in unit distance in the substance and in standard air, is approximately independent of the velocity of the particle. Again, if the energy losses are small, they are proportional to the range reductions so that

$$S = t_a/t = 1/t_e. \qquad (12\text{--}9)$$

Inasmuch as S does vary somewhat with the velocity of the alpha particles, the values given in table 6 at the end of the book are to be taken as averages over the range of energies of the natural radioactive alpha rays. The *mass stopping power* is the stopping power divided by the density of the substance.

The *atomic stopping power* is the stopping power divided by the number (n) of atoms per cubic centimeter of the substance. For a substance of density ρ and atomic weight A,

$$n = \rho N/A, \qquad (12\text{--}10)$$

where N is Avogadro's number. The *relative atomic stopping power* (s) is the ratio of the energy lost per atom of the substance to that lost per atom of a standard gas. Usually, air at 15° C. and 76 centimeters pressure composed of average atoms of atomic weight 14.4 $(= A_a)$ (but occasionally oxygen) is used as the standard. For equal energy loss (or equal reduction in range, when these quantities are small) and for equal areas

$$s = \frac{\rho_a A \, t_a}{\rho A_a \, t}, \qquad (12\text{--}11)$$

where the subscript (*a*) refers to the standard. Average values of *s* will be found in table 6. Bragg and Kleeman have shown that the atomic stopping power is approximately proportional to the square root of the atomic weight of the substance. This has been justified by theoretical work, particularly by Block.[4] Relative molecular stopping powers may be obtained by the addition of the separate values of *s* of the constituent atoms.

12-6. Ionization by Alpha Particles.—Alpha particles are very good ionizers. The ionization is so intense along a straight path that, in an expansion chamber, the individual water drops coalesce to give a straight line, as in figure 12-3. Ordinarily the alpha particle is able to plunge through the outer electrons of an atom, losing energy and speed as it ionizes or excites the atom, without suffering any deflection itself. But, occasionally, it passes sufficiently close to a nucleus to be deviated sharply from the straight path and the drop track shows a sharp bend.

The total number of ion pairs which can be produced by a single alpha particle in dry air at 15° C. and 76 centimeters pressure; i.e., the *total ionization* ($\mathcal{I}$), is directly proportional to the energy ($\mathcal{E}_0$) with which the particles leave the source. Thus,

$$\mathcal{I} = 1.80 \times 10^{10} \, \mathcal{E}_0. \qquad (12\text{-}12)$$

$\mathcal{I}$ is given as the saturation ionization current divided by the total number of particles emitted each second and $\mathcal{E}_0$ is measured by observations on the deflection of the particles in electric and magnetic fields. As an example, the long range, energetic particles from radium C' ($R = 6.92$ cm., $\mathcal{E}_0 = 1.225 \times 10^{-5}$ ergs = 7.7 Mev.) can produce a total of 2.20×10^5 ion pairs. Values of $\mathcal{I}$ range from 1.2×10^5 to 2.5×10^5 for the natural radioactive substances. (See table 4, at the end of the book.) The ratio of the total number of ion pairs produced in a gas other than air to the number produced in air is roughly independent of the energy of the alpha particles. As examples of this relative total ionization by alpha particles of 3.8 centimeters range, we have: helium, 1.15; oxygen, 1.09; neon, 1.30; argon, 1.45; air, 1.

Not all of the ions produced by an alpha particle are due to its direct action on the gas atoms. If drop tracks are examined closely and especially if they are made in an expansion chamber filled with helium at a low pressure, one can see small branches, close to the main track. These are due to the so-called delta rays or electrons ejected from atoms by the incident alpha particles with sufficient energy to account, in some cases for as much as two-thirds of the total ionization.

As alpha particles travel through a gas, they retain their double charge over more than 90 per cent of their path but, near the end, they capture and lose electrons, changing their charge several thousand times within the last few millimeters of their path.

An alpha particle travels slower and slower as it progresses through a gas because it is continually giving up energy in the processes of ionization and excitation of the gas atoms. The velocity of the particle can be measured by deflection in magnetic and electric fields. Figure 12–9 shows the velocity (v) as compared with the initial velocity (v_o) (1.922 × 10^9 cm./sec.) for alpha particles from RaC′ in standard air.

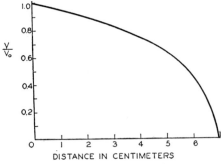

FIG. 12–9. Alpha particles slow down as they pass through a gas.

If the initial energy of an alpha particle from a given substance is divided by the total number of ion pairs which it can produce in a gas, there results an average value of the energy needed to produce one ion pair, which is called the *mean ionization energy*. Approximately the same value will be found when alpha particles from other radioactive substances are used. Thus, the mean ionizing energy is a characteristic constant of the gas and is approximately independent of the velocity of the alpha particle. Some values, in electron volts are as follows: hydrogen, 33.0; helium, 27.8; nitrogen, 35.0; oxygen, 32.3; neon, 27.4 and argon, 25.4. These values are appreciably larger than the ionization potentials of the corresponding gases (See section 7–5 and table 2) as might be expected, since the alpha particle not only gives up energy in the ionization of the gas atoms but also to excite them and to give the ejected electrons considerable kinetic energy.

The *specific ionization* is defined as the number of ions produced by a particle per unit path. The specific ionization of alpha particles is greatest just before the end of their paths; i.e., they are most efficient as ionizers just before they stop, because they are travelling slower. This phenomenon may be

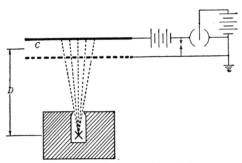

Fig. 12–10. To study the ionization produced by alpha rays at various points along their path.

studied with a shallow ionization chamber, such as *C* in figure 12–10. Here, the alpha particles from the source *X*, in a lead shield, traverse the distance *D* to the chamber (having a wire gauze for its lower plate) where they produce ions which are

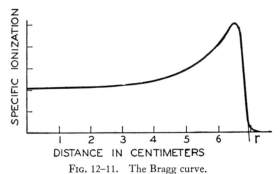

Fig. 12–11. The Bragg curve.

measured with an electrometer. The ionization current, divided by the number of particles per second at the various distances, gives the specific ionization. Figure 12–11 is for a special case, that of alpha rays from radium C′; whose (extrapolated) range (*r*) is equal to 6.96 centimeters at 15° C. and 76 centimeters pressure.

The general shape of this *Bragg curve* is the same for the alpha rays from various radioactive substances and is not altered by change of temperature or pressure or the kind of gas used, although its absolute value is altered.

Since the ionization by an alpha particle varies along its path, it is only possible to give a rough figure for the average specific ionization. If an alpha particle has a range of 7 centimeters it will produce an average of approximately 2440 ion pairs per millimeter in air at 15° C. and 76 centimeters pressure. Corresponding values [5] for other ranges are: 5 cm., 2540; 3 cm., 2880; 2 cm., 3440; 1 cm., 4800; 0.47 cm., 6000, and 0.21, 4500.

12-7.   Primary Beta Ray Spectra.—The ratio of charge to mass of beta particles has been measured from the amount of their deflection in a magnetic field as discussed in chapter 2. (See section 2-11.) It was found that they are *high-speed electrons* spontaneously emitted from the atoms of radioactive materials and that their mass increases with their velocity in accordance with the relativity equation

$$m = \frac{m_o}{\sqrt{1 - v^2/c^2}}. \tag{2-25}$$

The beta particles emitted by a given radioactive substance do not all have the same velocity, as is very nearly true for the alpha particles. Instead, it is found that the majority of the energy in the beta ray is carried by beta particles whose velocities range in a *continuum* from zero to a definite maximum.

The beta ray spectrum may be studied by means of a beta ray spectrograph, as in figure 12-12. In an evacuated metal box (*A*), radium C or some other concentrated source of beta rays is placed at *S* in a lead block. The beta rays pass through a slit at *B* and are bent by a strong magnetic field perpendicular to the paper, coming to a sharp focus * on a photographic plate (*P*). Several metal shields (*C*) are used to cut off secondary beta rays created

---

* Two circles of the same size whose centers are near each other will intersect at two diametrically opposite points. *The direction focus with this apparatus is, however, slightly imperfect, since only two circles intersect at the same point and the various beta rays, travel in a large number of circular paths indicated in the figure by the crescents.*

by the primary or gamma rays from S. The beta rays with least velocity are bent the most, reaching the plate near the slit and vice versa. A fogging of the plate is observed which extends away from the slit for a definite distance and then ceases at a

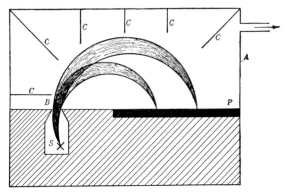

FIG. 12–12.   Beta ray spectrograph.

point characteristic of the emitting material. This background is of unequal intensity along the plate. In addition to this *primary spectrum*, several sharp lines are observed on the plate at positions which are also characteristic of the emitting substance. The latter form the so-called *line spectrum*.

The momentum of a beta particle, or the quantity Hr which is proportional to the momentum, may be determined from the position of the blackening on the photographic plate. It may be seen in figure 12–13 that

$$r = \sqrt{D^2 + a^2}/2 \cdot \qquad (12\text{–}13)$$

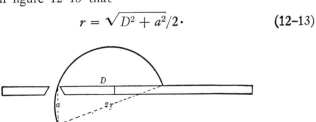

FIG. 12–13.   Velocity measurement in the beta ray spectrograph.

The centrifugal force mv^2/r on each beta particle rotating in a circle of radius r centimeters, is balanced by the magnetic force

Hev. The relativity mass equation (2–25) must be used. Then,

$$Hr = \frac{mv}{e} = \frac{m_0 v}{e}\left(1 - \frac{v^2}{c^2}\right)^{-\frac{1}{2}}, \qquad (12\text{–}14)$$

where H is the strength of the magnetic field in oersteds, m_0 is the rest mass and e is the charge of a particle of velocity v centimeters per second, and c is the velocity of light. The velocity of the beta particles may be determined by solving equation 12–14 for v.

The number of beta particles emitted each second in the continuous spectrum can be determined by substituting a Faraday chamber and electrometer for the photographic plate of figure 12–12. The number of atoms which disintegrate each second may be calculated from the transformation constant (λ) and the total number of atoms in the source. It is found that the number of beta particles which appear is the same as the number of atoms which are transformed into new and different atoms. It is thus established that these *disintegration electrons* come from the nucleus and not from the outer parts of the atom.

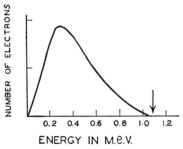

FIG. 12–14. Energy distribution among the disintegration electrons of radium E.

Their distribution of energy, as illustrated in figure 12–14 for the case [6] of radium E, is in strong contrast to the fine structure distribution observed in the case of alpha particles. The alpha particles which leave a disintegrating nucleus are confined to definite energies, whereas the beta particles from the nucleus are continuously distributed over a wide range of energies. A satisfactory explanation of the beta ray energy distribution has not yet been offered although several theories have been proposed. In one of these, it is assumed that when a beta particle is emitted, a new particle arises whose charge is zero and whose mass is very small. Pauli has called this hypothetical particle a *neutrino*.

The *maximum energy* of the electrons spontaneously ejected from a radioactive nucleus is a characteristic of the emitting substance. The more accurately determined values, in electron kilovolts, are: uranium X_2, 2300; radium B, 650; radium C, 3150; radium E, 1300; actinium C″, 1500; mesothorium 2, 2050; thorium B, 360; thorium C, 2250; and thorium C″, 1800.

Sargent has shown that there is a relationship between the maximum energy of the disintegration electrons and the decay constant, which is similar to the Geiger-Nuttall law for alpha particles (equation 12–5).

The beta particles which form the line spectrum are *photoelectrons* ejected from the parts of the same or of other atoms, which lie outside the nucleus, as will appear after the discussion of gamma rays.

12–8. Gamma Ray Wave-lengths.—The wave-length of gamma rays may be measured directly by the method of glancing angle reflection from a crystal, as with x-rays. Gamma rays from the source X in figure 12–15 pass through a long and narrow slit (S) made of two lead plates which are electrically charged to

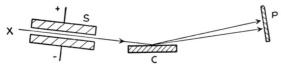

Fig. 12–15.   Measurement of gamma ray wave-lengths.

remove all beta rays. The rays are diffracted by a rock salt crystal C to the photographic plate (P) where they produce a series of lines, one for each wave-length.

The wave-lengths of gamma rays have also been measured by studying the beta rays which they eject from thin non-radioactive foils placed around the emitting material. A beta ray spectrograph like that in figure 12–12 is used. The energy ($\mathscr{E}_\beta$) of the beta rays in the line spectrum is measured with this apparatus and added to the energy (W) required to remove the electron from an x-ray level in the atoms of the foil. As is known from the Einstein photoelectric equation, the sum of $\mathscr{E}_\beta$ and W is equal to the energy $h\nu_\gamma$ in a photon of the gamma ray. Thus,

$$h\nu_\gamma = \mathscr{E}_\beta + W_K, W_L, W_M \ldots \qquad (12\text{–}15)$$

and $\lambda_\gamma = c/\nu_\gamma$. Values of λ_γ obtained by the two methods just described are in agreement. They range between 4.66 X units *

* An X unit is equal to 10^{-11} cm. or one one-thousandth of an angstrom.

for thorium C'' and 1323 X units for radium $B + C$, equivalent to 2.65 and 0.0093 million electron volts* respectively.

12–9. Secondary Radiations.—When an alpha particle is ejected from a nucleus, a readjustment takes place in the nucleus of the product atom which results in a gamma radiation. When the gamma ray photon leaves the nucleus, it may give up its energy to an electron in the K, L or other x-ray level of the same atom. This is known as *internal conversion*. *Photo-electrons* or beta rays are then ejected from the atom and can be studied with a spectrograph. They produce much sharper lines on the photographic plate than the electrons from the thin foils described in the preceding section and have been used extensively to deduce the wavelengths of the gamma rays which caused their ejection.

When the atom from which photo-electrons have been ejected returns to its normal state, *characteristic x-rays* are produced. These, in turn, may pass out of the radioactive material or, more often, they may eject other photo-electrons from still higher levels in their atom. This process of auto-ionization is called the *Auger effect* and the electrons are referred to as *Auger electrons*. The x-rays may also eject photo-electrons from other atoms. The complete beta ray line spectrum is, therefore, made up of a complicated system of photo-electrons. The velocities of the electrons range from 29 to 97 per cent that of light. The corresponding energies may be obtained by the use of equations 2–26 and 2–12 and Hr values may be calculated with equation 12–14. (See tables 9 and 10.)

12–10. The Absorption of Beta and Gamma Rays.—Alpha rays ionize profusely and are easily absorbed. Gamma rays produce comparatively few ions and are absorbed with difficulty. Beta rays are intermediate between the alpha and gamma rays.

The absorption of these rays by a solid substance, such as aluminum, may be measured by placing an appropriate radioactive substance in an electroscope, as at XXX in figure 17–1. Observe the rate of fall of the leaf as various thicknesses of aluminum and lead are placed over X. First, using thin sheets of aluminum foil, the observed rate of fall measures the ionization produced by the alpha, beta and gamma rays; i.e., the combined activity of the three rays. As additional sheets of foil are placed over the source,

---

* From the relation, volts = 12,336/angstroms.

the alpha rays are successively decreased but the other two are practically unaffected. With about 0.006 centimeter of aluminum, or a sheet of ordinary writing paper, all the alpha rays are absorbed. The beta rays may now be reduced by successive additions of aluminum sheets, 0.01 centimeter thick. A sheet of aluminum approximately 3 millimeters thick will absorb all the alpha and beta rays. The addition of lead sheets 3 millimeters in thickness will now serve to show the absorption of gamma rays alone. Gamma rays are more penetrating than x-rays and, with the exception of cosmic rays, are the most penetrating known today. They will pass through a block of iron one foot thick.

For the beta or the gamma rays from a radioactive substance, the intensity I of the beam after passing through d cm. of the absorber is

$$I = I_0 \epsilon^{-\mu d} \qquad (12\text{–}16)$$

where I_0 is the original intensity and μ is the *coefficient of absorption*. The intensities are measured by the amount of ionization which the rays produce after passing through the different thicknesses of

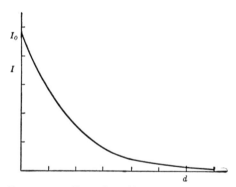

Fig. 12–16. Absorption of beta or gamma rays.

absorbing material. The law is shown graphically in figure 12–16 and may be tested by plotting log I against d as in figure 12–17 since, from equation 12–16, we have

$$\log_\epsilon I = \log_\epsilon I_0 - \mu d. \qquad (12\text{–}17)$$

This is the equation of a straight line. The ordinates are values of

$\log_\epsilon I$, the abscissae are values of d, $\log_\epsilon I_0$ is the intercept on the ordinate and μ is the slope of the line, the negative sign indicating

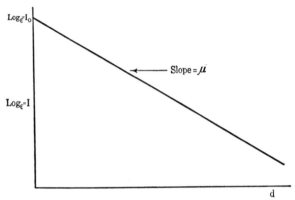

FIG. 12–17.   To determine the absorption coefficient (μ).

that the slope is downwards from left to right.   From the last equation,

$$\mu = \frac{\log_\epsilon I_0 - \log_\epsilon I}{d} = \frac{\log_\epsilon (I_0/I)}{d}, \qquad (12\text{–}18)$$

so that this constant is defined as the logarithmic ratio of the intensities at two points distant one centimeter in the absorbing medium.

In the case of successive additions of layers of absorbing material, one takes

$$I_1 = I_0 \epsilon^{-\mu d_1} \qquad I_2 = I_0 \epsilon^{-\mu d_2}, \qquad (12\text{–}19)$$

from which

$$\mu = \frac{1}{d_2 - d_1} \log_\epsilon \left(\frac{I_1}{I_2} \right), \qquad (12\text{–}20)$$

$$\mu = \frac{2.303}{d} \log_{10} \left(\frac{I_1}{I_2} \right), \qquad (12\text{–}21)$$

where I_1 is the intensity of the rays after passing through d_1 cm. of absorber, I_2 is the intensity after passing through d_2 cm., and 2.303 is used to change from the Naperian to the common system of logarithms.   Thus, the intensity is measured before (I_1) and after

(I_2) the addition of a sheet of the absorbing material of thickness $d(= d_2 - d_1)$.

The fact that *beta rays* obey an exponential law of the type just described, is entirely fortuitous since the rays consist of a complex mixture of the continuous or disintegration electrons and the characteristic line or photoelectric electrons whose velocities from any one substance vary over wide limits. In addition, the interaction of beta particles with matter is a complicated process. In practice, however, a logarithmic plot, such as that in figure 12–17, will show one or more nearly straight sections, each of which may be associated with a definite mean value of μ. The numerical values so obtained vary for beta rays from different radioactive substances passing through aluminum from 13.1 to 5500. Radium C, for example, sends out beta rays having coefficients of 13.2 and 53. These correspond roughly to groups of high and low velocity (energy), respectively. (See table 12.) Absorption coefficients for gamma rays are given in table 13 at the end of the book.

12–11. Interaction of Beta and Gamma Rays with Matter.— A comparison of the drop tracks produced by alpha, beta and

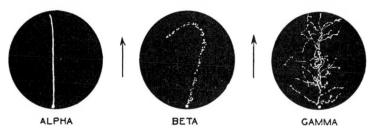

ALPHA   BETA   GAMMA

Fig. 12–18. A rough comparison of the drop tracks produced by alpha, beta and gamma rays.

gamma rays is shown in figure 12–18 and further details will be found in section 18–17.

The track of a *beta particle* is seen to be irregular and the total ionization spread throughout an appreciable volume of the gas. Although the beta particles possess approximately ten times the velocity of the alpha particles, they have such small mass, and hence such small momentum and energy, as to be easily deflected in their encounters with gas atoms. Sometimes they undergo a series of small deflections and at other times suffer radical changes

in direction.   Furthermore, several beta rays with different velocities leave any one substance so that a homogeneous beam cannot
be had without the use of magnetic or electric fields and consequent
diminution in intensity.   When a homogeneous beam of beta
particles passes through a layer of matter, it emerges with a wide
distribution of velocities.

The *range of beta particles* is defined as in the case of alpha
particles.   Values for aluminum and air are given in table 11.
The range of a beta particle is less well defined than that of an
alpha particle.   Straggling effects are much more pronounced and
successive particles each starting with the same energy will show
greater fluctuations in the range of penetration than will heavier
particles.

Average values of the *specific ionization* by electrons will be
found in table 11.   Beta particles of energies between 1.36 and
0.081 Mev $(Hr = 6000$ to 1000) produce from 45 to 200 ion pairs
per centimeter in air at 76 centimeters and 15° C.,* the specific
ionization varying inversely as the square of the velocity.   The
energy required to produce each ion pair in air is about 35 volts,
the same as for alpha particles.   Thus, the slower electrons lose
energy by the process of ejection of photo-electrons from the gas
atoms.

Faster electrons than those just mentioned lose energy not
only by the photo-ionization process but also by a radiation process.
The latter consists of the radiation of energy when the particles
suddenly change their velocity in an atomic impact, as in the
production of the continuous x-ray spectrum by the abrupt
impact of electrons on the anode of an x-ray tube.   For the faster
electrons, the stopping power is proportional to the logarithm of
their energy.

For exceedingly fast electrons, $(\mathscr{E} > 137mc^2)$, the pair production process discussed in chapter 14 most probably occurs.

The drop tracks produced by *gamma rays* (see figure 12–18)
are similar to those of x-rays.   The ionization is much less, about
one-hundredth of that produced by the beta rays from the same
source and the ions are more diffusely spread throughout the gas.

---

* This includes both the *primary* ions ejected by the beta particles themselves
and the *secondary* ions produced by the photo-electrons of the gas atoms.

It is largely a result of the secondary electrons which the gamma rays eject from the atoms.

The absorption of gamma rays in matter is the result of three processes whose relative importance depends on the energy in each photon and the atomic weight of the absorber. The predominant process, for lower-frequency gamma rays and for heavier elements,

TABLE 12–1.—SUMMARY OF THE NATURAL RADIOACTIVE RADIATIONS

Rays	Alpha	Beta	Gamma
Nature	Helium nuclei or $H_c{}^{++}$	Electrons	Very short electro-magnetic radiations
Charge	$+ 2e$	$- e$	None
Charge/Mass	$\dfrac{2e}{4M} = 4823 \dfrac{\text{e.m.u.}}{\text{gram}}$	$\dfrac{e}{m} = 1.76 \times 10^7 \dfrac{\text{e.m.u.}}{\text{gram}}$	
Velocity	1.42×10^9 to $2.06 \times 10^9 \dfrac{\text{cm.}}{\text{sec.}}$ about $\frac{1}{10}$ that of beta rays	$0.29c$ to $0.96c$ or 0.87×10^{10} to $2.88 \times 10^{10} \dfrac{\text{cm.}}{\text{sec.}}$	$c = 3 \times 10^{10} \dfrac{\text{cm.}}{\text{sec.}}$
Ionization	Great; along straight, narrow beams	Moderate; curved trajectories	Small; throughout the gas
Range	2.37 to 8.16 cm. in air (76, 0° C.)		
Absorbed	Easily; 0.006 cm. aluminum	Moderately; 3 mm. lead. $\mu = 13.1$ to 5500 in aluminum	With difficulty; 25 cm. iron. $\mu = 0.096$ to 2700 in aluminum
Wave-length	....	....	1.365 to 0.0047 angstroms

is the typical ejection of photo-electrons as in the case of alpha, beta and low-frequency x-rays. For higher frequencies and the lighter elements, the scattering of the gamma rays from free electrons (Compton effect) predominates. For exceedingly high frequencies, positron-electron pairs are formed, as discussed in chapter 14. At high energies, such as are to be found in cosmic rays or indeed in electrons accelerated by large betatrons, electrons give rise to high-energy photons which in turn interact with nuclei and produce both photo-neutrons and photo-protons by a nuclear photo-effect.

EXPERIMENT 12–1

RANGE OF ALPHA PARTICLES—SCINTILLATION METHOD

The apparatus for measuring the range of alpha particles at various pressures is shown in figure 12–19. An oil pump is con-

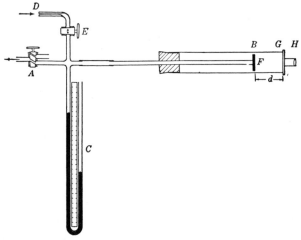

FIG. 12–19. Scintillation method of measuring the range of alpha particles.

nected to the stop cock *A*, partially evacuating the glass tube *B* (about 20 cm. long, 3.5 cm. diameter). The pressure in the tube is determined with the open-tube mercury manometer *C*. The pressure in centimeters of mercury is equal to the difference between the barometer reading and the difference in height of the mercury in the two arms. Air may be admitted to the tube slowly through the capillary *D* and stop cock *E*.

The active material is on a small metal plate (*F*), fixed with soft wax to a second plate supported by a long metal tube. The front of the source is covered with a brass disc pierced with a large number of holes in order to secure an approximately parallel bundle of alpha particles. The source and its collimator may be slid in and out through a rubber stopper. There is a small hole near the end of the tube to allow evacuation of B. The active material may be any substance emitting alpha particles but, because of the contamination of the walls of the tube by disintergation products or by recoil atoms, only certain substances should be used. A good source consists of ionium. Another may be made from the old, crushed tubes of the active deposit of radium used in medical work. These " needles " were originally filled with radium emanation which changed in the course of a few weeks through the short-life, active deposit to become radium D with a comparatively long life. Radium D is continually producing radium F or polonium (after an intervening substance) and this sends out the alpha particles whose range is to be measured. The metal disc is placed in a horizontal position and coated with a thin layer of water glass (sodium silicate). While this is drying, two or three pulverized radium D tubes are sprinkled over its surface. When dry it is ready for use.

The fluorescent screen G is prepared by placing the glass plate in a horizontal position, covering with a thin layer of gelatin. When thoroughly dry, soften its *surface* with alcohol and sprinkle with a uniform layer of green phosphorescent zinc sulphide. Shake off the excess powder, clear the edges and seal to the end of the tube with sealing wax, the luminescent material being inside. Scintillations produced by those alpha particles which reach this screen are observed through a small lens H.

Notes.—1. Turn the stop cock A to admit air to the oil pump before shutting off its motor; otherwise oil will be sucked up into the system.

2. The experiment must be performed in a good dark room. It will be necessary for the observer to remain in the dark at least ten or fifteen minutes to accustom his eyes to the darkness and to allow the screen to dim down before the scintillations will be sufficiently bright for accurate work. A second student should read the manometer and manipulate the stop cocks, using a shielded ruby light, or better, work in another room, the rubber tubing running through the wall.

3. There are always a few scintillations occurring at more or less rare intervals on the screen. These are to be disregarded.

4. Do not touch the surface of the active material with the fingers.

Procedure.—Read the barometric pressure and the temperature at the beginning and end of this experiment. Use the average value in the calculations.

Set the source at a distance d (see figure 12–19) which is to be about one centimeter greater than the range of the particles at atmospheric pressure Record the value of d. When the eyes have become accustomed to the darkness, lower the pressure slowly until the scintillations first appear. Note this pressure. Lower the pressure still farther, then let it increase slowly and observe the pressure when the scintillations first cease. Repeat these steps eight or ten times and average all values to find the pressure corresponding to the range d.

Repeat with the source at various distances farther away from the screen.

From the relation that the range is inversely proportional to the pressure and directly proportional to the absolute temperature, compute the range (r) at 76 cm. and 15° C. from each set of data. Average these readings and compare with the accepted value.

The final value will be found to be somewhat smaller than the accepted range because of absorbing films such as grease from the fingers, thin layers of water glass, etc., and because it is difficult to distinguish between the spurious scintillations and those of the alpha particles of maximum range.

EXPERIMENT 12–2

RANGE OF ALPHA PARTICLES—ELECTRICAL METHOD

Apparatus.—The shallow chamber BC of figure 12–20 is used to collect the ions produced by alpha particles from their source (S). The depth of the chamber is to be as small as possible, say 2 millimeters, yet sufficiently large that enough ions are produced in it to operate the current measuring instrument (E) (an electrometer or an electroscope) at a convenient rate. A potential (V) of approximately 200 volts, applied between B and C, is sufficient to draw over most of the ions. The collector plate (C) must be supported by an insulator of the very best kind (amber) and its lead wire should be enclosed in a grounded metal tube all the way to E, as usual in all small current measurements. If the current to C is too large to be measured accurately, either use a weaker source or add a small, well-insulated condenser in parallel with E. In front of the ionization chamber, at a distance of approximately 2 milli-meters, there is a grounded wire gauze A whose function is to pre-vent ions formed in front of B from entering the chamber. The collimated source (S) may consist of pulverized radium D tubes, as in the preceding experiment, and is supported by a rod passing through a rubber cork in the enclosing glass tube.

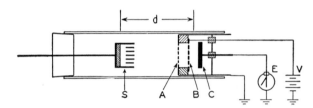

Fig. 12–20.   Electrical method of measuring the range of alpha particles.

Experiment.—Record the temperature and pressure. Measure the ionization in terms of the rate of fall of the leaf of the electro-scope or movement of the electrometer needle (corrected for the natural leak) when the source is at various distances (d). Plot, with ionization currents as ordinates and distances (d) as abscissae. Record on the graph the extrapolated range (r) reduced to 15° C. and a pressure of 76 centimeters. If desired, the pressure in the glass tube may be lowered to, say 30 centimeters of mercury, and the straggling effect near the end of the path of the alpha particles studied in greater detail.

Experiment 12–3

AIR EQUIVALENT AND STOPPING POWER FOR ALPHA RAYS

A thin foil is to be introduced in the path of an alpha ray and the reduction in range measured by the scintillation method.

Apparatus.—The various parts of the apparatus may be con-veniently mounted as in figure 12–21. The radioactive source (A) may consist of two radium D tubes, pulverized and stuck uniformly in the bottom of a shallow brass cup of approximately one centimeter in diameter. A disc of brass, perforated with many small holes and, say, 5 millimeters thick, covers the top of the cup and collimates the alpha rays. This source is mounted between two guide rods and is moved back and forth by means of a rack and pinion when the knob, indicated by the circle is turned. A vernier is mounted on *A* and moves along the scale indicated. Across the ends of the rods, a brass bar supports a low-power eye-

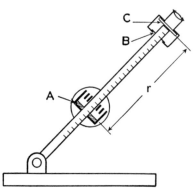

FIG. 12–21. Stopping power apparatus.

piece which, by rotation, may be focused on the fluorescent screen (*C*). The preparation of a suitable screen was described in experiment 12–1. The brass bar also supports the thin foil (*B*) whose stopping power is to be measured. A sheet of thin spring brass is doubled over and pierced with a central hole about 1.5 centimeters in diameter. Various foils may be slipped between the sheets and the whole slid into guides at a distance of, say, 2 millimeters from the screen. The apparatus is to be used in a dark room.

Procedure.—(1) Mount the foil in its holder. Two sheets of aluminum such as used for electroscope leaves will prove satisfactory. Hold them up to the light and see that there are no obvious holes or areas of unequal thickness.

(2) Record the barometric pressure and the temperature.

(3) Without the foil (*B*), place the source (*A*) two centimeters from the screen (*C*) and wait (about 15 minutes) in the dark room until scintillations can be seen clearly. Move the source back and forth and determine the distance (*d*) between the surface of the active substance and that of the fluorescent material where scintillations just cannot be seen. There will always be a few spurious flashes of light which are to be disregarded. The cessation of scintillations will not be sharp and a large number of rapid settings will give better results than a single reading taken with great care. The lack of sharpness in the cut-off is due not only to the straggling of the particles but also to their lack of parallelism

and to slight absorbing layers, perhaps grease, on the source and screen.

(4) Insert the foil in its holder in the path of the rays and repeat the range measurement as in (3). This distance is d'.

(5) Compute the air equivalent, t_a, equation 12-7.

(6) Determine the thickness (t) of the foil by weighing a known area on an accurate balance. The density of aluminum is 2.70 grams per cm^3. The quantity ρt in equation 12-11 is equal to the mass in grams of one square centimeter of the foil ($\rho t = m/a$).

(7) Compute the equivalent and the relative atomic stopping powers from equations 12-8 and 12-11, and compare with the accepted values.

EXPERIMENT 12-4

ABSORPTION OF BETA RAYS

The source of the beta rays may consist of a shallow cup whose bottom is covered uniformly with pulverized radium D tubes held in place with a very thin layer of binding material such as gelatin or sodium silicate. A sheet of aluminum 0.006 to 0.01 centimeter thick is placed over the cup to cut off all alpha rays.

This source is placed in an electroscope of the type shown in figure 17-1. The student should read the discussion on electroscopes given in chapter 17 before performing this experiment.

The activity is measured as successive sheets of aluminum, each about 0.007 centimeter thick, are placed over the source. Twelve of these sheets will be sufficient for a good curve. Care should be taken that the sheets are not and do not become contaminated by direct contact with the active material.

Place a non-contaminated sheet of lead about 3 millimeters thick over the source and make sure that there are no appreciable gamma radiations; i.e., the fall of the leaf is the same as the natural leak. If it is not, the gamma activity as well as the natural leak must be subtracted to obtain the beta ray activities.

Plot a curve of the beta ray activities as ordinates (vertical) and the thickness of the aluminum as abscissae. Also, using semilogarithm paper, plot logarithms of the activities *vs.* total thicknesses of the absorbing screens. Common logarithms may be used. Then, the slope of the line is 0.4343 times the coefficient of absorption of these beta rays in aluminum. Equation 12–21 may be used instead of the graphical method if desired. Take an average of the coefficients computed for various thicknesses. Compare your value of μ with the accepted value.

If the source emits gamma rays of sufficient intensity, measure the absorption coefficient of lead for these rays, using sheets approximately 2 millimeters thick.

EXPERIMENT 12–5

ABSORPTION OF GAMMA RAYS

Read the discussion of Counter Tubes in Chapter 18.

Danger.—Continued exposure to radioactive rays can cause serious burns. Consult the instructor as to the precautions necessay with the source which you are to use.

Apparatus.—A small Geiger-Müller tube with its amplifier and high speed counter, sheets of lead or aluminum and the gamma ray source. The strength of the source and the maximum counting rate will determine whether lead or aluminum is to be used and the proper thickness. For example, with a particular source of radio-thorium located 35 centimeters from a counter tube, whose residual count was 10 and maximum was 150 per minute, 8 sheets of lead, each 1 centimeter thick were found to be satisfactory.

Experiment.—When the apparatus is functioning properly, (1) measure the residual count, using as long a time interval as possible, say 10 minutes.

(2) In the absence of the source, place each of the absorbing blocks near the counter and again measure the residual count in order to be sure that none of the absorbers are radioactive.

(3) Then, with the source at a fixed distance, insert successive sheets of absorbing material and record the counting rate over as long time intervals as possible.

(4) Plot the above data, with the net counting rates as ordinates and centimeters thickness of the absorber as abscissae. Compute the absorption coefficient. Plot, also, the logarithms of the net counting rates against thickness of the absorber. If desired, the absorption coefficient may be obtained from the slope of the resulting line rather than from the equation for this quantity. Equations 12–18 or 12–21 are used.

The same equipment may be used for other experiments, such as a test of the inverse square law. For this, measure the net counting rate with the source at various measured distances from the counter tube. Plot counting rates vertically and inverse squares of the distances horizontally. An approximately straight line should result. It will deviate from linearity because of the absorption of the rays by the air. The deviation will be pronounced when a weak source, such as three or four radium D tubes (emitting mostly beta rays), is used.

The absorption coefficient of air can be measured as follows: due to the inverse square law, the net counting rate will be given by $I/I_1 = 1/d^2$ and due to the exponential absorption, $I_1 = I_0 \epsilon^{-\mu d}$, where I_0 is the counting rate at the origin and d is the distance from the source to the tube. Then, $Id^2 = I_0 \epsilon^{-\mu d}$ or $\log_\epsilon (Id^2) = -\mu d + \log_\epsilon I_0$. A straight line will be obtained when $\log_\epsilon (Id^2)$ is plotted against d. The absorption coefficient (μ) can be calculated from the slope, as in previous cases.

REFERENCES

1. S. Rosenblum, Jr. de Phys., **1**, 438 (1930). Compt. Rend., **190**, 1124 (1930); **194**, 1919 (1932).
2. Rutherford, Wynn-Williams, Lewis and Bowden, Proc. Roy. Soc., **A139**, 617 (1933).
   Lewis and Bowden, Proc. Roy. Soc., **A145**, 235 (1934).
3. See General Reference D, page 116, General Reference B, page 534 and (7) below.
4. See General Reference D, page 62.
5. See General Reference A, page 78.
6. See General Reference A, page 408.
7. M. G. Holloway and M. S. Livingston, Phys. Rev., **54**, 18 (1938).

GENERAL REFERENCES

A.—Rutherford, Chadwick and Ellis, *Radiations from Radioactive Substances*. The Macmillan Co. (1930).
B.—Madame Pierre Curie, *Radioactivité*. Hermann and Co. (1935).
C.—Geiger and Scheel, *Handbuch der Physik*, Vol. XXII/2 Springer (1933).
D.—F. Rasetti, *Elements of Nuclear Physics*. Prentice-Hall (1936).
E.—J. D. Stranathan, *The Particles of Modern Physics*. The Blakiston Co. (1942).

CHAPTER 13

THE ACCELERATION OF IONS*

THE MULTIPLE ACCELERATION OF IONS

13-1. Linear Multiple Acceleration.—The same potential may be used repeatedly to accelerate ions to high speeds.[1] In the apparatus of figure 13-1, positive ions from the source at the left pass in a parallel beam through the discs and cylinders mounted along the axis of the highly evacuated tube. The electrodes are alternately connected to a high frequency generator whose period is so adjusted that during the time the ions are travelling inside a given cylinder, the polarity of the next one

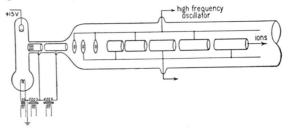

FIG. 13-1. The Sloan-Lawrence linear accelerator tube.

changes from positive to negative. The ions are thus accelerated at each gap by the same amount. The lengths of the cylinders (including the gaps) increase from left to right as the square root of the odd integers. Gaps of 20 per cent of these distances give effectively 96 per cent of the applied potential. Near the source, it is necessary to use discs instead of cylinders, at a sacrifice in efficiency, in order to provide homogeneous electrostatic fields. With a 20 kw. oscillator delivering 42 kv. at 30 meters on 30 accelerator electrodes, a current of 10^{-7} ampere of 1.26 Mev† singly charged mercury ions has been produced. Recently it has been proposed to build a linear accelerator, similar to the above, but with fewer sections and driven at much higher frequencies. By using the modern microwave oscillators developed during the war

* Includes electrons as well as the heavier positive ions.
† Mev = million electron volts. See chapter 2, section 5.

for radar transmitters, it should be possible to obtain high energies with an accelerator of reasonable dimensions.

13–2. The Cyclotron.—The principle of operation of the magnetic resonance accelerator or *cyclotron* of Lawrence [2] may be understood by referring to figure 13–2. The duants or " dees " (*A* and *B* of figure *a*) consist of a pill-box shaped copper chamber split into two parts. They are placed in an evacuated chamber, between the poles of a strong electromagnet, as in (*b*). Ions from a source near the center (in the gap between the two halves) are accelerated by a comparatively low potential (say 10,000 volts) to one of the dees, say *A*. Due to the magnetic field they rotate inside the dee in a circular path. Meanwhile the polarity of the dees is being reversed since they are connected to a short-wave vacuum-tube oscillator circuit of the type shown in figures 13–3 and 13–11. The magnetic field strength and the frequency of the

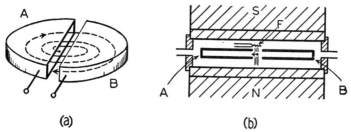

(a)   (b)

Fig. 13–2. The principle of the cyclotron of Lawrence.

oscillator are so adjusted that the ions travel one-half of a circle during one-half the period of the oscillator. Thus, as they leave *A*, they are again accelerated toward *B* by the same potential (10,000 volts). They now travel in a larger circle, in *B*, at a higher speed. But *the time* to rotate through 180 degrees *is the same* whether the ions are travelling in a small circle, at low velocity, or in a large circle at higher velocity, as proved below. Hence, during each half cycle, the ions are accelerated in the gap by the same voltage and travel in progressively larger semi-circles until, after many revolutions they approach the outer walls and are drawn off for use by an electrostatic field.

The time (t) for the ions to travel in a semi-circle of radius (r), at a velocity (v) is

$$t = \pi r/v. \tag{13-1}$$

Since the centrifugal and centripetal forces are then equal to each other,

$$\frac{Mv^2}{r} = HEv. \tag{13-2}$$

Solving for v and substituting in the previous equation gives

$$t = \frac{\pi}{H}\frac{M}{E} \text{ seconds,} \tag{13-3}$$

where H is the magnetic field strength in gausses, M is the mass of the ion in grams and E is its charge in e.m.u. Thus, *the time of running is independent of the radius of the circle.* The angular velocity ω of an ion is

$$\omega = \frac{v}{r} = H\frac{E}{M}, \tag{13-4}$$

a constant for a given ion and field intensity. When magnetic resonance exists, $2t$ is equal to the period of the oscillator. Then, the frequency (f) of the oscillator is

$$f = \frac{\omega}{2\pi} = \frac{H}{2\pi}\frac{E}{M}, \tag{13-5}$$

and its wave-length is ($\lambda = c/f$, $c = 3 \times 10^{10}$)

$$\lambda = \frac{2\pi c}{H}\frac{M}{E}. \tag{13-6}$$

$$\lambda^2 V = (3170r)^2 \tag{13-6'}$$

The energy of an ion in electron volts is

$$V = \frac{E/M}{2 \times 10^8}(Hr)^2 \tag{13-7}$$

since $10^8 VE = Mv^2/2$. The radius of path of these ions is

$$r = \frac{1}{H}\left(\frac{2 \times 10^8 V}{E/M}\right)^{\frac{1}{2}}. \tag{13-8}$$

The amplification factor (A), is the ratio of the final voltage (V) of the ions to the peak voltage (V_1) across the dees, and is equal to twice the number of revolutions n of the peak ions. Thus,

$$V = 2nV_1 = AV_1. \tag{13-9}$$

V_1, although difficult to estimate, ranges approximately from 10 to 100 Kv., in practice, and n varies from 25 to 400.

Protons are accelerated to an energy (V) of 2 Mev when $r = 16$ centimeters, $H = 13$ kilogauss and $\lambda = 15$ meters. Estimating a peak oscillator voltage of 10 Kv., the peak ions made 100 revolutions (n) and the amplification (A) was 200. For 6.8 Mev deuterons, $H = 18$ kilogauss, $\lambda = 22$ meters, $r = 30$ centimeters and, assuming $V_1 = 100$ Kv., $n = 34$ and $A = 68$. The lighter the ion, the shorter the wave-length required for a given magnetic field and outer radius. The resonance conditions for singly charged deuterons are the same as for doubly charged helium nuclei (alpha particles) since both the charge and the mass of the latter are twice as great as the former.

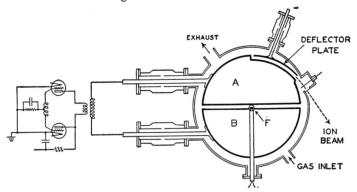

FIG. 13–3. Some details of a cyclotron. Top view.

An ion which crosses the gap from one dee to the other when the applied potential is not at its peak value will require the same time to travel in a half circle as those at the peak and will, therefore, receive multiple resonance accelerations. The ions which receive a smaller acceleration at each half cycle must execute more revolutions to arrive at a given radius; yet, when they do, they will have the same energy as those which were accelerated by the peak voltage. If, then, a deflector plate is placed at a given radius, as in figure 13–3, the emergent beam will contain ions of essentially one energy only. Theoretically, the spread of energies in this nearly " monochromatic beam " is approximately equal to twice the peak voltage across the dees.

There is a focusing action[16] on the ion beam each time it crosses the gap between the dees, due to the electro-static field. (See Electron Optics in chapter 6.) As a result, the emergent beam contains a large percentage of the ions which left the source.

The cyclotron chamber (figures 13-2 and 13-3) is evacuated at first to 10^{-5} to 10^{-6} millimeter after which a gas, such as hydrogen, deuterium or helium, is admitted to a pressure of 10^{-4} to 10^{-3} millimeter of mercury (just below the glow point). Electrons from the filament F, focussed into a vertical column by the magnetic field, bombard the gas and create positive ions. The ions are then accelerated by the negative dee. Their number depends on the number of bombarding electrons, the gas pressure and the effective length of the electron beam (somewhat less than the distance between the top and bottom plates of the dees). Output currents up to 500 microamperes have been obtained.

The deflecting plates have a radius of curvature from fifteen to thirty per cent greater than that of the ions to be deflected. Since the ions are of high energy, large electro-static forces are needed, say 20 to 100 kilovolts per centimeter.

The strength of the emergent ion beam may be measured by means of a shallow faraday chamber or a collecting wire of tungsten (to avoid excessive production of neutrons) connected to a micro-ammeter or electrometer. The energy may be reduced by introducing absorbing foils in the path of the beam. Materials to be bombarded by the ions may be located either inside the chamber or in the open air beyond a thin platinum window (say 0.000,1 inch thick) supported on a water cooled grid. Several microamperes of 5.8 Mev deuterons will produce a lavender colored glow for 25 centimeters in the air. A vacuum tube for the beam may be fastened to the side of the cyclotron and experiments carried out many feet away from the strong magnetic field. However, iron pieces or focussing coils are needed to concentrate the beam upon a small area, since it is divergent as it leaves the cyclotron.

THE PRODUCTION OF HIGH VOLTAGES

The familiar static machine, the induction coil, the transformer and the Tesla coil, as sources of direct, uni-directional, alternating and high frequency voltages of high value need not be discussed here.

13–3. D. C. Types.—*Rectifiers.*—Figure 13–4 shows the basic circuits used in radio and x-ray machines for the production of direct or semi-direct voltages from lower *a.c.* voltage supplies, together with the output wave-forms. In all cases, E is the peak voltage across the entire secondary of the transformer. Output voltages in practice are lower than the values given by an amount equal to losses in the circuit, such as the drop across the tubes. In A, the rectifier tube allows current to flow only during the half cycles in which its plate is positive; the condenser serving to partially sustain the current through the load on the negative half cycles. In B, the condenser and transformer add their voltages during alternate half cycles. In the full wave circuit of C, which is widely used,[3] the tubes take turns each half cycle in delivering current to the load. The use of a center tapped transformer may be avoided by the addition of two more tubes, as in D. In E, the condensers are each charged to half the peak voltage of the transformer (minus the drop across one tube) and in such direction that they add their potential to that of the transformer every half cycle. In F, the condensers are each charged to the full voltage E and, in series with each other and the transformer, deliver a peak output voltage of $3E$.

The full wave doubler circuit (G), of figure 13–4, is widely used. The condensers are charged in turn on alternate half cycles and in such a manner that they add their voltages. The

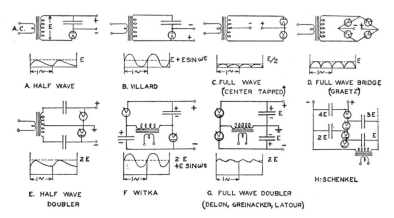

FIG. 13–4. Some basic rectifier circuits.

output is comparatively constant, the ripple amounting to approximately 5 per cent of $2E$ with the circuit shown and only to a fraction of one per cent when simple filter chokes and condensers are added.[4]

In order to obtain still higher voltages with rectifier-condenser circuits, several full wave doublers have been stacked on top of each other. Machines have also been built using a multiplicity of Villard circuits (B in figure 13–4). However, the problem of insulation between the primary and secondary of those transformers in the higher voltage parts of the circuit limits the application of these ideas. In H of figure 13–4, the condensers are so

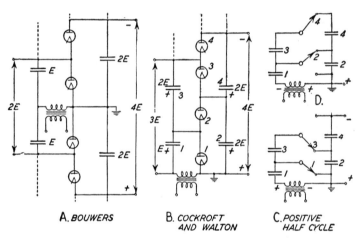

A. BOUWERS   B. COCKROFT   C. POSITIVE
               AND WALTON   HALF CYCLE

FIG. 13–5.   High voltage circuits.   (For negative half cycle.)

arranged that the lower ones are in series with the transformer and the next one above, on the half cycles. Here, however, the upper condensers must be capable of standing high voltages.

The full wave doubler circuit (G of figure 13–4) has been generalized by Bouwers [5] to give $4E$, $6E$, etc., as shown at A in figure 13–5. The upper part of this circuit (with one side of the high potential grounded) was independently conceived of and used by Cockcroft and Walton [6] in their pioneering work on nuclear disintegration. (See B of figure 13–5.) The operation of this circuit may be understood by referring to C and D of this figure, where the rectifier tubes have been replaced by switches. On alternate half cycles, condenser *1* is charged through switch (tube) *1*, then shares its charge with condenser *2*, through tube *2*; condenser *2* shares its charge with *3* through switches *1* and *3*; and *3* charges *4* through switches *2* and *4*.

The first condenser, near the transformer must be capable of standing the peak voltage of the transformer and each of the remaining condensers, as well as each rectifier tube must stand twice this value. The output voltage is very nearly constant, the ripple amounting to approximately $1\frac{1}{2}$ per cent when the supply frequency is 60 cycles per second. From theory and experiment it is known that the ripple is inversely proportional to the frequency of the supply line. The wave form is similar to that of the half-wave doubler circuit, with one " saw-tooth " per cycle. A peak voltage of 700 Kv. has been obtained.

All of the rectifier tubes of figure 13–5 can be contained in a single vacuum chamber. In the particular type [7] shown in figure 13–6, the filament can be replaced with ease by pulling it out of its copper tube. Since the filaments are at high potential, their currents must be supplied from a battery or a generator which is well insulated above ground and is surrounded by a corona shield. The generator can be rotated by means of an insulator rod, as in the figure, or with a belt, from a motor at ground potential. The tube is continuously evacuated, below approximately 10^{-4} millimeter of mercury.

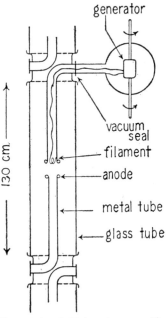

generator

vacuum
seal
filament
anode
metal tube
glass tube

130 cm

Fig. 13–6. A high voltage rectifier tube.

Belt Generators.—In the Van de Graaff electro-static generator,[8] electrical charges of one sign are sprayed onto a long, wide, endless belt made of insulating material and are carried into the inside of a large hollow, metal sphere where they are removed and, by

mutual repulsion, spread to the surface of the sphere, raising it to
a high potential.

Referring to the left half of figure 13–7, there is a supply of
comparatively low voltage, say 10 to 20 kilovolts from a trans-
former-rectifier-filter circuit. This voltage is applied to two
electrodes located on opposite sides of the belt, at *A*. The arrow
represents, either a row of needle points or a wire stretched parallel
to the belt and normal to its motion. The dot represents a metal
surface with rounded, smooth edges and is called the " inductor
plate." The system at *A* is called " the spray," since the brush

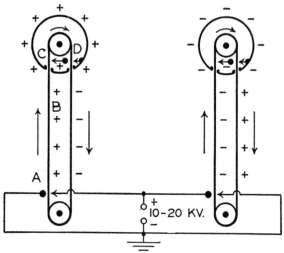

Fig. 13–7.   The Van de Graaff electro-static generator.

or corona discharge sprays charges of one sign onto the belt.
The belt (*B*) is made of paper, rubber, silk, etc., is often several
feet in width and travels at the rate of, say 5000 feet per minute.
The limit of charge which may be applied to the belt is of the order
of 10^{-9} coulomb per square centimeter on each surface and is set
by the breakdown of the air. At *C* in figure 13–7, the positive
charge is removed from the belt by means of a collector consisting
of sharp points or a wire. Thus, the collector becomes charged
positively and draws a negative charge from the spray at *D*,
which, in turn, is supplied from the sphere. In a similar manner
the sphere on the right of figure 13–7 is raised to a high negative

potential above the ground. The total potential difference between the spheres is thus doubled, and, in one installation, with spheres 15 feet in diameter, has reached the value of 5 megavolts. An upper limit to the voltage is set by the corona breakdown at the surface of the spheres, which is less when they are large and smooth. The voltage may be varied by changing the voltage of the supply. The generator may be made self-exciting by arranging the sprays in such a manner as to give a cumulative separation by induction of small charges on the belt. The rate of charging the spheres is given by the product of the surface charge density and the areal velocity with which the belt enters the spheres. Several belts are used instead of one to increase this rate.

Two modifications of the belt generator are shown in figure 13–8. At A,[9] the belt runs through a large, hollow, oval shaped

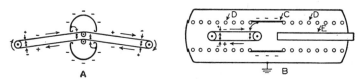

Fig. 13–8.   Two modifications of the belt generator.

conductor supported on a tall insulator (not shown). The charging rate is increased since negative charges are carried in at two places and positive charges are removed at two places. At B,[10] the entire apparatus is enclosed in a large metal tank, pumped to a pressure of, say 100 pounds per square inch. The high pressure reduces the corona losses to such a point that it has been possible to reach 2 megavolts in a tank $5\frac{1}{2}$ feet in diameter and 20 feet long. The high potential electrode C is in the form of a metal cylinder instead of a sphere. To prevent breakdown at the ends of this cylinder, metal rings are mounted axially and parallel to each other as shown at D. Each of these is provided with a point facing a small plate on the next hoop to provide a small corona leak and to give a smooth potential gradient from C to the grounded tank. Ions may be accelerated down the highly evacuated tube E.

A number of installations exist, at the present time, in which the several possible combinations of size and pressure have been tried out.   The large units frequently operate either without a pressure tank or at low pressures, of say two or three atmospheres, while smaller units have been put into tanks with pressures of several atmospheres.   The corona breakdown may be pushed toward higher voltages by filling the tank with freon or some other gas with good dielectric properties.

An important advantage which electrostatic generators have over other types of accelerating devices is that they operate on a true d.c. high potential.   The voltage is constant and the beam is steady and more nearly "mono-energetic" than the pulsing cyclotron beams.

13–4.   Impulse Type.—In figure 13–9, the condensers C are charged in parallel through the high resistances RR.   When the potential across the condensers has risen to a sufficiently high

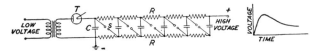

FIG. 13–9.   The Marx impulse generator.

value, the spark gaps (S) break down in succession, starting at the transformer end, connecting the condensers in series.   The voltage of the output is then the sum of the potential drops across the condensers, minus the losses in the spark gaps.   One impulse is generated each time the condensers discharge, usually once each cycle.   The rectifying tube (T) serves to make the impulses unidirectional.   The wave-form is shown at the right of the figure, where the peak is reached within, say, one-half micro-second[11] and the slow discharge lasts for as much as one hundred microseconds.   Obviously, the values given can be varied over a wide range by suitable choice of the circuit constants.   Peak voltages as high as 2 Mev have been produced.

13–5.   A. C. Type.—A single transformer capable of raising the voltage from, say 1,000 to 1,000,000 volts would require such excellent insulation between the primary and secondary as to become costly and inefficient.   On the other hand, a succession of transformers whose secondaries are connected in series (with the proper phasing) may be used.[12]   As shown in figure 13–10, the primary of a transformer is supplied from a comparatively low voltage (3 Kv.) secondary winding on the preceding transformer.

Each transformer must be insulated from ground for its respective potential. With four, 250 Kv. transformers, an r.m.s. voltage of 1 Mv has been obtained.

13–6. High - Frequency Type.

—The Tesla coil circuits[13] which generate high-voltage, high-frequency, damped oscillations are well known. It is also possible to generate *undamped*, high voltages at high frequencies

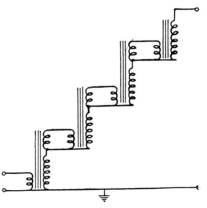

Fig. 13–10. Cascade transformers.

by means of vacuum tube oscillators and resonance transformers.[14] An x-ray machine of this type is shown in figure 13–11.

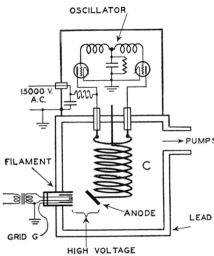

Fig. 13–11. A high-voltage high-frequency machine.

The oscillator is of the tuned plate-tuned grid type, has considerable power (100 Kw.) and is supplied with unrectified a.c. A single turn of copper tubing is used to couple to the quarter wave resonance coil (*C*). The coil is grounded at its upper end and is water cooled. A grid (*G*) is provided with a.c. so that electrons can leave the filament only when the lower end of the coil (*C*) is positive. In this way, 800,000-volt electrons have been produced. The machine may also be used for ion acceleration by the substitution of a horizontal tube for the anode and of a source of ions for the filament.

13–7. Betatrons and Synchrotrons.

—The betatron is an electron-accelerator which makes use of the fact that an electron

in a changing magnetic field experiences a force. A large magnet,
arranged similarly to a large cyclotron magnet but constructed of
laminated steel, is operated on a.c. In the early part of one
half cycle, while the current and hence the magnetic field are
increasing, a spurt of electrons is directed by an electron gun or
" injector " into the space between the poles of the magnet.
These electrons revolve in an orbit and experience an acceleration
as long as the field continues to change. The radius of the orbit
does not change appreciably, for, while the velocity of the elec-

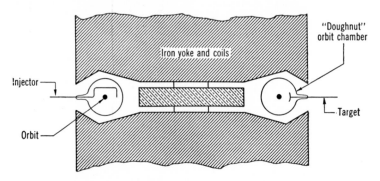

Fig. 13–11A.   Cross section of typical betatron.*

trons is increasing, the field is also increasing at a rate sufficient
to keep the radius constant. As the end of the quarter cycle is
approached, and before the time-rate of change of the current has
become zero, an auxiliary vacuum-tube circuit passes a sudden
heavy pulse of current through an auxiliary coil which acts as an
" orbit-expander " and causes the radius of the orbit to change
until the electrons strike a target. Thus the injector and expander
function once per cycle and the electrons are accelerated during
something less than a quarter of a cycle. The big magnet is
operated on a comparatively low frequency, 60 to 600 cycles
depending on the size of the installation. In order to correct the
power-factor difficulties introduced by the fact that the magnet
constitutes a large inductive load, a big bank of condensers is used.
In big installations these condensers constitute a large fraction of
the total cost and occupy a good deal of space. Electron energies

* After D. W. Kerst, Rev. Sci. Inst., 13, 388 (1942).

of 100 megavolts have been produced in existing units and larger installations are contemplated.

Finally, modifications employing various features of cyclotrons and betatrons have been proposed. Several such devices are at present having their design features studied preparatory to building. In particular a "synchrotron" promises possible particle energies of 300 megavolts in an instrument of reasonable size and such a unit may be under construction by the time this edition is printed.

ACCELERATOR TUBES

13–8. The Accelerator Tube.—The acceleration of ions by means of a high voltage generator involves the use of a special vacuum tube. First of all, the tube itself must be sufficiently

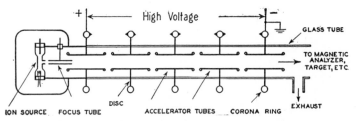

FIG. 13–12. Construction of an ion accelerator tube.

long that sparkover does not occur from one end to the other in the air outside. The source of ions and the target may be mounted on long supports very near to each other in the center of the highly evacuated tube, since exceedingly high voltages are needed to break down even a few millimeters of good vacuum (10^{-5} millimeter pressure or lower). High voltage x-ray tubes and rectifiers (see figure 13–6) are often built in this manner.

The salient features of the tubes used at very high voltages may be explained with the aid of figure 13–12. It is understood, of course, that this is but one of the many possible tube constructions. A single insulator tube (usually pyrex) is not only costly but will break down, even though very long. This is presumably due to the fact that the potential gradients are not only non-uniform along the tube but are different along the inner and outer surfaces. In order to obtain uniform and equal gradients, an ideal tube would consist of some (unknown) high-resistance material which would give a constant leakage current along the tube. In practice, a series of tubes are used, as in the figure. Now, ions which strike the walls will give it a charge of the same sign as that which they carry, or, in some cases, may cause sufficient secondary emission to set up a charge of opposite sign. Therefore, metal "accelerator" tubes with rounded ends are used. They are supported along the axis by means of an insulating rod. Lead wires or metal discs at their centers pass through the insulator walls and are fastened to corona rings or shields. It is one of the well-known principles of insulation practice that the electrical fields must be small wherever there is a joint between a dielectric and a conductor. (See chapter 19; Some Insulation Problems.)   In the structure of figure 13–12, the ions are speeded up, step by step, in the gaps between the accelerator tubes. Thus, the strong fields in the gaps are kept away from the weak regions.

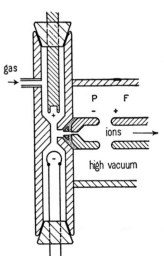

FIG. 13–13. An ion gun.

Points and planes are often used on the corona rings to give a small steady leakage and hence, a more uniform gradient in the air outside the tube. The insulator sections are sometimes corrugated instead of straight in order to increase the surface distance from one section to the next and, thereby, reduce leakage currents on the walls.

13–9. Ion Guns.—A large number of ions are to be withdrawn from their source and then focused into a parallel beam. One[15] of the many ion guns is shown in figure 13–13. The source consists of a low voltage, capillary arc, using electrons from the hot filament to bombard the gas atoms. Positive ions in the plasma in the capillary are withdrawn by the negatively charged "probe" (P) and are then focused by the electrostatic lens between P and the positively charged cylinder (F). In this manner positive ion currents of 1.5 milliamperes have been obtained. The intensity of the ion beam is controlled by the potential on P and the focus is varied by the potential on F.

A stream of lithium ions is directed from a furnace at 400 to 500° C. onto a large, flat tungsten filament heated to approximately 1100° C. Positive lithium ions are then emitted from the filament and are focused by means of electrostatic fields. One milliampere of positive ion current has been obtained by this method.

See also Electron Optics in chapter 6.

REFERENCES

1. Wideroe, Arch. f. Electrotech., 21, 387 (1929). D. H. Sloan and E. O. Lawrence, Phys. Rev., 38, 2021 (1931).
2. E. O. Lawrence and N. E. Edlefson, Science, 72, 376 (1930).
   E. O. Lawrence and D. Cooksey, Phys. Rev., 50, 1131 (1936).
   M. S. Livingston, Rev. Sci. Inst., 7, 55 (1936).
3. The Radio Amateur's Handbook. Power Supply Equipment.
4. J. B. Hoag and V. J. Andrew, Rev. Sci. Inst., 3, 750 (1932).
5. See J. M. Ledeboer, Physica, 13, 145 (1933).
6. J. D. Cockcroft and E. T. S. Walton. Proc. Roy. Soc. A136, 619 (1932).
7. S. K. Allison. Unpublished.
8. Van de Graaff, K. T. Compton and Van Atta, Phys. Rev., 43, 149 (1933).
   Van Atta, Northrup, Van Atta and Van de Graaff, Phys. Rev., 49, 761 (1936).
9. Tuve, Hafstad and Dahl, Phys. Rev., 48, 315 (1935).
10. Herb, Parkinson and Kerst, Phys. Rev., 51, 75 (1937).
11. Foust, Kuehnl and Rohats, Gen. Elec. Rev., 35, 358 (1932).
12. R. W. Sorensen, Jr., A. I. E. E., 44, 373 (1925).
    Lauritsen and Bennett, Phys. Rev., 32, 850 (1928).
13. Breit, Tuve and Dahl, Phys. Rev., 35, 51 (1930).
14. D. H. Sloan, Phys. Rev., 47, 62 (1935).
    Sloan, Thornton and Jenkins, Rev. Sci. Inst., 6, 75 (1935) (Tube Construction).
15. Tuve, Dahl and Hafstad, Phys. Rev., 48, 241 (1935).
16. M. E. Rose and H. A. Bethe, Phys. Rev., 53, 206A (1938).

GENERAL REFERENCES

A.—E. Pollard and W. L. Davidson, *Applied Nuclear Physics.* John Wiley & Sons (1942).

CHAPTER 14

ARTIFICIAL TRANSMUTATION

14–1. The First Artificial Transmutation.—The small metal box shown in the center of figure 14–1, contains a sample of radium C'. Alpha particles whose range is 6.9 centimeters (air equivalent) are spontaneously ejected from the radioactive source and pass through a small hole into the chamber A. They travel outward for a few centimeters but are all absorbed by the gas in the chamber long before reaching the thin foil window C. Yet, when certain gases are used, flashes of light can be seen on the zinc sulphide screen B. These scintillations are obviously produced by particles of unusually long range. With hydrogen in the chamber, the particles were found to have a range of 28 centimeters (air equivalent). It is reasonable to suppose that these particles

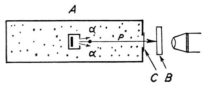

Fig. 14–1. The transmutation of nitrogen. Rutherford, 1919.

are protons (hydrogen nuclei) projected forward by the head-on, elastic collision of alpha particles with the gas atoms. This is shown to be true by deflecting the long range particles with a magnetic field (to get e/m) and by the application of the laws of conservation of momentum and energy for this type of collision. These high speed, long range protons are called "H particles."

H particles can also be observed with the apparatus of figure 14–1 when gases other than hydrogen are used in the chamber or when solids, in the form of thin foils over the hole in the source box, are under alpha particle bombardment. Rutherford took great care to eliminate all traces of hydrogen from a sample of nitrogen, yet still found long range protons. Of great significance was the fact that the range of some of these particles, when calculated from their absorption in the gas and the window, was 40 centi-

318

meters (air equivalent), which greatly exceeds the maximum value of 28 centimeters to be expected from the head-on elastic collision of an alpha particle with a hydrogen atom.

In 1919, Rutherford[1] proposed that the exceptionally long range protons had been driven out of the nuclei of the nitrogen atoms by occasional violent blows of the incident alpha particles. This, the first evidence for an atomic transformation accomplished by artificial means, has been amply verified by later work. We shall refer to these as alpha-proton (α-p) transmutations.

14–2. Early Alpha-Proton Transmutations.—Rutherford and Chadwick, as well as Kirsch and Pettersson, carried out extensive studies[2] of the disintegration of the lighter elements under alpha particle bombardment. Protons were the only particles observed leaving the various elements. Since the number of protons projected by elastic collision decreases very rapidly on either side of the direct path of the alpha particles, observations made at right angles and in the backward direction, as in figure 14–2, were comparatively free from these disturbing particles. Also, the disturbing influence of the alpha particles was eliminated. Attention could then be focussed on the disintegration protons, even though their range was less than 28 centimeters. As examples, alpha particles of 6.9 centimeters range ejected protons whose ranges (in centimeters) are as follows:

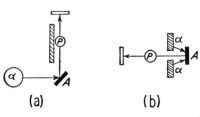

(a)   (b)

Fig. 14–2. Variations of the apparatus of figure 14–1.

	B	N	Fl	Na	Al	P
Forward	58	40	65	58	90	65
Backward	38	18	48	36	67	49

The range (energy) and also the number of protons was found to be less when they were ejected in a given direction from elements of even atomic number than from those of odd atomic number. It was concluded that the even numbered nuclei (of the lighter elements) are more stable than those of odd atomic number for this type of transmutation.

The *yield* or number of protons ejected by each alpha particle was found to be very small. It was estimated that from one to twenty out of each million incident alpha particles collided inelastically with nuclei to give rise to protons. In one year all of the alpha particles from one gram of radium could only cause the ejection of protons equivalent to approximately 3×10^{-4} cubic millimeters of hydrogen.

In several cases, the kinetic energy of the ejected protons was found to exceed that of the incident alpha particles. Now, protons with a 70 centimeter range have the same energy as the alpha particles from radium C' (see tables 4 and 8 in the back of this book). Thus, the 90 centimeter protons from the transmutation of aluminum were found to have an energy approximately seventeen per cent greater than that of the incident alpha particles; and the residual nucleus must also have been given kinetic energy. The excess energy must have been given up by the nuclei during the transmutation.

14-3. The Alpha Particle Is Captured by the Nucleus.—In 1925, Blackett[3] studied the passage of alpha particles through nitrogen gas used in an expansion chamber.* Stereoscopic photographs were taken of 415,000 alpha particle tracks. Among these there appeared a considerable number of forks due to elastic collisions, i.e., to the scattering of alpha particles by nitrogen nuclei. Of especial interest, however, were eight collisions of the type illustrated in figure 14-3. In some cases the track B was in the forward direction, as shown, while in others it was in a backward direction. It is to be noticed, that there are two, not three tracks, after the collision. Track B was long and thin, whereas track C was short and somewhat thicker than that of the alpha particle (A). The difference in appearance of the three tracks suggested that three different particles were involved; i.e., that the alpha particle disappeared or was *captured* when it collided with a nucleus. It was assumed that the capturing nucleus was nitrogen since that gas was used in the expansion

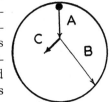

Fig. 14-3. Drop tracks of a nitrogen transmutation.

* A discussion of the expansion chamber will be found in section 18-15.

chamber and it was further assumed that the long thin track B was due to a proton, as in the H particle work described in the preceding sections.

14-4. Conservation of Momentum and Energy.—The three tracks (figure 14-3) were found to lie in the same plane. Thus, the momentum before the collision was equal to that after the transmutation. To test this, the angle θ between the proton track and the forward direction of the alpha track, and the corresponding angle ϕ for the residual nucleus were determined from the stereoscopic photographs. (ϕ is negative if θ is positive.) In the forward direction, we have

$$m_\alpha v_\alpha = m_r v_r \cos \phi + m_p v_p \cos \theta \qquad (14\text{-}1)$$

and in the normal direction

$$O = m_r v_r \sin \phi + m_p v_p \sin \theta, \qquad (14\text{-}2)$$

where m_α, m_r and m_p are the respective masses of the alpha particle, residual nucleus and proton while v_α, v_r and v_p are their velocities. The masses of the alpha particle and of the proton were known and the velocity of the alpha particle could be deduced from the distance which it had traveled from the source to the collision (see figure 12-9). With less certainty, the velocity of the proton was calculated from the range of track B. The momentum $m_r v_r$ of the residual nucleus was then calculated from equation 14-2 and found to satisfy equation 14-1. Thus, momentum was conserved during the transmutation.

Similarly the equations for the conservation of energy may be written

$$\tfrac{1}{2} m_\alpha v_\alpha{}^2 = \tfrac{1}{2} m_r v_r{}^2 + \tfrac{1}{2} m_p v_p{}^2 + Q_2 \qquad (14\text{-}2a)$$

where Q_2 is the energy evolved in the reaction, i.e., the potential energy within the nucleus which is transformed into kinetic during the process. As in chemical reactions, Q_2 may be negative, zero or positive. Negative Q_2 reactions are called endoergic, positive ones exoergic, and zero Q_2 values occur in the case of elastic scattering. The values observed for Q_2 range from several million electron volts (Mev) negative to a like amount positive for most reactions. The reaction in the case of nuclear fission has the highest Q_2 value now known, around 200 Mev.

14–5. The Reaction Scheme.—The identity of the particle causing track C (figure 14–3) was deduced from the law of conservation of electric charge. Thus, the nitrogen nucleus of charge 7 (= Z, the atomic number) added to the alpha particle of charge 2 gives a compound nucleus of charge 9 from which a proton of charge 1 is ejected to leave a residual nucleus of charge 8, i.e., an oxygen nucleus.

As a first approximation to the masses of the particles, mass numbers are used (= A, the nearest whole numbers to the weights of the isotopes). When these are used as superscripts, the reaction may be written as

$$_7\mathrm{N}^{14} + {}_2\mathrm{He}^4 \rightarrow {}_9\mathrm{F}^{18} \rightarrow {}_8\mathrm{O}^{17} + {}_1\mathrm{H}^1 \qquad (14\text{–}3)$$

Original nucleus + incident particle $\rightarrow$ compound nucleus $\rightarrow$ residual nucleus + ejected particle.

In general,

$$A + P \rightarrow C \rightarrow B + R + Q_2 \qquad (14\text{–}4)$$

where A and B are the original and residual nuclei, P and R the incident and ejected particles, respectively, and Q_2 the energy (or its mass-equivalent) liberated in the reaction. As we shall see later, R may be a photon, in which case the process is described as a *radiative capture*. If P is a photon and R is a material particle we have a *photoelectric effect*. If R and P are identical particles the process is one of *scattering* while if they differ, we have a *capture* transmutation.

From the range of the residual nucleus (track C, figure 14–3) a crude estimate was made of its velocity (v_r). Then, from its momentum ($m_r v_r$), as computed in the preceding section, its mass was calculated and found to be, approximately that of oxygen seventeen. This isotope (O^{17}) was not discovered until four years later. (See section 10–8.)

Conversely, when the residual nucleus was chosen as oxygen-seventeen, its velocity and its kinetic energy could be calculated with fair accuracy. It was then found that the total kinetic energy after the collision was less than that of the incident particle by approximately nineteen per cent. Using the same symbols as in equation 14–1,

$$E = (\tfrac{1}{2}m_r v_r^2 + \tfrac{1}{2}m_p v_p^2) - (\tfrac{1}{2}m_\alpha v_\alpha^2). \qquad (14\text{–}5)$$

The loss of energy (E) during the reaction amounted, in this case, to 19 per cent of $\frac{1}{2}m_\alpha v_\alpha^2$.

14–6. The Number and Energy of the Ejected Protons.—The number of protons which are able to pass through a thin sheet of absorbing material such as mica or aluminum can be determined with an ionization chamber and its associated electrometer or amplifier, as in chapter 18. The measurement is repeated as successive sheets of the absorber are inserted in the path of the particles and a curve plotted, as in figure 14–4a. Here, the total

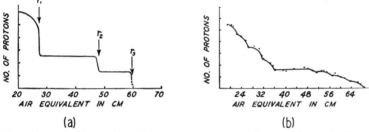

FIG. 14–4. An integral-distribution-in-range curve. Protons from aluminum bombarded by alpha particles.

thickness of the absorbing material has been converted into the equivalent thickness of air of standard density which will produce the same absorption. Also, from the range-energy relationship (table 8, at the end of this book), the abscissae may be expressed in ergs or in electron volts.

All of the protons have sufficient energy to penetrate a small thickness of the absorber. The number of protons penetrating the absorber remains constant as more and more absorbing material is introduced until a critical thickness of absorber is reached; then, the number of protons drops rapidly to a lower, constant value. Thus, there are a number of protons in the beam which are all stopped together, or nearly so. This means that there is a group of protons with a definite range (r_1). The remaining protons have greater energy and are able to penetrate a greater thickness of the absorber. Then, a second group, whose maximum range is r_2, is stopped, etc. A plot of the slope of the curve in figure 14–4a will show three peaks from which the mean ranges, R_1, R_2 and R_3 of the three proton groups can be determined as in figure 12–4. This differential-distribution-in-range curve will also show in what manner the energies of the protons in a given group are distributed about the average value.

If the integral-range curve has a continuous slope downward, rather than the step-like form of figure 14–4a, the protons have a wide range of velocities instead of a group structure.

In a number of transmutations, protons are emitted in groups, each with a definite energy.   For example, with the reaction

$$_{13}Al^{27} + _2He^4 \rightarrow _{15}P^{31} \rightarrow _{14}Si^{30} + _1H^1, \qquad (14\text{–}6)$$

Pose,[4] in 1929, obtained a curve like that in figure 14–4a.   Later, Chadwick and Constable[5] improved the experiment, obtained the curve of figure 14–4b, and thus showed that at least eight groups of protons ($_1H^1$) were emitted when a thick target of aluminum ($_{13}Al^{27}$) was bombarded with alpha particles ($_2He^4$).   The use of a thick target means that alpha particles of all energies from the maximum (5.3 Mev, for polonium) down to zero are in use, due to their retardation as they enter the aluminum.   Inasmuch as the protons did not leave the nuclei (at a given angle of emission) with a continuous distribution of energies similar to that of the incident particle, there must be certain favored energy groups of the incident particles which cause copious emission of protons; i.e., there is a *resonance phenomenon* between the protons and the alpha particles.   This is brought out clearly in figure 14–5.   This is called the *excitation curve* of the transmutation.   The yield is the number of protons per alpha particle and the peaks show the *resonance excitation* of the protons for alpha particles of definite energies.   The curve was obtained[6] with a thin aluminum target bombarded by mono-energetic alpha particles.   The various energy values of the alpha particles were obtained by slowing down fast alpha particles with thin foils or with a layer of gas of variable density.

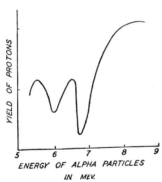

FIG. 14–5. Resonance phenomena.

As a matter of fact, alpha particles of suitable energy can cause the emission, not only of one group but of several groups of protons simultaneously. An example, when an aluminum target was used, is given in table 14–1 where it may be seen that pairs of proton groups are ejected by alpha particles of but one energy (± 0.3 Mev).

14–7. Resonance Penetration.—In studies of the scattering of alpha particles from aluminum foils (section 7–3) it has been shown that the Coulomb or inverse square law of repulsion breaks down when an alpha particle approaches to within approximately 10^{-12} centimeter of the center of the nucleus of the aluminum atom. Since alpha particles are occasionally captured by these nuclei, an attractive force must exist for the alpha particles inside the nucleus. The potential of the nucleus must, therefore, have the form shown

TABLE 14–1.

Alpha particles, resonance		Proton groups
Range (cm.)	Energy (Mev)	Range (cm.)
3.9	5.25	34 and 66
3.45	4.86	30.5 and 61
3.1	4.49	26.5 and 55
2.7	4.00	22 and 49

in figure 12–8. The top of the potential barrier, in the case of aluminum, has been estimated at approximately 8 Mev. But, in the preceding section, it has been seen that alpha particles of smaller energy can cause transmutations provided their energy lies within suitable narrow ranges. Thus, *resonance penetration* can occur through the potential barrier at favored energy levels below its summit. Resonance energies indicate virtual energy levels of the compound nucleus.

14–8. Excited States.—The emission of groups of protons, each with a definite energy, is analogous to the emission of a line spectrum of light rays, in contrast to the emission of a continuous spectrum, and suggests that energy levels exist inside the residual nucleus. With the emission of protons of maximum energy, the nucleus is left in its " ground " or lowest energy state. When protons of lesser energy are emitted, the nucleus is left in an *excited state*, with an energy (E_x) greater than the ground state. E_x is

called the *excitation energy*. The nucleus returns to its ground
state with the emission of gamma rays whose energy is

$$E_x = h\nu. \tag{14-7}$$

Studies made with counter tubes and absorbing screens have
shown that gamma rays are emitted in many alpha-proton disintegrations and that in certain cases, such as boron, the energies
of the gamma ray photons agree at least approximately with the
differences in energies between the ejected proton groups.

14-9. Calculation of Nuclear Masses.—The maximum reaction energy may be determined experimentally. Then, equation 14-10 may be used to compute one of the nuclear masses,
provided the others are known. For example, using mass units
from the mass spectrograph, or from other nuclear reactions, in the
equation

$$_{17}Cl^{35} + _2He^4 = _{18}A^{38} + _1H^1 + E_0 \tag{14-8}$$

we have

$$34.9811 + 4.0039 = A^{38} + 1.0081 + 0.000107. \tag{14-9}$$

It follows that[7] the isotopic weight of the argon thirty-eight isotope (A^{38}) is 37.9768 mass units. Compare with value in Table
15.

Also, for example, we have the reaction

$$D^2 + _1D^2 \rightarrow He^{4*} \rightarrow _2He^3 + n^1 + Q_2 \tag{14-10}$$

where the asterisk above He denotes that this is formed in an
excited state and will probably disintegrate. Again using masses
from the mass-spectrograph, $D = 2.01473$ and $He^3 = 3.01707$ and
Q_2 is 0.00342 mass units. We find for the mass of the neutron
1.00897. Hence, this reaction may be used to determine the mass
of the neutron, a quantity which cannot be obtained by the
deflection measurements because of its lack of charge.

14-10.   Discovery of Positrons ($_+e$).—In 1932, Anderson[14]
mounted an expansion chamber (see chapter 18) in a vertical
position between the pole pieces of a strong electromagnet, as in
figure 14-6a. The chamber C was illuminated by a strong light
source at x and photographs of drop tracks were taken with the aid
of a lens system, through a hole in the pole piece or from the side

when a mirror M was used.   A sheet of lead was placed in a horizontal plane inside the chamber. A large number of photographs were taken of the tracks due to cosmic rays coming down from above (chapter 15).   Among these, there appeared a few tracks, originating in the lead sheet, which were curved by the magnetic field in the direction to be expected of negatively charged particles and, simultaneously, tracks of identical appearance (thin and dotted) with an opposite curvature. Calculation from the measured curvature and the strength of the field showed that both kinds were

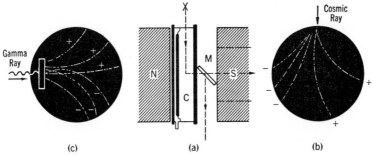

FIG. 14–6.   Experiments with an expansion chamber in a strong magnetic field.

due to particles of the same charge-to-mass ratio as that of electrons. The particles which curved in the opposite direction were, therefore, identified as positively charged electrons, now called positrons ($_+e$). Sometimes the negative electron ($-e$) is called a negatron and the term "electron" is used as a general word for both positrons and negatrons.

The discovery by Anderson of the positron was very shortly verified by Blackett and Occhialini.[15]   Two Geiger-Müller counter tubes (chapter 18) were mounted, one above and the other below the expansion chamber and connected in a coincidence circuit whose output operated a mechanism for expanding the chamber and taking photographs of drop tracks.   Thus, the chamber was operated only at a time when drop tracks were formed in it by the passage of a particle in a vertical direction through both counter tubes.   Many photographs of the type shown in figure 14–6b were obtained.   If the magnetic lines of force are, for example, directed into the paper, the tracks curved to the left are due to negative electrons and those to the right are due to positrons. Stereoscopic photographs show that the tracks originate within a small area above the apparatus.

Positrons can also be produced by the action of gamma rays,[16] as illustrated in figure 14–6c. Here a lead sheet is placed in an expansion chamber located in a strong magnetic field (perpendicular to the paper) and is bombarded with gamma rays. Nearly equal numbers of $_+e$ and $_-e$ tracks are observed.

Positrons can also be obtained from artificial radioactive substances, as discussed in a later section.

14–11. Pair Production and Annihilation.—The number of positrons and the number of negative electrons produced simultaneously by the bombardment of various substances with gamma rays has been found to be very nearly equal to each other (figure 14–6c). It is assumed that each gamma ray photon ($h\nu$) can materialize in the form of one *electron pair*.[30] The process has only been observed to take place in the electro-magnetic field of a nucleus, i.e., in the presence of matter. Since the self-energy of each electron is mc^2 (equation 2–27) (~ 0.5 Mev), the gamma ray must have an energy $2mc^2$ (~ 1 Mev) or more in order to form one pair. Any additional energy appears in the form of kinetic energy of the two electrons and the small recoil energy given to the nucleus. Thus, the kinetic energy KE is

$$KE = h\nu - 2mc^2, \qquad (14–11)$$

where h is Planck's constant, ν is the frequency of the incident gamma ray, m is the mass of an electron and c is the velocity of light. The number of pairs produced increases as the square of the atomic number. Hence, the use of lead in figure 14–6c.

Thibaud and Joliot have sent a known number of positrons toward heavy metal foils and counted the average number of photons ejected. They found two photons for each positron, emitted in opposite directions. It is assumed that a positron and an extra-nuclear electron are *annihilated* in the presence of the nuclear forces. Thus,

$$2mc^2 = 2h\nu. \qquad (14–12)$$

Each photon has been found to have the proper energy; i.e., 0.5 Mev, or a wave-length $\lambda = 0.024$ angstroms

14-12. Discovery of Neutrons (*n*).—In 1930, Bothe and Becker[8] bombarded lithium, beryllium and boron with alpha rays from polonium. By means of a point counter (*D*) as in figure 14-7*a*, they observed a radiation whose penetrating power, through an absorber *A*, was three times that of the hard gamma rays from radium *C*. They assumed that the radiation was of the gamma ray type because of its tremendous penetration. From the measured absorption coefficients of the rays and the Klein-Nishina formula (x-ray chapter), the wave-length λ was deduced. Then, from the relation that $V = 12336/\lambda$, each photon of the postulated gamma rays was found to have an energy of 15 Mev.

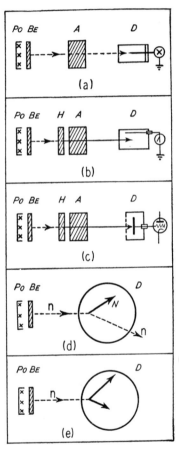

Fig. 14-7. Some experiments with neutrons.

The Joliots*[9] studied the new radiations with a deep ionization chamber (*D*) capable of detecting heavy charged particles, as in figure 14-7*b*. They found that the rays from beryllium, which could penetrate to great distances in heavy materials such as lead (at *H*), were readily absorbed by light materials such as paraffin; which contain many hydrogen atoms. In the latter case many long range protons were ejected. The range of the protons was found (with the absorber, *A*) to be 26 centimeters, corresponding to a velocity of 2.9 × 10⁹ centimeters per second or an energy of 4.3 Mev. Assuming that the particle was a recoil proton set in motion by the reversal of the incident radiation in a Compton collision, they found

* Dr. F. Joliot and his wife, Dr. Irene Curie Joliet, daughter of Madame Curie.

the energy of the unknown radiation to be 50 Mev. This does not agree with the value of 15 Mev obtained by Bothe and Becker, nor with that of the alpha particle (5.3 Mev), nor with the reaction energy to be expected when an alpha particle is captured by a beryllium nucleus.

In 1932, Chadwick[10] suggested that the radiations were uncharged particles of mass comparable with that of protons. These are called neutrons ($_0n^1$). He proposed the following reaction:

$$_4Be^9 + _2He^4 = _6C^{12} + _0n^1 + E_0 \qquad (14\text{--}13)$$

The absorption of neutrons in a hydrogen-rich material, H in figure 14–7c, was assumed to occur with the expulsion of recoil protons which were detected with a shallow ionization chamber (D) after having passed through an absorbing material, at A. The range, and hence the energy of protons was measured. Similarly, the range and energy of recoil nitrogen nuclei were measured. This gives two equations in which the mass and velocity of the neutrons occur. The evaluation of these equations lead to a neutron mass of 1.15 (now 1.009) mass units. In addition, the assumption of a particle of unit mass ruled out the 50 Mev value. Thus, he identified the " radiations " as particles of approximately the same mass as that of protons.

The tremendous penetrating power of these particles in heavy elements and their inability to ionize a gas led Chadwick to believe that they were uncharged (neutrons). Without any electrical field of their own, neutrons do not interact with the electrical fields of atoms through which they are passing and hence do not eject electrons. A nuclear impact is required to stop a neutron. It has been estimated that one collision with a nucleus may be expected in every three or four hundred yards of air and that several miles would be required to stop all the neutrons in a group. This is to be compared with a distance of one foot needed to stop the protons in a group of the same velocity (3×10^9 cm./sec.).

The work of Chadwick was confirmed by Feather,[11] in 1933, with an expansion chamber, as in figure 14–7d. The neutrons ejected from beryllium (Be), were used to bombard nitrogen atoms in the chamber D. Neutron tracks were not seen (hence the dotted line) but nitrogen recoil tracks (N) were observed Their range was found to be 3.3 millimeters of standard air, equivalent to 4.4×10^8 centimeters per second and an energy of 1.4 Mev. The angle of recoil was measured on the steroscopic photographs and the laws of conservation of energy and momentum applied to this elastic collision (no loss of kinetic energy). The energies of the neutrons were computed and a check of the previous work resulted.

In other work[12] with expansion chambers two tracks have been observed, starting from the same point; the neutron can cause a transmutation. (See figure 14-7c.) Many cases have been observed, as discussed later.

Note that the experiments shown in figure 14–7 all measure the number of neutrons removed from the incident beam by the interposed substance. The neutrons may be absorbed by the substance or they may be scattered out sideways at an angle to the beam. The arrangement shown measures scattering plus absorption. To measure either scattering or absorption by itself, a different geometrical arrangement of source, absorber and detector is necessary. For example, scattering can be studied by placing the detector at an angle to the direction of the beam and arranging shields to prevent any neutrons, except those coming from a particular direction, from reaching the detector. Similarly, pure absorption may be studied by having the source at the center of a sphere of the absorbing substance, since then as many neutrons will be scattered in one direction as in another.

14–13. Scattering of Fast Neutrons.—In figure 14–8, x represents a small tube containing a mixture of radon and powdered beryllium. The neutrons from this source have a wide distribution

Fig. 14–8. A study of fast neutrons.

of energies. A lead block (Pb) about 3 centimeters thick is used to cut off gamma rays. A shallow ionization chamber (D), lined with lithium, is used to detect those neutrons which pass through a substance A. The neutrons may be scattered to the side or they may be captured in A. Measurements were made[13] of the number of neutrons reaching D as the length of A was increased. Then (as in section 7–1) calculations were made of the effective cross-section (σ) of the nuclei of A for neutrons. The cross-section of the neutron itself is included in the values obtained.

Figure 14–9 was made by using various elements at A and shows a regular increase of σ with atomic weight.

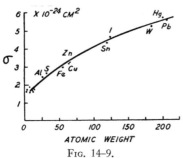

FIG. 14–9.

Nuclei-neutron cross-sections.

Of the neutrons which failed to reach the chamber D (figure 14–8), a majority (90%) were elastically scattered and the remainder were absorbed or captured in A. This was proved by using toroids of material, mounted axially with the dotted line, instead of solid cylinders as shown. Then, neutrons which were captured did not reach D. However, some of the neutrons which left the source at an angle with the axis were scattered by the toroids back into D.

14–14. The Discovery of Artificial Radioactivity.—In 1933, the Joliots[17] studied alpha-induced transmutations by means of a counter tube whose window consisted of a moderately thin foil of aluminum. They found that the counting rate gradually increased from the moment when the alpha source was first brought up and became essentially constant after fifteen minutes. The shape of the curve (figure 14–10) was the same as the formation curve of natural radioactive substances. Furthermore, when the alpha particle source was removed, the tube continued to give counts, the number decreasing as shown on the right of the vertical dotted line in the figure. By means of an expansion chamber, they found that the activity was due to the aluminum window, which gave out positrons. The positrons had an energy distribution similar to that of disintegration electrons from natural radioactive substances (figure 12–14) with an upper limit of 3 Mev and a most probable energy of 1 Mev. Their number was approximately 10^{-6} times the number of alpha particles; i.e., yield $= 10^{-6}$.

That the decrease in number of positrons emitted per unit time, after removal of the alpha particle source, follows an exponential law (equation 11–8) may be tested by plotting logarithms of the number of positrons vertically and time horizontally. If the exponential form is the correct one, a straight line will be obtained, whose (downward) slope is equal to the disintegration constant λ.

By means of equation 11-12, λ may be converted into the half-life T or time for one-half of the positron emitting nuclei to disintegrate. T was found to be three minutes and fifteen seconds when the target was aluminum.

When the energy of the incident alpha particles was decreased, the number of positrons emitted each second also decreased but the half-period remained unchanged. Here (as with spontaneous disintegrations) the half-period is a characteristic of the emitter.

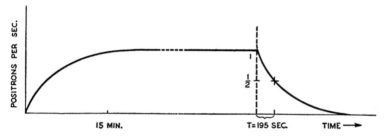

Fig. 14-10. Positrons emitted when aluminum is bombarded with alpha particles.

The positron emitter was identified by chemical means,[18] despite the exceedingly small number of atoms available. To do this, stable elements near aluminum were added to an active sample. Then, upon chemical separation, a comparatively small number of atoms of the positron emitter and a large number of atoms of a stable isotope of this element were precipitated together. The positrons, in this case, were found to be emitted by the phosphorus deposit and not by other precipitates. The reaction may, therefore, be written as

$$_{13}Al^{27} + {}_2He^4 \rightarrow {}_{15}P^{30*} + {}_0n^1 : {}_{15}P^{30*} \rightarrow {}_{14}Si^{30} + {}_{+1}e. \quad (14\text{-}14)$$

The asterisk is used to denote a radioactive substance, in this case " radiophosphorus."

Many radioactive substances have been artificially produced by irradiation of the elements with energetic alpha particles, deuterons, protons and neutrons. In some cases the ejected particle is a positron and in others it is a negative electron. Examples will be given later in this chapter. For collected results see reference 19.

Negative electrons are emitted when the mass number* of the radioactive isotope is greater than that of the heaviest (usually) stable isotope of the element. Positive electrons are emitted when the mass number of the radioactive isotope is less than that of the lightest (usually) stable isotope of the element. For example, in the case of carbon ($_2C^4$) the isotopes are: $_6C^{10}$, β^+ $T = 8.8$ sec.; $_6C^{11}$, β^+, $T = 20.5$ min.; $_6C^{12}$, stable, 98.9%; $_6C^{13}$, stable, 1.1%; $_6C^{14}$, β^-, $T > 10^3$ yr.

Note that the negative electron emitters lie along the upper side of the neutron-positron (N-Z) plot (see figure 10–11); the positron emitters lie below the stable isotopes on this chart. In general, the changes which occur due to the absorption or emission of various particles from the nucleus during nuclear transmutations are indicated on the neutron-proton chart as in Fig. 14–11.†

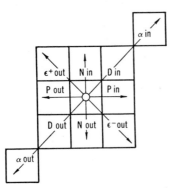

Gamma rays are frequently emitted during artificial radioactive disintegrations. They decrease in intensity at the same rate as that of the accompanying electron emission and, consequently, are not confused with the gamma rays emitted during the primary nuclear transmutation. It is assumed that when a radioactive isotope disintegrates with the emission of an electron, the final nucleus can be left in an excited state from which it shifts into the ground state with the emission of gamma rays.

FIG. 14–11. Absorption and emission of particles as indicated on the neutron-proton chart (see figure 10–11).

A given radioactive isotope has a characteristic half-life and emits either positive or negative electrons with a characteristic energy distribution. Hence, a study of the electron emission which follows a nuclear reaction serves as a valuable *indicator* in the identification of the residual nucleus. Many reactions have been discovered by detecting the subsequent electron activity.

* Mass number is the nearest whole number to the isotopic weight. Isotopic weight is the weight in comparison with O^{10} as 16.0000.

† See *Isotope chart*, Radiation Laboratory, Department of Physics, University of California.

Furthermore, the saturation activity (horizontal line in figure 14–10) is a measure of the number of residual nuclei produced

14–15. The Transmutation of Lithium by Protons.—In 1932, Cockroft and Walton[20] succeeded for the first time in accomplishing a transmutation by the use of particles which had been accelerated to a high velocity. It had just been shown by wave-mechanics, that charged particles can enter a nucleus, not only when they have energies equal to or greater than that at the top of the

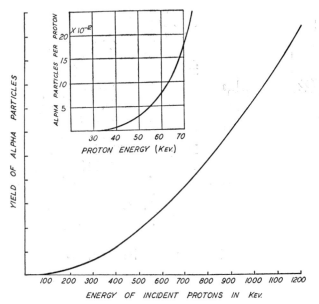

FIG. 14–12. Yield of alpha particles from lithium under proton bombardment.

potential barrier (figure 12–8), but also through the potential wall. In other words, a particle with energy less than that at the top of the barrier has a finite (though small*) possibility of entering the nucleus; the probability increasing as the energy approaches that at the top. Protons accelerated to 300,000 electron volts by a high-voltage machine (as described in the preceding chapter) were allowed to fall upon a lithium target. Alpha particles were observed by means of a scintillation screen to leave the lithium. The yield of alpha particles from a thick film of lithium (Li^7) is shown

* We are not considering resonance penetration at this time.

in figure 14–12.   Transmutations of this type have been observed when the incident protons had energies as low as 13 Kev.

A series of experiments were carried out by several workers[21] to determine the exact reaction which took place.   There are two isotopes of lithium, namely, lithium-six ($_3Li^6$) and lithium-seven ($_3Li^7$), the latter predominating.   They may be separated in small quantities by passing a beam of lithium ions through a velocity selector and collecting them in thin layers on metal plates.   Also, the hydrogen gas used in the discharge tube to produce the protons ($_1H^1$) contained a trace of the heavy isotope (deuterium) which would give a contamination of deuterons ($_1H^2$).   Other experiments have shown that even a few deuterons are very effective in producing transmutations.   A magnetic field has been used to exclude the deuterons, as in figure 14–13.   Here HV is the high voltage tube, and M is the area (shaded) over which the magnetic lines of force exist.   They are perpendicular to the paths of the particles. I is an ionization or expansion chamber. It was then possible to study the isolated reaction

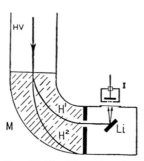

Fig. 14–13. Magnetic selection of accelerated particles.

$$_3Li^7 + _1H^1 = _2He^4 + _2He^4 + E. \qquad (14\text{–}15)$$

The kinetic energy (E_P) of the protons was measured in terms of the accelerating voltage, and the sum (E_T) of the energies of the two alpha particles was calculated from the range (8.3 centimeters, air equivalent) of their drop tracks in an expansion chamber or as measured from integral-range curves.   The difference between the energies, i.e., the reaction energy (E), was found to be 17.1 Mev (= 0.0183 mass units) = 0.0272×10^{-3} erg.   Using the masses of the isotopes given in table 15, it is seen that equation 14–16 balances.   Thus,

$$7.0180 + 1.0081 = 2 \times 4.0039 + 0.0183$$

$$= 8.0261 \text{ mass units} \qquad (14\text{–}16)$$

The masses of the isotopes, as listed in table 15, were obtained by calculation from many nuclear reactions and mass spectrograph measurements.

From the integral-range curves, two helium particles of ranges 0.82 and 1.15 centimeters have also been observed. These are from the reaction

$$_3Li^6 + {}_1H^1 \rightarrow {}_2He^4 + {}_2He^3. \tag{14–17}$$

14–16.   Effective-Cross-Section (σ).—The yield (Y), see figure 14–12, may be converted into the effective-cross-section (σ) for a given transmutation in the following manner. Let ΔN out of N incident particles accomplish transmutations, with the ejection of one particle each, from a target containing n atoms per cubic centimeter. Then

$$Y = \frac{\Delta N}{N} = n\,\sigma\,\Delta x. \tag{14–18}$$

where Δx is the thickness of the target material. This equation may be used directly to calculate σ provided the target is sufficiently *thin*; i.e., the particles suffer only a negligible percentage energy loss in it.

Most experiments are carried out with *thick targets*. The procedure to allow for the energy losses of the incident particles is as follows:[36]

$$\frac{\Delta Y}{\Delta E} = n\sigma\,\frac{\Delta x}{\Delta E} = n\sigma \Big/ \frac{\Delta E}{\Delta x}, \tag{14–19}$$

where ΔE is an increment in the energy of the incident particles corresponding to an increment ΔY in the yield. $\Delta Y/\Delta E$ is the slope of the excitation or yield curve (figure 14–12). The loss of energy per centimeter, $\Delta E/\Delta x$, may be obtained from the range reduction (ΔR) of the particles in a given thickness of material Δx and the relationship between the range R and the energy E (see reference 37, or the Geiger law, equation 12–4, for alpha particles; the tables of Mano,[22] or those in the back of this book). The range-energy law is not always known with accuracy, so that thin targets should be used whenever possible in this type of work.

The effective-cross-section is proportional to the yield and is also a measure of the probability of transmutation.

A numerical value for an effective-cross-section applies to a particular transmutation alone, i.e., to a given target, a certain incident particle of definite energy, and a known ejected particle. If several reactions are possible, with a given target and incident particle, there will be a corresponding set of σ's. If the energy of the incident particle is varied, σ will also vary; the curves of σ *vs.* E have the same shape as the excitation curves, for thin targets. In a resonance region, Y, σ and the probability of the transmutation are comparatively large.

Theoretical equations have been developed for σ. The σ *vs.* E theoretical relationship for charged particles is known as the Gamow function. Experimental and theoretical values are in good agreement. Values of σ range from zero to 10^{-24} cm.^{2} in the usual cases. In certain slow-neutron reactions, values of σ as great as 10^{-20} cm^2. have been observed. For the case of lithium-six bombarded by protons (see equation 14–17), σ increases exponentially from 2.2×10^{-26} to 8.2×10^{-26} cm.^{2} as the accelerating voltage is raised from 200 kv. to 400 kv.

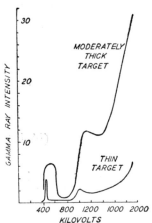

14–17.   Simple Capture and Other Proton Reactions.—Gamma rays have been observed when a thin target of lithium was bombarded with protons. It has been shown[23] that the number of gamma rays varies with proton energy, as shown in figure 14–14. The first sharp peak occurs at 440 Kev ($\pm$ 11Kev). The reaction is

$$_3\mathrm{Li}^7 + {}_1\mathrm{H}^1 \rightarrow {}_4\mathrm{Be}^{8*} \rightarrow$$
$$_4\mathrm{Be}^8 + \gamma. \qquad (14\text{–}20)$$

Fig. 14–14.   Yield from a simple capture process.

There are, of course, other cases of the simple capture of protons.   The reaction

$$_6\mathrm{C}^{12} + {}_1\mathrm{H}^1 \rightarrow {}_7\mathrm{N}^{13*} \rightarrow {}_7\mathrm{N}^{13} + \gamma : {}_7\mathrm{N}^{13*} \rightarrow {}_6\mathrm{C}^{13} + {}_{+1}\mathrm{e} \qquad (14\text{–}21)$$

has been well established[24] by observation of the gamma rays and the production of the active nitrogen. Two resonances are noted; for protons of energies 0.40 and 0.48 Mev. In general, this type of transmutation has a low probability as compared with those in which a particle is ejected. In all cases, the phenomenon of resonance is prominent.

There are four principal reactions induced by protons in the presently explored energy range. These are: proton in alpha out, five known cases; proton in deuteron out, one known case; proton in gamma out, ten cases; and, the most common, proton in neutron out, of which twenty-two cases have so far been reported in the literature. It seems certain that as proton energies are increased in the newer accelerating devices, more reactions of the above types and possibly still others will be discovered.

14–18. Transmutations Produced by Deuterons.—With a strong magnetic field in the apparatus of figure 14–13, the heavy-hydrogen nuclei (called deuterons, $_1H^2$) may be deflected onto the lithium target. The cyclotron (section 13–2) has also been used[27] to accelerate deuterons to high velocities for these studies. Two reactions were observed when lithium-six ($_3Li^6$) was bombarded by $_1H^2$; in one case, two alpha particles were ejected and in the other, a proton was ejected leaving a lithium-seven residual nucleus. Three reactions were obtained when lithium-seven ($_3Li^7$) was bombarded by deuterons; (1) two alpha particles and a neutron were found, (2) a neutron was ejected leaving beryllium-eight and (3) a proton was ejected leaving radio-active lithium-eight which became beryllium-eight after the emission of a negative electron.

Thus, a variety of reactions are possible when a given target is bombarded by particles of one kind. As illustrated by the case of magnesium bombarded by deuterons, the probability of neutron emission is greatest, that of proton emission is next and that of alpha emission is least. The neutron emission may be 100,000 times as probable as the other two.

Many transmutations have been produced with targets of the heavy as well as of the light elements. The residual nuclei are stable in certain cases and radio-active in others. A positron ($_+e$) is emitted in the reaction

$$_6C^{12} + _1H^2 \rightarrow _7N^{13}* + _0n^1 : _7N^{13}* \rightarrow _6C^{13} + _+1e \quad (14\text{–}22)$$

whereas the bombardment of sodium with deuterons gives

$$_{11}Na^{23} + _1H^2 \rightarrow _{11}Na^{24}* + _1H^1 :$$
$$_{11}Na^{24}* \rightarrow _{12}Mg^{24} + _{-1}e + \gamma. \quad (14\text{–}23)$$

The negative electrons ($_-e$) have a maximum of energy of 3 Mev and the gamma rays (γ) have an energy of at least 3 Mev (penetrating). The half-life of the radio-sodium ($Na^{24}*$) is approximately fifteen hours. One microampere of deuteron current at 1.75 Mev can give thirty million transmutations into radio-sodium each second. This material may be used in medical applications instead of natural radio-active substances.

The excitation energies of a residual nucleus are characteristic of that nucleus and not of the process by which it was formed. For example, the carbon nucleus $_6C^{12}$ in the transmutation

$$_7N^{14} + {}_1H^2 \rightarrow {}_6C^{12} + {}_2He^4 \tag{14--24}$$

has an excitation energy $E_x = E_1 - E_0 = 13.2 - 8.9 = 4.3$ Mev. In the reaction

$$_4Be^9 + {}_2He^4 \rightarrow {}_6C^{12} + {}_0n^1 + \gamma, \tag{14--25}$$

$_6C^{12}$ emits gamma rays whose three components have energies of 2.7, 4.2 and 6.7 Mev. The value 4.2 is in good agreement with 4.3 deduced from the preceding reaction.

Furthermore, the half-life of a radio-active substance is the same, regardless of the method of production. For example, $T = 10.5$ minutes for $_7N^{13}*$ when produced by deuteron bombardment of carbon-twelve or by alpha particles upon boron-ten.

Neutrons may be produced conveniently by bombarding light elements with deuterons. For example, if energetic (17 Mev) neutrons with a wide distribution of velocities are desired,

$$_3Li^7 + {}_1H^2 \rightarrow 2{}_2He^4 + {}_0n^1. \tag{14--26}$$

Sharper groups of lesser energy (4.5 Mev) may be obtained from

$$_4Be^9 + {}_1H^2 \rightarrow {}_5B^{10} + {}_0n^1. \tag{14--27}$$

A more homogeneous group, but of lesser energy ($\sim$1.8 Mev) may be had from

$$_1H^2 + {}_1H^2 \rightarrow {}_2He^3 + {}_0n^1. \tag{14--28}$$

For comparison with the above, the radon-beryllium source gives neutrons with a broad energy distribution up to 12 or 14 Mev. A very homogeneous group of neutrons may be had by bombarding beryllium with gamma rays. In this case, the energy depends on that of the incident photons ($h\nu$).

In order to explain the disintegration of heavier elements by means of deuterons, Oppenheimer and Phillips[28] assumed that at the collision the deuteron split apart, into a proton and a neutron, the latter entering the nucleus. This is called a *partial capture*.

There is some question as to whether the *emission* of deuterons is possible, because their binding energy is so small that they split into neutrons and protons very easily.

Again it will be noted that not all possible permutations and combinations of reactions, i.e., not all combinations of particles entering and leaving the nucleus, are observed to occur. Among the deuteron-induced reactions, the most usual ones are: deuteron in alpha out, 23 reported cases; deuteron in proton out, the most probable reaction with over 50 known cases; and deuteron in neutron out, with some 26 known cases. Less probable reactions at lower energies include deuteron in proton plus alpha out, one illustration; and deuteron in neutron plus alpha out, 2 reported cases. It appears probable that more of the latter reactions will be discovered when higher bombarding energies are available. It may also be added that reaction 14–28 can go two ways, yielding either He^3 plus a neutron, as shown, or H^3 plus a protron.

14–19. Photo-disintegration.—Gamma rays can cause artificial transmutations of elements, with the emission of particles. This is a nuclear photoelectric phenomenon. For example,

$$_1H^2 + \gamma \rightarrow _1H^1 + _0n^1 \qquad (14\text{–}29)$$

$$_4Be^9 + \gamma \rightarrow _4Be^8 + _0n^1. \qquad (14\text{–}30)$$

Very energetic gamma rays* are needed to disintegrate heavy elements. The 17 Mev gamma rays from proton bombarded lithium were found[29] to be very effective in ejecting neutrons from various elements. The cross-sections observed were of the order of 10^{-27} cm.².

Photon-induced disintegrations yielding protons have been noted in cosmic-ray studies, and have also been found in the laboratory when the high-energy photons produced by the betatron were studied. Photo-neutron and photo-proton production, or nuclear photo-effect, becomes more probable at photon energies in excess of 20 Mev. Indeed it has been recently reported that

* The 17 Mev gamma rays are much more energetic than those from natural radio-active substances (up to 2.62 Mev).

the entire oxygen nucleus has been " shattered " and the constituent eight protons and eight neutrons were emitted.

14–20. Multiple Reactions.—The alpha particles ejected from boron, bombarded by protons, are found to have an unusual energy distribution. There is (1) a mono-energetic group of approximately 5 Mev. (2) a moderately homogeneous group near 3.85 Mev and (3) a continuous distribution extending from 5 Mev down to very low energies. The 5 Mev *group* is composed of the alpha particles from

$$_5B^{11} + {}_1H^1 \rightarrow {}_4Be^8 + {}_2He^4, \qquad (14\text{–}31)$$

where the residual nucleus ($_4Be^8$) is left in its ground state, with a mass equal to that of two alpha particles. The yield is 13.5 alphas per 10^{11} protons at 200 Kv. and 128 at 400 Kv.

Other of the boron-eleven nuclei in the target undergo a multiple reaction,[25] as follows:

$$_5B^{11} + {}_1H^1 \rightarrow {}_6C^{12x} \rightarrow {}_4Be^{8*} + {}_2He^4 \rightarrow 3\ {}_2He^4, \quad (14\text{–}32)$$

in which the asterisk (*) has been used to indicate that the nucleus is in an excited state. The first helium nuclei appearing in this *three-particle* reaction form the group whose energies are near 3.85 Mev.

The Be^{8*} nucleus was left with an excited energy of 2.8 Mev which is greater than the *dissociation energy* required for a separation into two alpha particles. Therefore, after approximately 10^{-21} second, this nucleus breaks up; the alpha particles having the continuous energy distribution of (3) above.

Other multiple reactions are known.[26] In general, these may be written in the form

$$A + P \rightarrow C^* \rightarrow B^* + R \rightarrow D + S + R, \qquad (14\text{–}33)$$

where the notation of equation 14–4 has been used and D is the final nucleus. One or both of the ejected particles, S or R, may be the same as the incident particle P.

14–21. Transmutations by Fast Neutrons.*—We shall consider *fast* neutrons as those whose energy exceeds 0.1 Mev. These

---

* The comparatively large amount of hydrogen in the human body readily absorbs neutrons. The resulting recoil atoms produce ionization in the body whose biological effects are similar to those due to gamma rays. In order to reduce the intensity of fast neutrons by approximately fifty per cent, interpose a slab of paraffin six centimeters thick. The experimenter may protect himself from *intense* neutron sources by interposing barrels full of water between himself and the source.

neutrons have been used to produce a large number of different transmutations. For examples, see reference 19.

In 1934, Fermi[31] discovered the radio-activity of the residual nuclei produced in a large number of elements bombarded by neutrons. This has proven of great value, since the saturation activity (horizontal line of figure 14–10) is a measure of the number of residual nuclei produced each second and, hence, of the yields and cross-sections of neutron induced transmutations. The capture-cross-sections range from 10^{-26} to 10^{-24} cm.^{2} Furthermore, since the active nuclei continue to radiate positrons or negative electrons for appreciable lengths of time, it is possible to carry out extended chemical tests and obtain direct proof of the nature of the residual nuclei. Thus, it has been found that, if Z is the atomic number of the initial nucleus, then that of the residual nucleus is either (1) $Z - 2$, (2) $Z - 1$ or (3) Z.

(1) Alpha particles can be produced by fast neutrons in heavy and in light elements and also, by slow neutrons in certain of the light elements. For example, the reaction

$$_7N^{14} + _0n^1 = _5B^{11} + _2He^4 + E \qquad (14\text{–}34)$$

can only be produced by fast neutrons. The reaction is endothermic; i.e., $E = -0.3$ Mev. The equation, read backwards, gives the reaction for the production of neutrons by the bombardment of boron with alpha particles.

(2) Protons are emitted in those cases where Z decreases by one unit. These reactions are usually endo-thermic and can only be produced by fast neutrons (with one known exception, namely, with nitrogen). In the following example,

$$_8O^{16} + _0n^1 = _7N^{16*} + _1H^1 + E, \qquad (14\text{–}35)$$

very fast neutrons, above 12 Mev, are required.

(3) When Z does not change, we have (a) inelastic scattering, (b) simple capture or, (c) emission of two neutrons. In the first case, a neutron enters the nucleus and a neutron leaves. The nucleus is sometimes left in an excited state with subsequent emission of gamma rays. This process is very probable for light and medium-weight nuclei. In case (c), Heyn* has explained several

* Heyn, Physica, 4, 160 (1937).

reactions produced by fast neutrons as due to the emission of two neutrons.   The residual nucleus is usually positron active and is isotopic with the original nucleus, although reduced by one unit in mass.   The half-lives of the radio-active substances are the same as when produced in gamma-neutron reactions, in all cases where it has been possible to make a comparison.   Many cases of n-2n reactions have been observed by Pool, Cork and Thornton.[19]

14–22.   Slow Neutrons.—We shall consider *slow* neutrons as those whose energy ranges from zero up to a few thousand volts. Those whose energy is approximately 0.028 electron volts are known as *thermal neutrons*.

In 1934, Fermi[32] found that the saturation activity produced in a number of substances such as silver, cadmium, rhodium, etc., was greatly increased when the neutron source (radon + beryllium) was surrounded by several centimeters of a substance which was rich in hydrogen, such as paraffin or water.   He assumed that the neutrons were slowed down in the hydrogen-rich material and, hence, were easily captured.   We shall return to the proof of this a little later.

Slow neutrons can cause transmutations in which alpha particles are emitted.   Thus,

$$_3Li^6 + _0n^1 \rightarrow _2He^4 + _1H^3 \tag{14–36}$$

$$_5B^{10} + _0n^1 \rightarrow _3Li^7 + _2He^4. \tag{14–37}$$

For thermal neutrons, the cross-sections are very large, 900×10^{-24} and 3000×10^{-24} cm.^{2}, respectively, and hence, the reactions are very probable.   The heavy particles (He^4 and H^3) which are ejected are excellent ionizers of a gas.   Hence, lithium or boron (about 1 mm thick) is used as a lining in shallow chambers or electroscopes for the detection of neutrons.

Protons are emitted when slow neutrons bombard nitrogen. Thus,

$$_7N^{14} + _0n^1 \rightarrow _6C^{14} + _1H^1. \tag{14–38}$$

The simple capture of slow neutrons has also been observed. For example,

$$_1H^1 + _0n^1 \rightarrow _1H^2 + \gamma. \tag{14–39}$$

The energy of the gamma ray photon is equal to the binding energy of the deuteron ($_1H^2$), the energy of the slow neutron being negligibly small. The capture-cross-sections in this and other similar cases are very large.

The velocity of the slow neutrons which are strongly absorbed in cadmium has been measured directly with a velocity selector.[13]
As illustrated in figure 14–15, a Rn-Be source of neutrons is located at x in a large cylinder of paraffin. This is surrounded by a cadmium can which prevents the type of neutrons under test from traveling outward to the walls of the room from which they could be

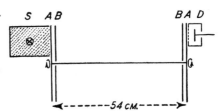

FIG. 14–15. Direct measurement of the velocity of slow neutrons.

scattered back to the detector D. However, the front of the source is open, so that slow neutrons can pass through two rotating discs AA and two fixed discs BB into the boron-lined ionization chamber D. Each of the duraluminum discs has on its surface 50 sectors of sheet cadmium. Each sector covers 3.7° and each gap between sectors covers 3.5°. Each pair of discs (AB) serves as a shutter for neutrons absorbable in cadmium. If n is the number of revolutions per second of the discs A, then $50n$ spurts of neutrons leave the first pair of discs each second. If they travel to the next pair, a distance d, with a velocity v such that an opening is present between the cadmium sectors, they will continue into the detector D. On the other hand, they will not enter D if

$$v = 100nd. \qquad (14\text{–}40)$$

For a thermal velocity of 2.2×10^5 cm./sec., and a distance $d = 54$ centimeters, the discs must rotate at 2500 r.p.m. The number of neutrons entering D was observed as n was varied from 0 to 83 r.p.s. and was found to follow the Maxwellian distribution law. The maximum number of neutrons in this thermal "C" (cadmium) group was found to be at the velocity given above ($\equiv 0.028$ electron volts). Furthermore, the maximum number was found to shift to lower velocities when the paraffin around the source S was cooled down.

In the experiment just described there was always a background of neutrons entering D whose number was not altered by the speed of the discs. These neutrons are, therefore, not absorbed to any appreciable extent in cadmium. Their velocities can be shown to lie in a range from about one to one thousand volts.

A modification of the velocity selector system has been developed consisting of an electronic circuit which modulates the beam of a cyclotron by an oscillator and produces spurts of neutrons when, for instance, a beam of deuterons falls on a heavy ice target. The sensitivity of the detector is similarly modulated by

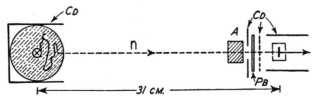

FIG. 14–16.   The absorption of slow neutrons.

applying to it pulses controlled by the same master oscillator which modulates the beam. The detector is suddenly rendered sensitive by a second pulse following the original pulse by a known and controllable time interval. Velocity selection can thus be achieved, for the neutrons requiring a certain time of flight from source to detector can be isolated and studied. Absorbers can be put into the neutron beam, and the absorption as a function of velocity determined. A group of cross sections has already been published, and a systematic investigation to explore the energy dependence of all cross sections is under way.

Measurements of the absorption of thermal neutrons were carried out by Dunning and his collaborators[13] with the apparatus of figure 14–16. A nearly parallel bundle of thermal neutrons was obtained with the source at the left and the Cd shields at the right. Gamma rays were excluded with the lead sheet Pb. The neutron intensity (number per second) was measured with a lithium-lined shallow chamber, with and without a sheet of cadmium in the dotted position. The difference is the intensity of the thermal group.

The intensity of the thermal neutrons was measured as increasing thicknesses of various elements were inserted at A, and was found to decrease exponentially. Then, as with electrons in section 7–1,

$$N = N_0 \, \epsilon^{-\mu x}, \qquad (7\text{-}6)$$

where N_0 is the number of neutrons incident upon and N is the number emergent from an absorber (A) of thickness x. The absorption coefficient μ is related to the effective-cross-section σ and the mean-free-path λ of neutrons in the absorber by the equation

$$\mu = n\sigma = 1/\lambda. \qquad (7\text{-}7)$$

The cross-section is a compound value of that of the nucleus of the element at A and that of the neutron itself. It has been shown

TABLE 14–2. FOR NEUTRONS

Element	Cross-section, $\times 10^{24}$, cm.^{2}			Main Process	Resonance Energy, Volts	Group Name
	Thermal	Resonance	Fast			
Li^6	900		1.8	α		
B^{10}	3000		1.6	α		
Rh	125	6000		44″		" D "
Ag	80 30 total 55	900 20 16		22″ 22″ 2.3′	5.0 16 45	" A " " B "
Cd	2600	7000		C	0.16	" C "
In	85 55 total 140	4000 200		54′ 16′	1.44 3.8	" D "
I	9.4	16	4.6		37	
Gd	30,000					
Ir	280	600		C 19 hr	1.9	" D "
Au	90	3000		C	4.8	" A "
Hg	440		5.8	C		

C = capture, α = alpha emission.

that the cross-sections obtained in this manner are largely due to the capture of neutrons, rather than to their scattering.

The nucleus thermal-neutron cross-sections do not vary in a regular manner with atomic weight as in the case of fast neutrons (section 14–13). In many cases they are only a few times larger than the fast neutron values; i.e., of the order of 1 to 10 $\times$ 10^{-24} cm.^{2} But, in certain cases, exceedingly large cross-sections have been observed, particularly among the rare earths. Selected values are given in table 14–2.

Fermi and his collaborators[33] have shown that there are certain selective absorptions of slow neutrons. Thus, the exceedingly large cross-sections observed in certain cases are due to the *resonance capture* of neutrons of a given energy. Neutron groups of this type are listed in table 14–2.

It has been shown, both experimentally and theoretically, that the effective-cross-section σ for the capture of slow neutrons is inversely proportional to the velocity v of the neutrons; i.e.,

$$\sigma = k/v, \qquad (14\text{–}41)$$

where k is the constant of proportionality. This law is valid except in the resonance regions.

14–23. Uranium and Thorium Bombarded by Neutrons.— Fermi found that when uranium was bombarded with neutrons, radio-active nuclei were produced. Several half-lives were observed and chemical tests proved that elements had been produced with atomic numbers greater than 92. These are called *transuranic elements.* Thus,

$$_{92}\text{U}^{238} + {}_0\text{n}^1 \rightarrow {}_{92}\text{U}^{239^*} \rightarrow {}_{93}\text{Np}^{239} + \text{e}^-$$
$$_{93}\text{Np}^{239} \rightarrow {}_{94}\text{Pu}^{239} + \text{e}^- \qquad (14\text{–}42)$$

The heavy U isotope is unstable and decays by the emission of a beta ray to a new transuranic element neptunium, which is also unstable and decays similarly to plutonium. The element plutonium is comparatively stable, and is an alpha-emitter like its parent uranium, with a long half-life. Both the light isotope of uranium $_{92}\text{U}^{235}$ and plutonium are " fissionable." If bombarded by neutrons, the nucleus splits into two parts of not exactly equal weight, but about half way down the periodic table. Thus a typical fission reaction might be

$$_{92}U^{235} + _{0}n^{1} \rightarrow _{92}U^{236} \rightarrow _{38}Sr^{88} + _{54}Xe^{148} + Q \quad (14\text{-}43)$$

The Q values for such a reaction are very large, yielding values of the order of 200 Mev. Hence these reactions have been employed when large energy-liberation was desired, as in the case of nuclear power devices. It will be further noted that one or both of the fission products is too heavy, the normal Xe isotopes in the case of 14-43 being of mass around 133. Hence the postulated Xe nucleus will emit neutrons and become a stable isotope. Since these neutrons may cause further fission reactions, the reaction, if once started in a mass of the substance sufficiently large so that neutrons do not all escape, will tend to become self-perpetuating. The name " chain-reaction " has been used to describe such a self-perpetuating system. The fission products postulated in 14-43 are not the only possible ones, and in general there will be many other ways the nucleus can divide. However, nearly any postulated division into two major fractions will have high Q values and heavy neutron-emitting isotopes.

When thorium is bombarded with neutrons, a new radio-active family is produced.[35] The actinium series is characterized by elements whose mass numbers are equal to $4n + 3$, where n is an integer: the uranium-radium series by $4n + 2$ and the thorium series by $4n$. The new family has mass numbers equal to $4n + 1$.

14-24. Theories of the Nucleus.—See sections 10-11 and 10-12. The size of the nucleus (distance where normal scattering no longer holds) proves to be consistent with the dimension derived from quantum mechanical computation of the uncertainty in position of the components of the nucleus. The assumption of electrons as components would lead to an entirely different dimension. Hence, electrons do not exist in nuclei; they are created at the moment of their emission and are accompanied by the transition of a proton into a neutron or vice versa, according to whether a positron or a negative electron is emitted.

Because of the comparatively wide separation of the extra-nuclear electrons, processes which deal only with the outer parts of the atom may be treated with simple collision considerations, between free individual particles; and the outer part itself may be thought of as though it were a gas. With nuclei, however, where the forces are of very short range and where many particles form a compact mass, it is better to consider the nucleus in terms of a *liquid drop*. This nuclear model was first advanced by Bohr. When a particle enters the nucleus its energy is divided among all constituent parts. Later, a sufficient excess of energy may concentrate on one particle as to permit its ejection; a process comparable to evaporation.

High-energy processes of any kind, such as photon-absorption, may induce high nuclear temperatures. The result will be the evaporation of one or more nuclear particles, protons or neutrons. Such nuclear evaporations are believed to be responsible for the protons and neutrons produced by the cosmic radiation. Indeed in some cases a considerable number of particles may be emitted, giving rise to a "star." Such stars are observed in cloud chambers, in the emulsions of photographic plates and in proportional counters in cosmic-ray experiments. More recent experiments have shown that similar effects can be produced in the laboratory with the high-energy radiations (electrons or quanta) produced in betatrons. In a crude analogy with photoelectric work functions and the ejection of electrons from metals, the ejection of particles from nuclei becomes probable when the energy of the bombarding entity becomes high compared to the potential barrier of the nucleus, i.e., a few tens of Mev.

14–25. The Physical Optics of Neutrons.—In a previous section we saw that electrons have associated waves, and indeed that any particle can be expected to have a wave system, the wavelength of which will vary inversely with its momentum. The problem therefore arose whether such waves were manifested by neutrons, and whether neutrons showed the same diffraction phenomena that charged particles do. The affirmative answer was provided by a series of neutron diffraction experiments in which the main experimental arrangements were similar to those used to demonstrate the diffraction of electrons. The main difference was in the detecting method. Since neutrons do not blacken a photographic plate very effectively, it was necessary to use a neutron detector, in this case a counter or particle-detector. By arranging this to have a narrow aperture through which the neutrons might enter, and allowing the detector to be moved about, the cones of the diffraction-maxima could be explored. Thus it was established that neutrons have waves associated with them, just as electrons and protons have, and that neutrons are preferentially scattered into those directions which ordinary diffraction theory would predict for waves of the corresponding length.

ARTIFICIAL TRANSMUTATION OF LITHIUM

In order to observe the alpha particles ejected from a lithium target bombarded with protons use the apparatus of figure 10–12. The magnetic and electric deflecting fields are not needed. Protons are to be accelerated in the same manner as described in detail in experiment 10–1. Tube E is removed and the apparatus of figure 14–17 is waxed into D. The brass tube F is closed at its

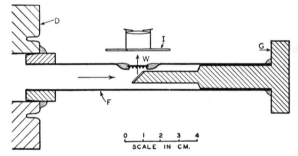

FIG. 14–17. Target assembly for an artificial transmutation.

end by the brass plug G; a waxed joint is sufficient. The end of this plug (G) has been reduced in diameter and beveled at 45°. The material to be bombarded is placed in a thin layer on this bevel. For this target, use a thin layer of metallic lithium, pressed into place, or a lithium salt such as lithium chloride (LiCl). Do not use lithium sulphate ($LiSO_4$). The lithium must be replaced after operating the tube for an hour or two because of a brown deposit which forms over its surface and greatly reduces the number of ejected alpha particles.

Immediately above the target, the tube F has been flattened and drilled with a hole of approximately one centimeter diameter. Five wires of 0.024 centimeter diameter (the dots in figure 14–17) are soldered across the hole to form a supporting grid for a very thin mica window, W, made vacuum tight with a hard wax ring. The mica should be as thin as possible and its stopping power, as measured with the apparatus of figure 12–21, should not exceed two centimeters, air equivalent. As close as possible above W place a scintillation screen I, with sensitive surface downward. This screen must have very few spurious or background scintillations. These are to be counted (in a dark room) before the target is bombarded with protons, but with the screen in place as shown, and should not exceed one or two per minute. Otherwise, the few alpha particle scintillations produced by the protons accelerated at the low voltages used will be masked. The counting of scintillations is to be carried out over a period of five or ten minutes and an average value used, to reduce statistical fluctuations, both for the background and when the target is under bombardment.

The voltage supply may consist of an x-ray power unit provided with rectification. Do not attempt the experiment with less than 50 kv. Satisfactory results can be obtained in the range from 50 to 70 kv.; the higher the voltage, the better.

The discharge tube is first evacuated to as low a pressure as possible. A Bunsen burner with a very low flame is clamped near the palladium tube and a small flow of hydrogen started into the discharge tube, with the pumps in continuous operation. If the rate of flow is too fast, the pressure in the tube rises, the voltage falls off and the tube and proton currents increase. A series kenotron, as used with the high-voltage supply of figure 3–6, serves to limit the current, protecting both the supply system and the discharge tube. The flow is decreased by moving the flame slightly farther away from the palladium tube. If the flow of hydrogen is slow, the voltage drop across the discharge tube will rise, which is desirable, as may be seen from figure 14–12. But, if the flow is too slow, the discharge current and the intensity of the proton beam will decrease below the point where the number of alpha particles ejected from the target is appreciably greater than the background count. A pressure of approximately 10^{-3} millimeter is satisfactory, at which time the glass walls show the characteristic green color produced by x-rays. A controlled leak of hydrogen from a tank of this gas would be better than the system described, but more complicated.

Unless the cathode *C*, figure 10–12, is water-cooled, it will over-heat and emit gases which not only lower the voltage but also introduce undesirable ions in the bombarding beam, and the heat may melt the wax holding the discharge tube to the cathode.

Precautions.—(1) The observation end must be the grounded side of the high voltage system and must be kept grounded at all times, as in figure 10–12. A small static spark, of no serious danger, may be picked up from the target tube even though it is grounded; hence, touch this tube with your hand before looking into the eyepiece.

(2) Keep away from the anode end of the tube at all times.

(3) Do not operate the apparatus for too long a period of time because of the x-rays produced at the anode.

(4) Be sure the cathode is water cooled while the high voltage is on.

Experiment.—(1) Evacuate the apparatus to a very low pressure. (2) Measure the background scintillations. (3) Turn on the high voltage, introduce hydrogen and adjust the flow as discussed above. This will require experience. (4) Count the number of scintillations per unit time and subtract the background count. The additional counts are due to the 8.3 centimeter (range) alpha particles from lithium-seven, as discussed in section 14–15. If a shallow ionization chamber and amplifier is available, this should be used instead of the scintillation screen.

14–26. Proposed Experiment on Induced Radioactivity.—Any laboratory having access to a cyclotron, Van de Graaff machine or radioactive neutron source can set up a number of instructive experiments on artificial radioactivity. For example, silver may be easily activated, and a silver coin may be exposed to neutrons. The coin will be found to emit beta particles for some time thereafter, which may be detected with a Geiger counter or with any electroscope system. If the counting rate of the counter is determined at several intervals, and the results plotted on semi-log paper, a straight line determining the half-life period should be found. A list of other substances which can be readily activated and which will show easily measurable half-lives will be found in reference K, chapter 14.

REFERENCES

1. Rutherford, Phil. Mag., **37**, 581 (1919).
2. General reference G, pages 284–301.
3. Blackett, Proc. Roy. Soc., **A107**, 349 (1925).
4. Pose, Phys. Zeit., **30**, 780 (1929).
5. Chadwick and Constable, Proc. Roy. Soc., **A135**, 48 (1932).   Kane, Phys. Rev., **52**, 266 (1937).
6. Duncanson and Miller, Proc. Roy. Soc., **146**, 396 (1934).
7. Pollard and Brasefield, Phys. Rev., **50**, 890 (1936).
8. Bothe and Becker, Zeits. f. Physik, **66**, 289 (1930).
9. Curie and Joliot, Compt. Rendus, **194**, 273, 708, 876 (1932).
10. Chadwick, Proc. Roy. Soc., **136**, 692 (1932).
11. Feather, Proc. Roy. Soc., **142**, 689 (1933).
12. Harkins, Gans, Kamen and Newson, Phys. Rev. **47**, 511 (1935); **50**, 980 (1936).
13. See Dunning, Pegram, Fink and Mitchell, Phys. Rev. **48**, 265, 704 (1935).
14. Anderson, Science, **76**, 238 (1932).
15. Blackett and Occhialini, Proc. Roy. Soc., **139**, 699 (1933).
16. Anderson, Science **77**, 432 (1933).
17. Curie and Joliot, Compt. Rendus, **198**, 254, 559 (1934).
18. General reference F, page 82.
19. General references: J; also A, page 272; also E, page 359.   Pool, Cork and Thornton, Phys. Rev. **52**, 239 (1937).
20. Cockroft and Walton, Proc. Roy. Soc. **137**, 229 (1932).
21. General reference A, page 242.   Doolittle, Phys. Rev. **49**, 779 (1936).
22. Mano, Jr. de Phys. et Ra. **5**, 628 (1934).   See also, general reference E, pages 266–270.
23. Herb, Kerst and McKibben, Phys. Rev. **51**, 691 (1937).   Gaerttner and Crane, Phys. Rev. **52**, 582 (1937).   Delsasso, Fowler and Lauritsen, Phys. Rev. **51**, 391 (1937).
24. Hafstad and Tuve, Phys. Rev., **48**, 306 (1935). (and Heydenburg), Phys. Rev., **50**, 504 (1936).
25. Dee and Gilbert, Proc. Roy. Soc., **154**, 279 (1936).   Williams, Wells, Tate and Hill. Phys. Rev., **51**, 434 (1937).
26. General reference D, page 216.
27. General reference A, pages 239–249.   Amaldi, Hafstad and Tuve, Phys. Rev., **51**, 896 (1937).
28. Oppenheimer and Phillips, Phys. Rev. **48**, 500 (1935).
29. Bothe and Gentner, Naturwiss, **25**, 90, 126, 191 (1937).
30. General reference A, pages 88–94.
31. Fermi and others, Proc. Roy. Soc., **146**, 483 (1934).
32. Fermi and others, Proc. Roy. Soc., **149**, 522 (1935).
33. See Amaldi and Fermi, Phys. Rev., **50**, 899 (1936).
34. Meitner, Hahn and Strassmann, Zeit. f. Physik, **106**, 249 (1937).
35. Curie, Alban and Fresiwerk, Jr. de Phys., **6**, 361 (1935).

36. Haworth and King, Phys. Rev., **54**, 38 (1938).
37. Holloway and Livingston, Phys. Rev., **54**, 18 (1938).

GENERAL REFERENCES

A.—Rasetti, *Elements of Nuclear Physics.* Prentice Hall (1936).
B.—Feather, *An Introduction to Nuclear Physics.* Cambridge University Press (1936).
C.—Bethe and Bacher, Rev. Mod. Phys., **8**, 82 (1936).
D.—Bethe, Rev. Mod. Phys., **9**, 69 (1937).
E.—Livingston and Bethe, Rev. Mod. Phys., **9**, 245 (1937).
F.—*International Conference on Physics*, Vol 1. Cambridge University Press (1935).
G.—Rutherford, Chadwick and Ellis, *Radiations from Radioactive Substances.* Macmillan (1930).
H.—Gamow, *Atomic Nuclei.* Clarendon Press, Second Edition (1937).
I.—Fleischmann and Bothe, *Ergenbisse der Exakten Naturwissenschaften*, Vol. XIII (1934) and Vol. XIV (1935).
J.—Glen T. Seaborg, Table of Isotopes, Rev. Mod. Phys., **16**, 1 (1944).
K.—E. Pollard and W. L. Davidson, Jr., *Applied Nuclear Physics.* John Wiley & Sons (1942).
L.—H. D. Smyth, Atomic Energy for Miliary Purposes. Rev. Mod Phys., **17**, 351 (1945).
M.—J. D. Stranathan, *The Particles of Modern Physics.* The Plakiston Co. (1942).

CHAPTER 15

COSMIC RAYS

15-1. Introduction.—The electroscope has been used for many years to measure small electrical currents. The leaves of this instrument repel each other, when charged with the same kind of electricity, and remain apart unless charges of opposite sign flow to them from the surrounding gas or a small current leaks across the surface of the insulating support to neutralize their charge. It is possible to prepare an insulator so that the latter leakage does not take place in measurable amount. In order to test this,[1] the leaves are charged to a definite potential by means

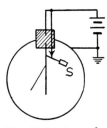

FIG. 15-1. A test for current leakage across the insulator of an electroscope.

of a battery, as in figure 15-1, and diverge to a fixed position. The switch S is then opened and the voltage of the battery greatly increased. This higher potential should drive charges of electricity across the insulator if this does have any leakage. The leaves would then diverge still more. But it is found that with a good insulator, properly cleaned, they do not diverge. In fact, they actually collapse at a slow rate, indicating that the current which flows to them and neutralizes their charge must come from the surrounding gas.

If an electroscope, which has a good insulator, is enclosed in an air-tight, grounded metal box, as in figure 15-1, the leaves are observed to continue to fall even though all the original ions inside have had time to be attracted to the leaves or to recombine with each other to form neutral particles. The continued fall of the leaves indicates that new ions are formed continuously in the chamber by some ionizing agency. That this agency does not reside in the metal used in the construction of the electroscope may be shown by placing the entire instrument in a second electroscope and observing that the latter's natural leak does not increase. It must be concluded that the ions are created by a radiation originating outside the chamber and capable of penetrating the metal walls. That a part of the natural leak is due to gamma rays from radioactive substances of the earth can be demonstrated [2] by placing ice or lead, free from radioactive contaminations and of great thickness, under the electroscope and also by surrounding it with several inches of lead. The natural leak is reduced but not entirely eliminated. It is obvious that the *residual leak*, which is observed after correction of the natural leak for local radiations, must be due to a very penetrating form of radiation.

In 1910, Gockel[3] measured the residual leak of an electroscope at different heights up to 4500 meters above the earth's surface, with the aid of balloons, and found that it increased slightly at the higher altitudes. Hess,[4] in 1911 and Kolhörster,[5] in 1913–1914, extended the observations to 5200 and to 9000 meters, respectively, and found an increase of as much as twelve times the sea-level value. The penetrating radiation which produced the residual leak must then indeed have originated at a great distance above the earth's surface.

It was Hess in 1912 who first definitely ascribed these effects to radiation coming from beyond the atmosphere.

In 1924, Millikan and his co-workers[6] measured the absorption of these penetrating rays by lowering an electroscope to different depths in each of two lakes at different altitudes. They found that some of the radiation had sufficient penetrating power to pass through the entire thickness of the earth's atmosphere several times and, further, that the layer of air between the higher and lower lakes did not contain sources of penetrating rays. The source of the ionization is, therefore, above the lakes. In the absence of any known mechanism for producing such exceedingly penetrating rays in the upper atmosphere, Millikan concluded that the radiation came from beyond the outermost boundary of the earth's atmosphere.

It is now known that the radiation reaches a given point on the earth's surface in essentially constant amount (± 10 per cent), day and night, year in and year out. It cannot, therefore, have originated in the sun. Further, there is no direct association of the radiation with any of the bodies in the solar galaxy. Together with other lines of evidence, it appears most probable that the radiation originates somewhere in inter-stellar space. It is, truly, a " cosmic " ray.

15–2. The Great Penetrating Power of Cosmic Rays.—Cosmic rays constitute the most penetrating radiations known today. They have been observed through 1418 meters of water. The energy of primary cosmic rays ranges from a few billion to at least

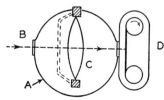

FIG. 15–2. A recording cosmic ray meter.

sixty and perhaps one thousand billion electron-volts, while the secondaries created in the atmosphere by the primaries range from 0 to 10^{12} e.v. Quantitative measurements are made by observing the intensity of the rays at different elevations both above and below the earth's surface.

Figure 15–2 shows a simple diagram of the self-recording electroscope used by Millikan.[6] Sky light which enters the ionization chamber A through the window B casts a shadow of the charged fibers C upon the slowly moving photographic film D. When carried aloft by a balloon, there is found to be an increase in the rate of collapse of the fibers, and when lowered below the surface of a lake there is a decrease in this rate. Millikan increased the

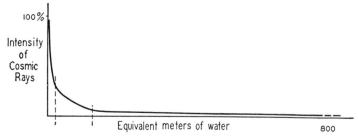

FIG. 15–3. The intensity of cosmic rays at various depths below the surface of the earth's atmosphere.

pressure inside the chamber A to several atmospheres in order that, with an increase in the number of ions produced each second, the instrument would be more sensitive. Regener[7] extended the test to higher altitudes (27 kilometers) and to greater depths (241 meters of water). Wilson made measurements in a mine to a depth of 1418 meters water equivalent.

A curve of the intensity of the cosmic rays at different depths (equivalent water depths) below the surface of the earth's atmosphere is shown in figure 15-3. From this curve, absorption coefficients have been computed and have shown that cosmic rays consist of several, probably three, components of varying degrees of penetrating power. Thus, some of the rays do not reach the surface of the earth, others can just penetrate the atmosphere and the third group are able to travel several hundred meters into the earth's crust before being absorbed.

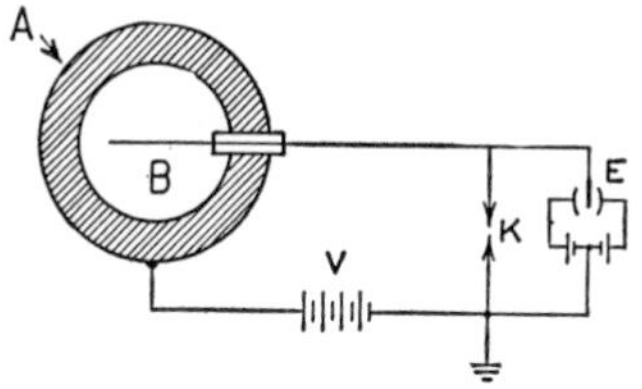

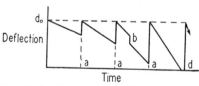

Fig. 15-4. Apparatus to measure the ionization produced by cosmic rays.

15-3. The Ionization of Gases by Cosmic Rays.—In the cosmic ray meter of A. H. Compton,[8] (figure 15-4), the mechanism used to observe the ionization produced by the cosmic rays has been separated from the chamber itself. The ionization chamber A consists of a hollow steel ball surrounded by one inch of bronze and two inches of lead. The effect of local radiations is then small compared with that of the cosmic rays. The chamber is filled with argon at a pressure of, say, 30 atmospheres. The ions produced in this ball are collected by a steel rod B. This is supported by means of a good insulator and is connected to a sensitive electrometer E, such as that of Lindemann. When the key

Fig. 15-5. Electrometer deflections from the apparatus of figure 15-4 at increasing altitudes.

K is closed, electrode B is charged by the battery V. The key is then opened and the electrometer needle is deflected by a large amount (d_0 of figure 15-5). The deflection then decreases regularly toward the undeflected position at a rate which is proportional to that at which the ions are formed in the chamber and are collected on the rod B. The original potential may be restored to the collecting rod by re-connecting the battery for a brief time by means of the key

K. This recharging is indicated at *aaa* in figure 15-5. The increasing rapidity of discharge of the electrometer as the apparatus is carried to higher and higher elevations is shown in this figure by the increasing slopes of the lines between each recharge. Thus, the increasing strength of the cosmic rays with altitude may be measured.

Occasionally, as at *b* in figure 15-5, a sudden loss of charge occurs. This abrupt ionization of the gas in the chamber is referred to as a cosmic ray *burst*. These bursts occur more frequently at the higher altitudes.

Another form of apparatus is shown in figure 15-6. The ionization current passes through a high resistance *R* and produces an e.m.f. between its ends, which is amplified and then recorded on the meter *M*.

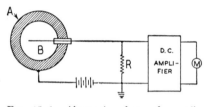

FIG. 15-6. Alternative form of recording apparatus.

Upon calibrating the electrometer or the amplifying equipment, it is possible to calculate the number of ions formed each second. When allowance has been made for the rate of recombination of the ions with each other, it is found that there are approximately two ion pairs produced at sea level in each cubic centimeter of air at standard pressure (760 millimeters) and temperature (0° C.) each second by cosmic rays received at a magnetic latitude of 50°. At the same latitude, but at an elevation of 19,000 meters (11.7 miles), the strength of the rays is found to be 170 times this value.

15-4. The Constancy of the Average Intensity of Cosmic Rays.—To the cosmic ray meter of figure 15-4, there is added a radioactive substance whose radiations produce a steady electrometer current in the opposite direction to that produced by the cosmic rays. The strength of the local ionization is adjusted until it is equal to the average intensity of the cosmic rays. The electrometer deflections will then show any change in the intensity of the cosmic rays from their average value. It is found that the rays are of nearly constant value but that some variations do occur.

It is found, to a close approximation, that the intensity is inversely proportional to the barometric pressure. Thus, when the air pressure is greater, there are more atoms present to absorb the rays and the intensity decreases. It may be concluded that the cosmic rays have come from beyond the earth's atmosphere. The *barometer effect* amounts to approximately one or two per cent per centimeter of mercury.

After the intensities of the cosmic rays have been corrected for barometric pressure, it is found that the average value is essentially constant at a given locality.

There is, however, a very small variation of the mean intensity, amounting to approximately 0.3 per cent, which follows *sun time* but has its maximum in the middle of the morning hours (there is a phase difference).[10] Several theories have been proposed to account for this diurnal variation, one of which assumes that the changes are due to fluctuations in the earth's magnetic field.

There is, also, a still smaller variation of the mean intensity, of approximately 0.03 per cent, which follows *star time*. It has been proposed [9] that this diurnal variation is due to the motion of the earth with the rotation of the galaxy and, hence, that cosmic rays originate from some region outside our galaxy.

15-5. Short-Time Fluctuations in Intensity.—When examined over comparatively short time intervals, the intensity of cosmic rays is found to fluctuate around the average value in a random manner. The deviations from the mean are sometimes large, and sometimes small. They range about the mean according to the Maxwellian distribution law; a law which deals with large numbers of individual particles. This suggests that cosmic rays are of a granular nature, reaching the earth as a host of particles rather than in a continuous stream.

The amount of the variation of the observed cosmic ray intensity at a given instant about the average value may be used to give a quantitative measure of the number of cosmic ray " particles." In order to understand the procedure, consider the following analogy. Water is collected in a pan placed outdoors in a steady fine rain or mist and weighed at regular intervals of, say, one minute. The weights are all found to be of nearly the same value, i.e., the variations from the average weight are small. Next, large hailstones are collected in the pan and weighted at regular intervals, so chosen that the average weight is the same as for the case of the rain drops. Now, however, the random variations from the average are obviously greater; i.e., the spread of the Max-wellian distribution curve about the average is greater. Statistical laws may be applied to compute the weight of the individual rain drops and the hailstones and also the total number of each. An analysis of this type has been made for cosmic rays.[10]

Figure 15-7 shows a Geiger-Müller tube, as used in cosmic ray studies. It is surrounded with a heavy lead sheath to eliminate a majority of the local radiations. When a cosmic ray particle

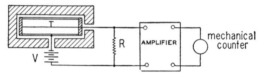

Fig. 15-7. A Geiger-Müller counter tube apparatus for cosmic ray studies.

passes through the gas in the tube, the ions which are created initiate an electrical discharge from the battery (V) through the resistance (R). The IR drop in the resistance quickly lowers the voltage across the counter tube and the discharge ceases. The sudden potential drop which appears across the resistance for each cosmic ray particle is then amplified and used to operate a counting mechanism. The number of counts per unit of time is found to agree with the number deduced from the variations in the ioniza-tion chamber currents. In addition, Regener has measured the absorption of cosmic rays in both water and lead by means of counter tubes and found agreement with the chamber method. It is to be concluded that the same phenomenon, a granular radiation, is responsible for both the chamber and the counter tube observations.

15-6. Coincidence Counters.—The ends of two counter tubes are indicated by the solid circles and central dots in figure 15-8. Iron and lead shields surround the tubes in order to exclude local radiations. The ionization current produced in each tube by a penetrating radiation is amplified in the usual manner and then sent into a common circuit. The latter is so arranged that the counter-meter will only operate when the two tubes are ionized simultaneously, or in practice, within a small fraction of a second of each other, say 10^{-4} second.

Triple coincidence counters may also be arranged so that

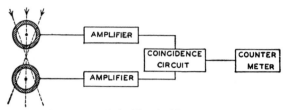

FIG. 15-8. A double coincidence counter.

the penetrating radiation must pass through all three tubes at essentially the same instant before a count is observed.

If radiations approach along the line joining the tubes, as indicated by the dotted lines of figure 15-8, a large number of *coincidence counts* will be recorded, whereas, if the radiations approach at right angles there will be very few counts. Thus, by mounting the tubes rigidly together and pointing them in different directions, it is possible to tell the line along which the penetrating rays are travelling.

With such a *telescope*, it was found that the radiation which produces coincidence counts, in the absence of all local sources, is much stronger in the vertical direction and that it decreases rapidly in strength until it is negligible at approximately ninety degrees.

Experiments with coincidence counters indicate that they are operated by charged and not by uncharged particles.[11] Expansion chambers and blocks of absorbing materials (such as lead) are placed at various positions, above and between the counter tubes.

15-7. The Earth as a Magnetic Spectrograph.—If cosmic rays consist of moving charged particles they should be capable of deflection in a magnetic field. Their great penetration suggests that they possess great energy. Therefore, in order to deflect them by a measurable amount, an exceedingly strong magnetic field over a small area or a weak field extended over a large area would be required. The earth's magnetic field, though not of great intensity, does extend over a large region and should serve as a huge magnetic spectrograph to sort out charged particles of various kinds. However, the earth has an atmosphere of variable density which acts as a filter to transmit the more energetic and to stop the less energetic particles. Further, secondary radiations may be expected to arise when the primary radiations are absorbed.

It can be shown [12] that the earth's magnetic field should act upon charged particles (and not upon photons), which approach the earth uniformly from all directions, in such a manner as to decrease the number which reach the surface of the earth near the equator, as compared with the number at higher latitudes. The *latitude effect* was discovered experimentally by Clay in 1927 and its significance was pointed out by A. H. Compton [13] who, with many collaborators, has made comparative tests of the strength of cosmic rays at stations all over the earth. Some of the data obtained in these extensive tests are shown in figure 15–9. The less energetic charged particles which approach the earth's atmosphere are greatly curved by the earth's field near the magnetic equator and fail to reach the observer, as indicated by the large dip in the higher altitude curve. The more penetrating rays, which follow straighter paths, are able to reach sea level in numbers sufficient to account for the 14 per cent dip.

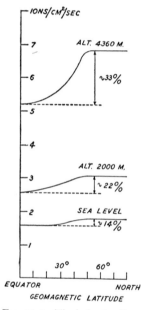

FIG. 15–9. The latitude effect.

In 1933, Alvarez and Compton, and Johnson, observed that the number of cosmic rays approaching the earth near the equator was greater from the west than from the east, by about 10 per cent. This *east-west* effect has been explained theoretically on the assumption that the cosmic rays near the equator consist, predominantly, of positive charges. Johnson [14] has found the effect to be much greater at higher than at lower altitudes.

There is also a variation of the strength of cosmic rays of a few per cent at different *longitudes*, as observed by Clay and Millikan. These variations follow the changes of the earth's magnetic field with longitude and, therefore, show that part, at least, of the rays consist of charged particles.

The various effects just mentioned cannot be accounted for quantitatively unless it is assumed that much the greater part of cosmic rays consist of charged particles. Further, if the observed rays had been secondary charged particles produced in the atmosphere, say by photons, the earth's field could not have curved them sufficiently before they reached the observer to account for the various phenomena. Just which charged particles are involved is not yet certain but there is some tentative evidence that protons and positive and negative electrons are present.

15-8. Showers.—It has been pointed out in the preceding chapter, in connection with the discovery of the positron, that large numbers of ionizing particles are occasionally observed in an expansion chamber. With a magnetic field, the tracks are curved, some to the right, some to the left, and in approximately equal numbers. As many as one hundred tracks have been observed in one of these " showers," diverging in a narrow angle from a small area. From the number and length of the tracks, the number of droplets on each, the curvature in a magnetic field and their absorption in various substances, it is possible to estimate the total energy in the shower. This is of the order of 10^8 to 10^{10} electron volts, the same as that deduced for the energy of cosmic rays.

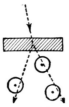

Fig. 15–10. To study the production of showers.

Showers may also be studied with counter tubes, as in figure 15–10. Three tubes [15] are placed as shown and connected in a coincidence circuit so that ionization must take place in all of them at practically the same instant to give a count. Rossi found that, when increasing thicknesses of lead were placed above the tubes, the number of counts increased until there was about one centimeter of lead, after which it decreased.

A latitude effect has been observed with showers and it is known that they increase with altitude.

The bursts observed in ionization chambers consist of one or more showers. They occur more frequently at the higher altitudes. When more and more lead sheets are placed above an ionization chamber, the number of bursts observed in unit time increases at first, then decreases, as with the shower experiment of figure 5–10.

Showers and bursts probably consist of secondary charged particles of great energy produced when primary cosmic rays or secondary photons strike the nuclei of atoms. Thus, cosmic rays, with their great energies, billions of volts, may be used in nuclear disintegrations.

15–9. Mesotrons.—The process of shower production is a characteristic of high-energy electrons. The action may be thought of as follows: A high-energy electron passes close to a nucleus and gives off a gamma ray. This radiation is called " bremsstrahlung," or deceleration-radiation. It is analogous to the production of the continuous x-ray spectrum. The electron loses the amount of energy now possessed by the quantum but in general this is less than its total energy, so it continues and produces yet other quanta near subsequent nuclei. The quanta, in turn, again in the neighborhood of nuclei, produce a pair of electrons, one positive and the other negative. The two electrons again may radiate, and the new quanta produce still more electron-pairs. Thus a " cascade " or shower, is developed from a single high-energy electron. Such cascade-showers may be photographed in cloud chambers or studied with counters and will occur whenever an electron penetrates appreciable quantities of matter. Thus, in general, it would be most unlikely that an electron should penetrate a centimeter or two of lead and not produce such a shower. This property can be made the basis for identifying electrons.

When Blackett and Anderson studied the particles involved in cosmic rays with the aid of cloud chambers they found a great number of electrons which were characterized by their shower-producing properties. However, they also found a second kind of particles which did not produce showers and which therefore could not have been electrons. These particles were not protons either, because they did not ionize as heavily as do protons. By applying magnetic fields to the cloud chambers, it was possible to measure the curvature of the tracks and hence to evaluate the e/m ratio of the particle. Assuming that the particles had a unit electronic charge, the mass was found to be approximately 200 electron-masses. Indeed the experiments show that the mass is not unique and that a range of masses between 50 and 250 electron-masses occurs. This particle, of mass intermediate between proton and electron, was called by a variety of names, the " barytron," the " yukon " or the " heavy electron "; but the names *meson* or *mesotron* are now most commonly applied to it.

Shortly thereafter it was found[16] that the mesotron was radio-active and that it had a mean life of one or two microseconds (10^{-6} sec). Since the cosmic-ray particles were moving with velocities approaching that of light, the relativistic time contraction extends the lifetime in the frame of reference of the observer to several hundred microseconds. The particles can therefore reach sea level if they are produced in the upper atmosphere, but the same radioactivity excludes the possibility that they are primary particles entering the earth's atmosphere from outside.

The discovery of these particles at once explained some puzzling aspects of the diurnal variation and the temperature coefficient exhibited by cosmic radiation. If the atmosphere warms up, it expands, the mesotron-producing layer rises, and the mesotrons have more time to decay on their way down to sea level. At the same time, the mesotron-producing process introduces some interesting problems in high-energy nuclear physics, which are by no means fully understood at the present time. These production processes are tied up with the disintegrations of nuclei—produced by the high-energy primaries—and mesotrons, neutrons and protons are all produced. These production processes are being actively studied today.

EXPERIMENT 15–1

THE ABSORPTION OF COSMIC RAYS

The circuit of figure 15–4 may be used. The chamber (A) may be constructed of seamless steel tubing $\frac{3}{8}$ inch thick, 2 to 3 inches in diameter and 12 inches long inside. The chamber is to be filled with a gas at high pressure and must, therefore, have carefully constructed ends. The gas pressure should be 30 to 50 atmospheres in order that sufficient ion pairs be produced to give an ionization current appreciably greater than the natural leak of the equipment. Air may be used. Oxygen is comparable to air, carbon dioxide or nitrogen somewhat better and argon very much better. If the gas is not free from radioactive contaminations, the natural leak will be found to be large. All parts of the equipment must be dry. The insulating plug is made of amber and so designed as to withstand the pressure in the chamber. The collecting rod (B) is a $\frac{1}{16}$-inch steel rod passing through the plug and running axially along the center of the cylindrical chamber to approximately one inch of the opposite end. Non-radioactive metals, tested with an electroscope, are placed around and under the chamber. Three to four inches of lead or of iron slabs should be used. As is usual with electrometer technique, and especially true here, the lead wires to the insulated quadrants of the electrometer as well as the switch (K) must be carefully shielded in grounded metal tubes or cases. The voltage (V) is to be of the order of 100 to 200 volts. The experiment should only be attempted with a sensitive electrometer, as the currents are of the order of 10^{-14} amperes and less. It should be carried out in a room which is free from radioactive contaminations.

Slabs of iron, free from contamination, of $\frac{1}{2}$ to 1-inch thickness, which cover the chamber are to be placed over it. The rate of deflection of the electrometer is observed as increasing layers of iron are added, up to about one foot total. These rates are proportional to the cosmic ray intensity and are to be plotted against the total thicknesses of iron to obtain a curve of the absorption of the softer cosmic rays which reach the earth's surface.

The experiment may also be carried out with a double coincidence counter, as in figure 15–8, adding successive layers of absorbing material above the counters and observing the number of counts per second. Single and double coincidence counters can now be purchased on the market. For further details, see chapters 17 and 18.

15–10. Proposed Experiment on Cosmic Rays.—A laboratory equipped with a Geiger counter coincidence circuit may set up a number of instructive experiments. For example, the students can verify the cosine-squared zenith angle distribution by orienting the set at various angles to the zenith, and determining the counting rates in each position. The background of accidentals and showers is determined by setting the counters in the case of a triple or higher multiplicity coincidence set with the counters in any out-of-line arrangement so that a single straight line cannot be drawn through all counters. In the case of a double-coincidence unit, the counters can be arranged at right angles to each other and in the same horizontal plane, and very few single rays will actually pass through them. The background thus determined must be subtracted from observations at the various zenith angles. A second experiment will consist of placing the counters in a vertical line and interposing various thicknesses of absorbers between them. The absorption coefficients of various substances may thus be determined.

At the present time counters are available on the market, and it is to be hoped that they will before long be sold commercially at low enough prices to permit such experiments to be widespread. The circuit itself can easily be constructed by students familiar with the assembly of electronic equipment, and all the parts can be purchased at radio supply stores. Various circuits are described in reference C, chapter 18.

REFERENCES

1. C. T. R. Wilson, Proc. Roy. Soc., **68**, 151 (1901).
2. Rutherford and Cook, Phys. Rev., **16**, 183 (1903).
   McLennon and Burton, Phys. Rev., **16**, 184 (1903).
3. Gockel. Phys. Zeit., **11**, 280 (1910).
4. Hess, Phys. Zeit, **12**, 988 (1911); **13**, 1084 (1912).
5. Kolhörster, Phys. Zeit, **14**, 1066, 1153 (1913).
6. Millikan, *The Electron* (+ *and* −), pp. 301 and 404.
7. Regener, Naturwiss, **11**, 183 (1929); Phys. Zeit., **34**, 306 (1933).
   V. C. Wilson, Bul. Amer. Phys. Soc., **12**, 7 (Nov. 1937).
8. Bennett and Compton, Rev. Sci. Inst., **4**, 491 (1933).
9. A. H. Compton and I. A. Getting, Phys. Rev., **47**, 817 (1935).
10. R. L. Doan, Phys. Rev., **49**, 107 (1936).
    See also R. D. Evans and H. V. Neher, Phys. Rev., **45**, 144 (1934).
11. Boethe and Kolhörster, Zeit. f. Physik, **56**, 751 (1929).
    Rossi, Proc. Lond. Conf. on Nuclear Phys. (1934).
    Hsiung, Phys. Rev., **46**, 653 (1934).
    Auger and Ehrenfest, Compt. Rend., **199**, 1609 (1934).
    Street, Woodward and Stevenson, Phys. Rev., **47**, 891 (1935).
    A. H. Compton, Phys. Rev., **50**, 1120 (1936).
12. Lemaitre and Vallarta, Phys. Rev., **43**, 87 (1933); **50**, 493 (1936).
    Störmer, Zeit. f. Astrophys., **1**, 237 (1930).
13. Clay, Physica, **1**, 363 (1934).
    Compton, Bennett and Stearns, Phys. Rev., **38**, 1565 (1931).
    Compton, Phys. Rev., **43**, 387 (1933).
    R. A. Millikan, Phys. Rev., **50**, 15 (1936).
14. T. H. Johnson, Phys. Rev., **48**, 578 (1935).
15. Rossi, Zeit. f. Phys., **68**, 64 (1931).
16. Rossi, Hilberry and Hoag, Phys. Rev., **56**, 837 (1939).

GENERAL REFERENCES

A.—A. H. Compton, Proc. of the Phys. Soc., **47**, 747 (1935).
B.—K. K. Darrow, Bell System Tech., Jr., **11**, 148 (1932).
C.—J. D. Stranathan, *The Particles of Modern Physics*. The Blakiston Co. (1942).

CHAPTER 16

VACUUM TECHNIQUE

THE PRODUCTION OF VACUA

16–1. Introduction.—Some pumps operate from atmospheric pressure, while others require that a "fore pump" reduce the pressure considerably before they will start pumping.

The speed of a pump may be measured by observing the rate of fall of pressure during the evacuation of a flask of known volume (V, liters). With a constant leak of gas into the flask, Gaede's equation is

$$S = \frac{V}{t_2 - t_1} \log_\epsilon \frac{p_1 - p_0}{p_2 - p_0}, \qquad (16\text{–}1)$$

where S is the speed in liters per second at the mean pressure $(p_1 + p_2)/2$, p_1 is the pressure in millimeters of mercury at the time t_1 (seconds), p_2 is the pressure at a later time (t_2) and p_0 is the lowest pressure attainable by the pump. With pumps requiring a fore vacuum, the speed depends on the vacuum produced by the fore pump.

The speed of evacuation of an enclosed system depends not only on the speed of the pump but also on the size of the connecting tubes and the gases and vapors present or given off by the walls.

16–2. Pumps Working from Atmospheric Pressure.—The *water aspirator* or filter pump shown in figure 16–1 may be used if only a moderate degree of evacuation is desired. Water, under a pressure of ten to twenty

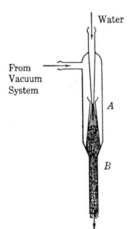

Water

From Vacuum System

A

B

FIG. 16–1. The water aspirator.

pounds per square inch, passes through the constricted tube at
A, dragging along the air in the surrounding chamber. This air
forms a sheath around the water for a short distance, then mixes
with it to pass out at *B*. Such pumps are fast but cannot reduce the pressure much below that of the vapor pressure of water
at the existing temperature. This amounts to 9 mm. at 10° C.
and 20 mm. at 23° C.

The *Toepler* pump, *EFGH* of figure 16–13, may be used to reduce
the pressure to as low a value as 2×10^{-5} mm. but works slowly
as the operation is carried on by hand. It is more often used in
the collection of gases as described in connection with the figure.
However, its action as a pump in evacuating the bulb *D* is as
follows. The gas in *F* is compressed by lifting the mercury reservoir *E* and is forced out through the capillary tube *H*. *E* is then
lowered, gas expands from *D* into *F* and the process is repeated.
The side tube *G* serves to prevent excessive bumping of the mercury as it is being lowered, which is caused by the gas from *D*
expanding into *F* when the pressure in the former exceeds that in
the latter.

One of the many forms of *oil pumps* is shown in section in figure
16–2. A rotor *A*, mounted eccentrically on its shaft, moves in the

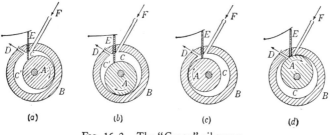

FIG. 16–2. The "Cenco" oil pump.

direction of the curved arrows inside the cylinder *B* at 200 to 300
revolutions per minute. In stage *a* of the figure, gas from the
chamber to be evacuated enters the chamber *C*, which it continues
to fill in stages *b* and *c*. As the cylinder *A* continues its rotation,
this gas occupies the chamber *C'* which becomes smaller in the
successive stages. In this way the gas is compressed and forced
out through the valve *D*. The inlet and outlet chambers, *C* and

C', are isolated from each other by the oiled vane E, which is held in close contact with the rotor by a spring at its top. Two such pumps are mounted on the same shaft with a small phase displacement to each other, connected in series and immersed in oil. A valve is provided at the inlet F to prevent oil being sucked back into the evacuated system. Such pumps operate at approximately six liters per minute and, when new, can reduce the pressure to 10^{-3} mm.

16–3. Pumps Requiring a Fore Vacuum.—The principle of *molecular pumps* may be seen in figure 16–3. The cylinder A

FIG. 16–3. Principle of molecular pumps.

rotates clockwise in its casing B with such velocity that a point on its periphery travels faster than the molecules of the gas in the partially evacuated groove C. Such particles as strike this moving drum are given a tangential velocity in the direction of motion. Hence, particles which enter at D are given a motion toward the outlet E where they are removed by the fore pump. The forms of molecular pumps designed by Gaede and by Holweck are described on page 152 of Electron Physics (1929).

By far the most outstanding pumps today are the *condensation or diffusion pumps*, as shown in figures 16–4, 5, 6, 7 and 8. Their speed at the jet C is very large, so that the rate of diffusion of the gases through the tubes of the system and the gases given off by the walls set the limit to the speed of evacuation. Theoretically, these pumps can create a perfect vacuum. Further, the only moving part is a stream of mercury or oil vapor. In figure 16–4 the mercury vapor rising from the boiler A passes through the heat-insulated tube B to travel with considerable velocity through the constriction C. From here, it is condensed by the water jacket D and returns in liquid form through the U-tube E to the boiler, where it is reheated. The fore pump F maintains a pressure in the tube G considerably lower than that of the mercury vapor in the boiler. Gas from the chamber to be evacuated (H) *diffuses* to the region around the constriction C where it is entrained by the mercury vapor and carried away by the fore pump. Since the velocity of the mercury vapor particles at the mouth of the jet C

is considerably greater than the diffusion rate of the gas molecules around it, the chance of diffusion of the gas molecules in the opposite direction is very slight (computed as 1 in 10^{20}). Further, the mercury, being *condensed* immediately below the jet, exerts no greater vapor pressure in H than that which it has at room temperature. This is around 10^{-3} mm. and, for lower pressures, the

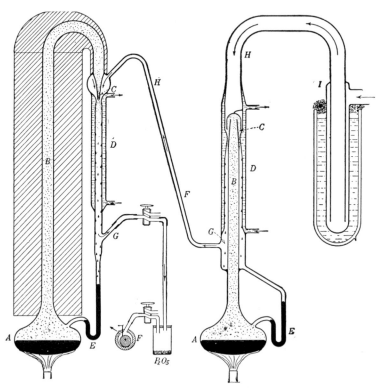

FIG. 16–4. Mercury condensation pumps.

liquid air trap I is used to prevent mercury vapor from entering the remainder of the vacuum system.

In practice, it is found that the speed of these pumps depends on the size and shape of the jet. Pumps of the type shown at the right in figure 16–4 do not usually "take hold" until the fore vacuum is lower than that created by water aspirators or mechanical oil pumps.   Thus, a first stage pump of the type shown at the left is used as its fore pump.   This insures the maximum speed of operation of each pump.

There are many forms of these mercury condensation pumps, some of which are constructed entirely of steel and contain two to four stages in series.   These are used when a high rate of pumping at low pressures is desired.   Figure 16–5 shows a glass

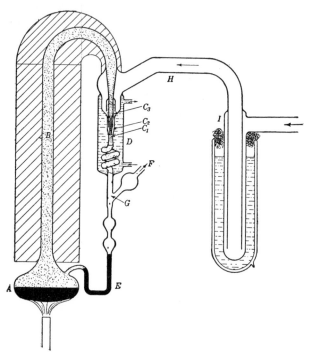

Fig. 16–5.   A three-stage condensation pump.

pump containing *three stages* in one.   The mercury is divided into three parts, that which passes through C_1 creating the fore vacuum for the second stage at C_2 which, in turn, lowers the pressure for the third stage C_3.

A three-stage, mercury diffusion pump with excellent speed and compact form is shown in figure 16–6.

Instead of mercury, certain oils[1] may be used in diffusion pumps.[2] These special oils have a very low vapor pressure at room temperature so that liquid air or CO_2 traps are not needed.

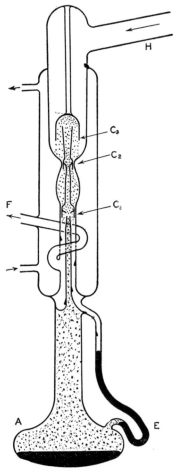

FIG. 16–6. A compact three-stage pump.

A two-stage metal system is shown in figure 16–7. The annular area at the jet (C) between the umbrella and the main (outer) wall will determine the range of pressures over which the pump is most effective. This gap is small in the first stage (annular area of 5.6 cm.²) and large in the lower pressure pump (diffusion area = 12.3 cm.²). The boiler should have a large surface and only a small quantity of oil is to be used, say 100 cc. of Apiezon oil " *A* " in the first stage and an equal amount of " *B* " in the second stage. A central copper rod which rests on the floor of the copper boiler serves to support the umbrella (*U*) and to keep it hot. A glass heat insulator (*I*) is used around the outside of the

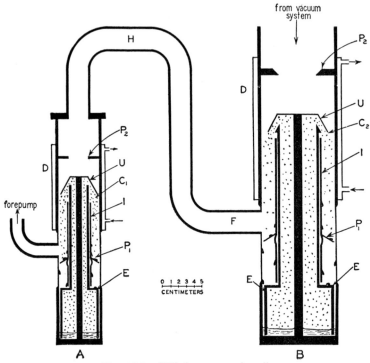

Fig. 16–7.   Diffusion pump using oil.

inner, copper tube to prevent volatilization of the oil after it has condensed below the jets. A copper baffle plate at *P* also assists in keeping the returning oil in liquid form. The liquid oil returns to the boiler through several small slots pressed in the side of the boiler wall. This feature is exaggerated in the drawing, at *E*.

Only a small amount of cooling is needed in the thin water jacket (*D*). A cold baffle plate (*P₂*) is essential to keep traces of oil out of the high vacuum system (H). In fact, for very high vacua, it has been found necessary to add a bend in the large tube leading from the second stage to the system to be evacuated, or to use a trap cooled with ice water. The main tubing of the pump may be made of stainless steel and should be thinned down, as shown in figure 16–7, to keep the boiler heat from the water jacket. It is silver soldered to the copper base plate. The particular pumps shown operated at maximum speed (21 liters/sec.) when 135 watts were used to heat (A) and 150 watts for (B). A fore pressure of 0.05 millimeter of mercury was used.

A more volatile oil should be used in the first stage than in the second stage diffusion pump. A pumping system[3] in which this is accomplished by fractional distillation is shown schematically in figure 16–8. The vapor in A contains a larger percentage

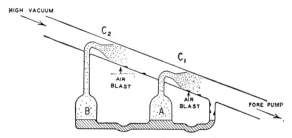

FIG. 16–8. Fractionating oil condensation pump.

of the more volatile component of the oil than does that in B. In one pump of this type, the clearance between the jets and the outer wall was 2 millimeters at C_1 and 3 millimeters at C_2.

16–4. The Elimination of Occluded Gases.—At low pressures, the layer of water which sticks to glass surfaces begins to evaporate rapidly. After this has been removed, it is found that pumps, though capable of low pressures, cannot reach their limit. If the system is sealed off, the pressure slowly rises. This is due to the liberation of gases occluded in the glass and metal parts of the system. This takes place slowly at room temperatures and may be greatly hastened by heating the system. To " bake out " the glass it is raised for several hours to as high a temperature as it will stand without collapsing. Lead glass may be heated to 350° C., soft glass to 400° C., and pyrex to 550° C. Metal parts may be heated by passing an electrical current through them, by continued bombardment by electrons from a hot filament or by the use of an induction furnace which uses high frequency currents produced by the discharge of a condenser or by a vacuum tube oscillator.

16–5. The Sorption Processes.—Sorption is a property of certain substances for occluding and retaining gases and vapors. *Absorption* is a true solution in a solid and takes place rapidly at first, then more and more slowly. *Adsorption* consists of a condensation on the surface and is practically instantaneous. Certain *chemical reactions* may occur to reduce the amount of gas or vapor in a chamber. These three sorption processes may occur simultaneously.

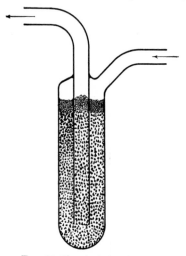

Charcoal which has been previously freed from gases has the property of adsorbing large quantities of gases, especially at low temperatures such as produced by liquid air. Ordinary wood or cocoanut charcoal does not show this property to any appreciable extent until it has been subjected to a heat treatment at about 800° C., called "activation." Activated charcoal can be purchased on the market. Samples which adsorb appreciably at atmospheric pressure (as in gas masks) are not necessarily satisfactory for the production of high vacua. For use in this latter connection, the charcoal is placed in a tube (figure 16–8') in the vacuum system and heated to a dull red temperature for several hours, the pumps being kept in operation. The system is then sealed off from the pumps and the charcoal is cooled with liquid air. It then removes a large part of the remaining gases. With gases such as hydrogen and nitrogen, the pressure may be reduced to values between 10^{-6} and 10^{-7} mm. of mercury, each gram of charcoal adsorbing from 10 to 120 cc. of the gas (reduced to 0° C. and 76 cm. pressure) but with neon or helium

FIG. 16–8'. A charcoal tube.

the adsorption is small, from 0.1 to 8.0 cc. per gram. This offers a method of isolating these gases when mixed with others. Dewar found that considerable quantities of helium were taken up by charcoal cooled below liquid air temperatures, say 15° absolute. Oxygen, once adsorbed, is only given up by prolonged heating at high temperatures. In addition to the high adsorption capacity of the large surface offered by the porous nature of charcoal, it also serves to remove water vapor by capillary action.

Certain samples of *palladium black* have the property of absorbing hydrogen to a very marked extent.   For producing high vacua, the palladium is heated to 100° C. in the system which is being evacuated. The pumps are then cut off and the palladium cooled with liquid air.   Starting at 10^{-4} mm., the pressure will be lowered to around 5×10^{-7} mm. Under certain conditions nickel, copper and iridium will also absorb appreciable quantities of hydrogen.

There are several methods for reducing the pressure after the vacuum chamber has been sealed off from the pumps. In one of these, zirconium, thorium or calcium is placed in the system before evacuation. After evacuating and sealing off, the substance is volatilized by the external application of heat, when all except the rare gases such as argon, neon and krypton disappear. The initial pressure must not exceed a few millimeters if a high vacuum, say 10^{-7} mm., is to be obtained.

When an *electrical discharge* passes through a sealed Geissler tube, the common gases slowly disappear until the pressure is so low that the discharge ceases.   This effect is observed in gas-filled x-ray tubes, so that it is occasionally necessary to admit traces of gas to prevent the tube from " hardening." The explanation of this " clean-up " is not known although the walls of the tube and the electrodes undoubtedly play an important part.   This type of clean-up usually accompanies the process of sputtering.

Gases may be removed from a partially evacuated tube by the use of *getters*. These consist of red phosphorus, *magnesium, barium, calcium,* strontium, aluminum and various mixtures or alloys of these.   The getter is volatilized just before the tube is sealed off from the vacuum system, forming chemical combina- tions with the air molecules which are then condensed on the inner walls of the tube. If the getter is " flashed " in a well-evacuated tube, it will condense on a small area, but in a poorer vacuum, it will spread all over the inside. The getter will take up gases evolved during the life of the tube. The effectiveness of getters is approximately in the order of their chemical activities. Barium is widely used as a getter. Magnesium, which deposits as a bright silvery coat, does not adsorb gases appreciably after deposition. Calcium is not as effective as barium or magnesium but has the advantage that its deposited calcium salt is non-conductive.

Nitrogen, oxygen and hydrogen slowly disappear from a low pressure tube in which a tungsten filament is maintained at high temperature. Pressures of the order of 10^{-6} mm. can be obtained by the use of such *incandescent filaments* when the preliminary pressure was only about 0.1 mm. Despite the great care in manufacture, x-ray tubes and kentoron rectifying tubes have a slight tendency to soften. But, if used from time to time, the slight traces of gas are removed and the tube remains hard.

PRESSURE GAUGES

16–6. Pressure Units.—The pressure in a vacuum system may be measured in millimeters of mercury (*mm.*), *microns* (μ) or *bars*. The micron is one one-thousandth of a millimeter of mercury. The bar* is the pressure exerted by a force of one dyne uniformly distributed over one square centimeter.

$$1 \text{ mm. Hg.} = 1000\mu = 1325 \text{ bars.} \qquad (16\text{–}2)$$

The pressure in a chamber may be measured with the usual (1) closed and (2) open manometers shown in figure 16–9, if it is not too low. Increased sensitivity may be had by mounting the manometers off the vertical. For pressures where a Geissler discharge passes through the tube, the length of the cathode dark space may be used as a rough measure of the degree of evacuation.

16–7. The McLeod Gauge.—Figure 16–9 (3) shows a McLeod Gauge in which the low pressure gas is compressed to a pressure easily observed. The large bulb with capillary tube on top has a volume V, determined at the time of construction. The gas, whose low pressure p is to be measured, enters this bulb freely through the tube A. It is compressed by raising the mercury reservoir B

---

* This is sometimes called a barye. (Meteorologists use a unit which is 10^6 times larger, which they call a " bar." They refer to the bar, as defined above, as one " microbar.")

up to a point C, where it occupies a small volume v at a pressure P. Then from Boyle's law,

$$pV = Pv. \qquad (16-3)$$

The volume v is equal to $\pi r^2 h$, where r is the radius in mm. of the uniformly circular capillary bore (determined when the gauge was being manufactured) and h is the distance in mm. to the top of the

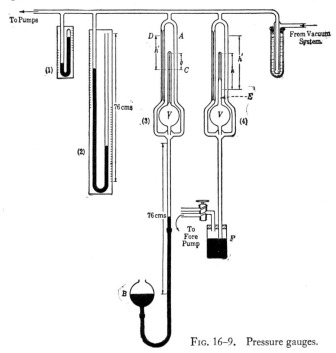

FIG. 16-9. Pressure gauges.

capillary. In the other side tube, the mercury rises to D, so that $P = h'$, in mm. of mercury. This side tube is made of the same capillary tubing as C in order that there shall be equal capillary depression on both sides. We then have,

$$p = \frac{\pi r^2 h h'}{V} \text{ mm. of mercury,} \qquad (16-4)$$

V being measured in cubic millimeters. The gauge may be operated conveniently by making $h' = h$. Then we have

$$p = Kh^2 \qquad (16-5)$$

where K is a constant $(=\pi r^2/V)$. Then a scale calibrated for pressure may be placed along the central capillary tube. The instrument may be built to cover ranges extending from 1 mm. to 10^{-6} mm. With a bulb of 200 cc. capacity and a capillary whose radius is 0.5 mm. and length is 20 cm., $K = 3.93 \times 10^{-6}$ and the gauge reads conveniently from 10^{-5} to 0.16 mm. Two ranges of pressure may be measured by the same instrument if constructed with the larger tube E of (4). This figure also shows a different

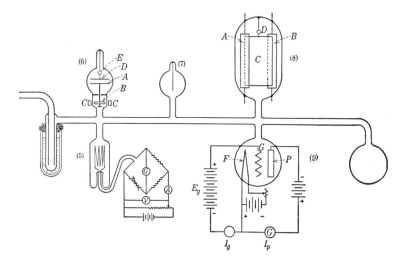

FIG. 16–10.   Pressure gauges.

method of raising the mercury. Air is removed from F as the main system is being evacuated, and is admitted through the stop cock or pumped out to raise or lower the mercury. This gives a more convenient form of gauge and prevents air leaks through the rubber tube of (3). An air trap may be used, as shown at the bottom of P_3 in figure 8–16 (chapter 8). Plungers have also been used to raise the mercury. *McLeod gauges do not measure vapor pressures.* It is important that the glass, rubber and mercury parts be scrupulously cleaned before assembling.

16–8. The Pirani Gauge.—The Pirani gauge (5) of figure 16–10 operates on the principle of thermal conductivity; the higher the pressure, the greater the rate at which heat is conducted away from a hot filament sealed in the vacuum system, and vice versa. Maintaining constant current through the filament, its temperature and also its resistance change with the pressure of the gas and may be measured with a Wheatstone Bridge. The greater the pressure, the lower the resistance. The gauge is calibrated by comparison with a McLeod gauge, a liquid air trap being placed between the two to freeze out the mercury vapor. It has been found better to maintain the filament at constant temperature, observing the voltages V necessary to do this as the pressure changes. The greater the pressure, the greater the reading of the voltmeter. If V_0 corresponds to the lowest pressure attainable and V to a higher pressure, it is found that $(V^2 - V_0^2)/V_0^2$ plotted against the pressure gives a straight line below 0.05 mm. which is the same for all gases containing no hydrogen. However, separate curves for each gas containing hydrogen must be made. Pressures as low as 10^{-5} mm. can be measured. Readings may be obtained quickly, especially by the first method described, if the gauge is placed in a constant temperature bath. Recording meters may be used to obtain permanent records. In practice, a tungsten filament lamp (10–40 watts) with rigid filament may be used for this gauge. Using the constant temperature method, the bridge is balanced at the start so that the filament is around 100° C., i.e., below red heat.

A convenient *thermocouple gauge*[4] for use in the pressure range from 0.1 to 10^{-3} millimeter of mercury is described in reference 4.

A modification of the above types is the " thermal gauge," a device often found useful. In this device, a junction is made at which four wires are spot-welded together. Two of these are of any convenient material for producing heat, such as german silver. The other two are any two dissimilar elements, iron-copper, iron-nickel, or chromel-alumel. A current is passed through the pair serving as heaters, thus raising the temperature of the junction. The potential developed thermoelectrically by the junction of the two dissimilar wires may be measured on any sensitive device such as a microammeter. Since the temperature attained by the junction, for a fixed current through the heater, is determined by the number of collisions which the molecules of the surrounding gas make with the heater-wires, the readings of the microammeter may be directly calibrated in terms of pressure. Such a gauge may develop 150 microamperes with a heater current of 100 to 250 milliamperes, depending on wire diameters. The gauge is sensitive in the pressure-region useful for leak-testing. Further, it is much easier to operate than a McLeod, is continuously sensitive, and, unlike some types, will not be damaged if it is inadvertently left " on " when gas is admitted to the system. Moreover, the microammeter can be located at any convenient place not necessarily near the system, and indeed micro-relays can be connected to sound alarms or shut off pumps should the pressure rise beyond a predetermined amount. The operating limits of the gauge are about 1 mm. to 10^{-4} mm., the limits being determined by the number of collisions required to produce effective changes in equilibrium temperatures. Except over small ranges, the scale is not linear.

16–9. Molecular Gauges.—The molecular gauges (6) and (7) of figure 16–10 operate on the principle of viscosity. In (6) the disc A is rotated by the magnet B turned by the rotating magnetic field C. As a result, the light disc D, supported by a quartz fiber, is deflected by the viscous drag of the intervening gas. The distance between the discs must be small in comparison with the mean free path of the molecules at the existing pressure. The speed of A remaining constant, the angle of twist of the suspension, as observed by the reflection of light from the mirror E, is proportional to the pressure. This gauge, like that of (7), is calibrated by means of a McLeod gauge and is delicate, requiring skill to operate.

The vibrating fiber gauge (7) consists of a quartz thread suspended in the system. The rate at which its vibrations are damped down gives a measure of the pressure of the gas. The instrument has a range from 1.0 mm. down to 10^{-4} mm. but is not satisfactory for lower pressures.

16–10. Radiation Gauges.[10]—A type of Knudsen radiation gauge is represented by (8) of figure 16–10. This operates on the principle of the repulsion between a hot and cold plate due to molecular bombardment. The electrically heated platinum strips A and B act as the hot plate and the mica sheet C as the cold plate. The latter, supported by a quartz fiber, is rotated by the unequal bombardment on the sides adjacent and away from the hot plate, as observed by light reflected from the mirror D. The amount of rotation is proportional to the pressure, other conditions remaining constant, and the distance between it and the hot plate being small in comparison to the mean free path of the molecules at the existing pressure. When the gauge has been properly designed, the pressure may be calculated directly from the rotation, spacing, temperature difference, etc., so that it serves as an absolute manometer from 10^{-3} mm. to 10^{-7} mm. and possibly lower. This is the most accurate absolute instrument for work at extremely low pressures but requires skill in construction and use.

16–11. Ionization Gauges.—The ionization gauge (9) of figure 16–10, due to Buckley,[5] has been found particularly useful, especially at low pressures. Electrons from the hot filament F are accelerated toward the grid G by the battery E_g. Some of these reach the grid and constitute the current I_g (0.5 to 20 milliamperes) while others pass through into the region between the grid and negatively charged plate P where they are repelled back to the grid. The gas in this region is ionized by these electrons in proportion to the number of particles present and hence in proportion to the pressure. The positive ions so formed are drawn over to the plate giving a reading on the galvanometer of amount I_p. Calibration of the gauge by comparison with a standard gauge at pressures around 10^{-4} millimeters gives values of K in the equation

$$p = KI_p. \qquad (16\text{–}6)$$

Under certain conditions K will be a constant. It is usually expressed in millimeters of mercury per ampere of positive ion current.

In order that the positive ion current shall be directly proportional to the pressure of the gas, the following conditions must be fulfilled:

1. The pressure must be lower than that critical value for which the mean-free-path of the electrons in the gas is less than the distance between the grid and plate. If the pressure is greater, an electron may suffer more than one collision with gas molecules, destroying the desired one-to-one relationship. This is avoided by proper spacing of the electrodes and restriction of the range of pressure used, to below approximately 10^{-3} millimeter of mercury. There are commercial tubes especially designed for this purpose,

such as the FP62.   But certain tubes, such as the 101D, 102D, 205D, 216A and 45, may also be used.

2. The number of ions produced by each electron must not change appreciably with variation of the energy of the electron. The latter is usually expressed in terms of the accelerating voltage between the grid and the filament.   The probability of ionization for electrons of different speeds is zero up to a small accelerating voltage, called the minimum ionizing potential, and rises to a broad maximum somewhere between 100 and 500 volts.   For still higher voltages, the chance that an electron will ionize a gas atom decrease slowly.   Best operation of the gauge is, therefore, obtained in the region of the broad maximum where the probability is nearly constant.   This maximum occurs at different voltages and is of different magnitude for different gases, necessitating a separate calibration for each gas or combination of gases.   For air, a maximum exists between 250 and 300 volts.   This, however, is not critical and 160 volts has been found satisfactory in actual operation.

3. The number of electrons bombarding the gas, as measured by the grid current, must be kept constant.   This cannot be brought about by simply maintaining constant voltages on the tube, since the temperature, and hence the emission of the filament varies with the pressure, due to the cooling effect of heat convection by the gas.

The grid current (I_g) can be kept approximately constant by using small changes in its value to control the heating of the filament.   When I_g rises above the desired constant value, its increase is used to reduce the filament current which, in turn, reduces the emission, and vice versa.   Figure 16–11 shows one method[6] by which I_g is maintained constant with a mechanical relay.   Whenever the grid current is excessive, it closes the contacts of a (100 ohm) relay and shorts the filament.   Then, the filament cools, the emission decreases, the relay opens and the filament is reheated.

A gas-filled triode (thyratron) can be used[7] to maintain a nearly constant current, without the use of moving mechanical parts.   The a.c. operated thyratron plate circuit is connected in series with the filament of the ionization gauge.   The grid potential of the thyratron is obtained from a resistor through which the grid current of the gauge tube is flowing.   An increase in I_g

makes the thyratron's grid more negative, decreases its average plate current and hence lowers the temperature of the filament, and vice versa. This gives a rapid and smooth control of I_g.

The gauge constant (K) for a 216A tube operated with a filament voltage of 5.5, a grid current of 20 ma., a grid voltage of +100 and a plate voltage of −7.5, is 5.25 millimeters per ampere. Values for other tubes can be determined by plotting a curve of pressure (McLeod gauge; liquid air trap between the gauges) against the plate current and measuring the slope of the resulting

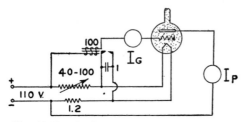

FIG. 16–11. A relay-controlled ionization gauge.

straight line. Since K is a constant at the lower pressures (below about 5×10^{-4} millimeters of mercury), as can be shown both theoretically and experimentally, equation 16–6 can be used to measure pressures below those used in the calibration. A recording instrument may be used for I_p.

The gauge can be used for rough measurements without outgassing, but for accurate work it is necessary to drive out all gases occluded in the glass walls and metal electrodes.

Vacuum Technique

16–12. Care Required to Produce Vacua.—The lower the pressure to be obtained, the greater the care needed in the assembly of the vacuum system. For comparatively high pressures, above say 0.1 mm., rubber tubing, greased stop cocks, waxed joints, etc., may be satisfactorily used. But for lower pressures, all connections should be made of glass or metal parts. Waxed joints, stop cocks and other sources of vapor pressure should be eliminated wherever possible. For very low pressures, all parts must be baked out for long periods of time to drive out the occluded gases. These requirements are greatly reduced or even unnecessary when some of the modern fast pumps are used. With mercury condensation pumps or mercury gauges, it is necessary to freeze out the mercury vapor with liquid air or carbon dioxide snow if the pressure is to be lowered below 10^{-3} mm.

16–13.   Hunting for Leaks.—Despite great care in the assembly of a vacuum system, it is usually found that there remain small holes or cracks too small to be visible. When these are comparatively large, blow into the system through a drying tube or apply a few pounds of compressed air and go over the outside with soap suds. Bubbles appear at the leak.

When the pressure can be reduced so that a discharge passes through, the leaks may be located with a spark coil. This should have a spark gap in parallel with its secondary to prevent high potentials which would spark through weak spots in the glass. Connect one terminal of the secondary of the coil to an electrode sealed in the system. If there is no electrode, stick a pin through the rubber tubing of the fore vacuum line and wax around it. A wire from the other terminal is held by a long glass rod and carefully moved over all parts of the system. The pressure being low enough, a bright spark occurs through the hole and the system lights up when the exploring wire is near the leak.

The Geissler discharge at the lower pressures in an air tube has a reddish color if there is a leak but is pale blue, almost white, if the system is tight.

When a system is first evacuated, it is more difficult to lower the pressure than after it has been pumped out a number of times. This is due to a surface layer of water on the inside of the tubes. The presence of water vapor is often mistaken for a leak in the system itself. Phosphorous pentoxide (P_2O_5) in a side arm or in a bottle as in figure 16–4 is very effective in absorbing water vapor. The oil in a fore pump should be freed from moisture by removing and boiling whenever the pump fails to operate at its normal rate.

Another method for hunting leaks is to pass a discharge through the system and sponge over it with ether or water. With air in the tube, the color changes from a pinkish to a bluish when the water passes through the hole.

When the leak has been found, let in the air and fuse the hole. For quick repair, the leak may be eliminated by covering it with one of the low vapor pressure waxes; but this method cannot be used for very low pressure work, especially on parts which are to be heated.

Stop cocks should be tested for leaks before sealing into the system by holding in a vertical position, pouring a drop or two of ether or alcohol into the tube (the cock being greased and closed), quickly sucking on the same tube, putting the tongue on the end and watching if any bubbles come through the liquid. Turn a stop cock leisurely when using it and as seldom as possible for the grease is ultimately squeezed out, leaving rings which leak. Never twist the stopper unless the grease is present, otherwise the glass walls will be scratched and the cock will leak.

Cast iron leaks badly and should be avoided. Brass, aluminum, copper, steel, nickel, etc., may be used but must be baked out when dealing with very low pressures.

Pyrex has a great tendency to contain minute pin holes where it has been fused, even though carefully worked in an oxygen flame.

Rubber tubing connections to glass should be made as follows. The glass is warmed gently so that a ring of wax can be melted around it a short distance from the end. The rubber tubing is slipped over this and gently flamed at its end. Rubber tubing, even of the thick walled " pressure " type, permits the passage of air through its walls at low pressures and should be used only in the fore-pressure lines. Red sealing wax may be used or a good wax may be made of about 10 parts rosin and 90 parts beeswax. The beeswax is melted in boiling water to free it from sugar granules. When cooled, it forms a cake on top of the water and is taken off and dried, then melted with the rosin. A pan of this mixture is kept on hand and melted whenever needed. The liquid may be applied to warmed parts of a vacuum system with a brush. Softer waxes are formed by using a larger percentage of beeswax. DeKotinsky, Everett, Apiezon and Picein waxes of low vapor pressure may be purchased on the market. See, also, section 16–15.

16–14. Flow of Gases at Low Pressure.—In experiments at low pressures, the rate of flow of the gas through various sizes of tubing is often of great importance. In many experiments pure gas is admitted continuously through a fine capillary or otherwise and pumped away by a mercury vapor pump. An equilibrium pressure is thus established in the experimental tube. If various parts are connected together, the pressure may be very different in the different parts. In calculating the rate of flow with a good vapor pump, the pressure at the pump itself may be considered as maintained at zero. The flow through the various tubes may be computed from the following formula of Knudsen which may be derived kinetically. When the pressure is so low that the free path is large compared with the radius of the tube,

$$n = 2.22 \times 10^{19} \frac{R^3}{L} \frac{P_2 - P_1}{\sqrt{MT}} . \qquad (16\text{–}7)$$

Here n is the number of molecules of a gas of molecular weight M passing per second through a tube of length L cm. and radius R cm. under a pressure difference $P_2 - P_1$ bars at a temperature of $T°$ absolute. If $\dfrac{P_2 - P_1}{n}$ is defined as the " resistance " of the tube, it is easy to show that the " resistance " of a network of tubes connected in series and parallel is obtained by the same laws as for the combination of electrical resistances in series and parallel. It may be seen from the formula that large tubes are needed and that a short narrow constriction offers as great a resistance to the flow of a gas as a long tube of larger radius. Thus, one centimeter of 0.1 cm. tubing offers the same resistance as ten meters of 1.0 cm. tubing. Thus, stop cocks and mercury cut-offs should be made of as large bore as possible.

A similar formula holds for the number of molecules flowing through an aperture of area A sq. cm. in a thin disc:

$$n = 0.264 \times 10^{19} A \frac{P_2 - P_1}{\sqrt{MT}} . \qquad (16\text{–}8)$$

For most vacuum engineering, the resistance of $1\frac{1}{2}$–3 inch elbows may be neglected,[11] whereas a $1\frac{1}{2}$ inch Kinney bellows valve offers a resistance equal to about five pipe diameters.*

* Reference 11 also gives an equation applicable not only at the low pressures just considered but also at the higher pressures where Poiseuille's equation is generally used. Confirmation is given by comparison with the literature on the flow of gases in glass tubes and also by measurements with copper pipes of about 1 cm. radius and iron pipes as large as 10 cm. radius for pressures from 0.1 to 1000 microns. The equation is

$$Q = \frac{\pi g_c R^4}{16 \mu L} (P_1{}^2 - P_2{}^2) F,$$

In using a pressure gauge, it is important to have it connected as closely as possible to the experimental chamber and to wait a sufficient length of time before taking a reading to allow the pressure in the gauge to reach its new value.

16–15. Vapors.—Impurities in the system exert a constant vapor pressure below which it is difficult to lower the pressure, even with fast pumps and large tubing. For instance, if there is moisture in a tube at 20° C., the lower limit of pressure would be around 17 mm. The obvious solution of this very important vapor tension problem is to eliminate as much as possible the causes of vapors and then to lower the temperature in a portion of the system. As water is cooled from 20° C. to −20° C., its vapor tension drops to 0.9 mm. At the temperature of carbon dioxide snow (−78° C.), it is 0.001 mm. and at liquid air temperature (−195° C. to −182.7° C.), it is below 10^{-6} mm. It is, therefore, necessary to remove water vapor with a tube of phosphorous pentoxide unless liquid air is available.

Next to water vapor, mercury vapor presents the greatest problem. Cooling methods must be used when mercury is used in the condensation pumps and McLeod gauges. The following table gives the vapor pressure of mercury at various temperatures.

°C	P mm.	°C	P mm.
40°	6.0×10^{-3}	−40°	6.7×10^{-6}
20	1.8×10^{-3}	−78	4.1×10^{-8}
0	3.5×10^{-4}	−190	nil

Other gases such as those from stop cock grease and fore-pump oil have a pressure of only 10^{-4} mm. at 0° C. and are negligible at the temperature of carbon dioxide snow. Thus, if the water vapor is removed, carbon dioxide snow will serve excellently as a refrigeration agent although liquid air is still better. The liquid air in its

---

where Q = rate of flow of gas, in micron-cu. cm./sec; g_c = 1.33; R = tube radius in cm.; μ = gas viscosity at atmospheric pressure in poises; L = tube length in cm.; P_1 and P_2 are the upstream and downstream pressures in microns, respectively; and $F = 1 + 4 \sqrt{\pi/2} (2/f - 1) \mu/P_m R \sqrt{\rho_{1c}}$, where P_m is the arithmetic mean pressure = $(P_1 + P_2)/2$; ρ_1 is the gas density at one micron, in gm./cu. cm.; and f is the fraction of molecules striking the wall which is diffusely reflected (0.77 − 0.90).

Dewar flask or thermos bottle is raised around the trap slowly (see figure 16–4) so that it does not boil too rapidly. After it has become quiet, a cotton or waste plug is added around the top of the flask to reduce the evaporation. It is best to reduce the pressure to a few centimeters before applying the liquid air.

To form carbon dioxide snow (CO_2), a cloth bag of about a liter capacity is tied over the opening of the drum of gas. The drum is tipped up at an angle of 30° or more with the valve at the bottom so it is below the level of the liquid CO_2 inside. The valve is opened wide when the liquid, rushing out under high pressure, soon turns to snow and collects in the sack. Break up the snow (do not pinch it with the fingers), put it in the Dewar flask and add ether, *acetone* or alcohol to form a slush. This insures good contact with the trap. A pint of CO_2 snow and alcohol will keep for about a day and a half. In many large cities, carbon dioxide snow is supplied commercially under the name of " dry ice."

The following table[8] gives the vapor pressure p in millimeters of mercury of various materials at room temperatures.

Substance	$p \times 10^4$ mm.	Wax	$p \times 10^4$ mm.
Pyrex..................	0.58	Picein.................	2.9–3.3
Brass..................	0.83	Dennison's Royal Scarlet	3.7
Iron...................	2.9	Beeswax 1 part, rosin 1	
Rusty iron.............	210.0	part...............	4.6
Glyptal...............	1.7–5.8	Express sealing wax.....	8.7
Stop-cock grease:		Universal wax..........	10.
Cenco..............	5.8	Dennison's *#* 2.........	10.
Lubriseal.............	6.2	de Khotinsky..........	12–21

16–16. Mercury Cut-offs.—Figure 16–12 shows two forms of mercury traps. When the vacuum chamber A is to be sealed off from the pumps, apply air pressure at B, raising the mercury above the cut-off level C.

16–17. Metal-to-Glass Seals.—Since the linear expansion coefficients of platinum and soft glass are the same, many lead-in wires are of this type. Dumet wire may be used similarly.

For lead-in wires with pyrex, tungsten may be used. (See D of figure 16–12.) The tungsten is heated red hot and cleaned by rubbing with a stick of potassium nitrite. It is then washed, and warmed in a broad oxygen flame, when it quickly turns straw colored or purple. A thin tube of pyrex or G702P glass, which just fits over it, is slipped on and fused in a strong oxygen flame, starting at the middle and working towards both ends. When cool, the joint should have a smooth golden brown color if it is to be free from leaks. It may then be sealed into the walls of the vacuum chamber, glass to glass.

At the upper left of figure 16–12, a copper tube E is prepared by giving it an inside taper of $2\frac{1}{2}°$, followed by thinning on a lathe

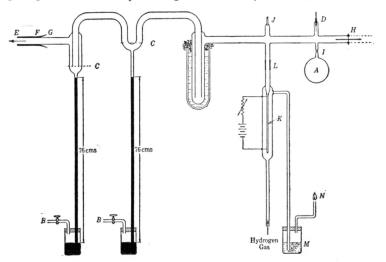

Fig. 16–12. Vacuum technique.

with an extremely sharp tool until it is only 0.001 in. thick at the end. The end of the glass tube G is coned sharply inward and inserted into E, making contact just inside the end of the copper tube, where it is fused in place. The glass is then cut with a flame a short distance outside the copper and paddled open. The paddle is also used to press the glass against the copper almost to the beginning of the taper (nearly to F in the figure). The glass is then fused to the copper all along the taper. Then the main glass tube is resealed onto G and the joint cooled down slowly. Either hard or soft glass may be used.

At H in the same figure, a copper foil is placed between the ends of two tubes. The glass is fused, then the right tube (dotted) is blown out and drawn away leaving a ring of glass on the face of the copper which is now fused to the other tube. Various electrodes may be put through this foil and soldered in place.

An alloy of iron, nickel and cobalt, called " Fernico," is used as an intermediary metal between the iron shell of radio tubes and special glass beads through which the lead-in wires pass.

Many other metal-to-glass seals are possible. Platinum can readily be sealed to soft glass, but expensive graded seals are required to seal soft glass to modern pyrex systems. An alloy called " Kovar " and a fairly hard glass to which it seals readily has been extensively used. Further, when the highest vacuum is not required or heating of the joint can be avoided, ordinary red sealing wax may be used to seal glass-to-metal joints. If the parts are heated slightly above the melting-point of wax before the wax is applied, it will wet both surfaces and make a satisfactory and tight joint. Such a joint cannot, of course, be heated after the wax has set, and the vapor-pressure of the wax constitutes the limiting vacuum attainable in a system thus equipped. However, for quick repairs to complex systems, and in many experiments for which the very highest vacuum is not essential, wax joints are useful.

16-18. Sealing Off.—When a chamber is to be sealed-off from the system, a narrow constriction is made in the tubing as close as possible to the chamber, as at I in figure 16-12. After pumping out, this constriction is warmed all over, the pumps being in operation to remove gases given off by the heated walls. Then a small flame is applied to the constriction, the tube fused together, and the chamber pulled off.

16-19. Introducing Gases.—When a small but constant leak of gas into a vacuum system is desired, one may use a long, fine capillary tube. For a slower rate of leakage, a value may be used in which a fine needle nearly closes a small, gently tapered hole. The mechanical device to adjust the position of the needle in the hole, to control the rate of leakage, may be made air tight with a sylphon bellows.

As shown in figure 3-6, a small piece of lavite, pointed on the end, may be waxed in the end of a glass tube and surrounded with mercury, leaving such an amount of the tip projecting as to give the desired rate of leakage through this semiporous material into the vacuum system.

A bent, flattened metal tube may be used as a valve to control the rate of flow of a gas into a vacuum system. The more it is bent, the slower the leak.

A small crack in a glass tube may also be used as a valve. Twisting the tube will open the crack and increase the flow of gas through it.

In order to introduce hydrogen into a vacuum system, a palladium tube is sealed into the system as at J, figure 16–12. If a bunsen flame is applied with the tip of its inner cone (the oxidizing part) on the palladium, hydrogen will be drawn out of the system. If the outer part of the flame is applied, hydrogen will pass into the vacuum. The palladium thimble should not be heated red hot.

K in figure 16–12 is a platinum tube, some 20 cm. long, 1 mm. in diameter, with walls 0.1 mm. thick, sealed in a soft glass tube and attached to the pyrex system through the graded seal L. Tank hydrogen flows over the platinum tube at a rate indicated by the bubbling in the water M and is burned at N. If the platinum is heated to 500° C. by a battery (20 volts, 15 amperes) or a step down transformer, it allows pure hydrogen to flow slowly into the system. The hotter it is, the faster the hydrogen goes through. Thus, it may be used as a valve and also as a purifier of the gas entering the vacuum system.

16–20. Purifying Gases.—The main things to remove from tank hydrogen are oxygen and water vapor. Pass the gas through a calcium chloride tube, then over hot copper shavings or a hot copper wire (heated dull red), then through a phosphorus pentoxide tube. The first and last tubes take out the water vapor and the copper combines with the oxygen to form copper oxide. Hydrogen mixed in proper proportion with oxygen or air is explosive so that the hydrogen should be passed through the system for a short time before heating up the copper. The safe condition may be determined by passing the gas, as it leaves the last tube, into an inverted test tube. When the gas has flowed for a short time, remove the test tube a few feet away, keeping it inverted, and apply a match. If the hydrogen burns rather than giving a gentle explosion it is safe to start the heating.

Tank nitrogen contains oxygen and water vapor which are removed as with hydrogen. It is not necessary to take any precaution against explosions.

Tank helium contains hydrogen and water vapor. The latter is removed with calcium chloride and phosphorus pentoxide as before. The middle tube should contain black copper oxide heated to dull red. The copper oxide combines with the hydrogen to form copper and water. Another way is to circulate the gas over heated, out-gassed charcoal, using liquid air to freeze out the vapors.

To reduce the amount of oxygen in tank argon or tank helium (from say 6 to 1 per cent), pass the gas slowly through a liquid air trap. For further purification, expose the gas for 12 hours to a hot tungsten filament operated at approximately 1100° C.

Any one of the rare gases may be purified by passing it through a chamber in which a spark is occurring between misch metal electrodes, or an arc between calcium electrodes. Misch metal is a mixture of rare earths and absorbs nitrogen very readily.

Tank oxygen, made from liquid air, contains nitrogen which is difficult to remove. Water vapor should be taken out with phosphorus pentoxide. Oxygen from electrolysis contains water vapor and hydrogen which are removed with CaCl, P_2O_5 and heated copper oxide as in the case of helium.

Sticks of potassium hydroxide (KOH) in a side tube serve to remove carbon dioxide from the system.

Deuterium gas is obtained by passing the vapor of heavy water through zinc filings at 350° C, (or by the electrolysis of heavy water, in which case it is collected the way hydrogen is normally recovered in such processes). The deuterium oxide decomposes into zinc oxide and deuterium (D_2). If the system is connected at D in figure 16–13, the D_2 gas may be transferred with the Toepler pump and stored in the flask (J).

16–21. Collection of Gases.—Figure 16–13 shows the construction of a Toepler pump used in the collection of gases. The entire system is evacuated by applying a fore pump at A. Mercury is then forced above the cut-off point B by blowing at C. The gas is then generated at D. The mercury reservoir E is then raised so that the gas in F and G is cut off and compressed through the mercury in the capillary tube H into the chamber I. E is then lowered, more gas expands into F and the process is repeated until the approximate pressure desired is obtained in I, as measured by the difference in height of the mercury in the U-tube. By

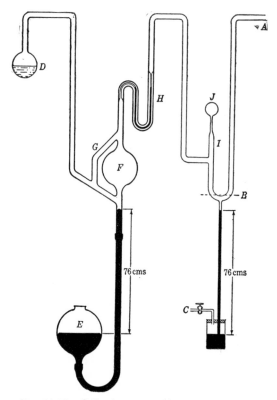

Fig. 16–13.   Collecting gases with a Toepler pump.

changing the pressure at *C*, the gas in *J* can be brought to the
exact pressure desired and sealed off at the constriction.

16–22. Cleaning Processes.—Rubber tubing should be washed
with a solution of caustic potash (sodium hydroxide, NaOH), then
carefully washed in distilled water and dried.

For cleaning glassware, a saturated solution of potassium
bichromate in sulphuric acid is used.   This is much more effective
if used hot.   When cleaned, the glass should be carefully washed
in distilled water and dried by drawing warm dry air through it.

A very simple and effective way of cleaning mercury is shown
in figure 16–14.   Dry air from a calcium chloride ($CaCl_2$) tube is
bubbled through the mercury *A* in a long tube (around 2 meters)
for several hours.   A heavy scum will form on the surface which

contains practically all the impurities.   The mercury is then
filtered through small holes punched in filter paper held in a funnel.

A good but more tedious method of cleaning mercury is to
filter it, and shake thoroughly in a bottle with chromic acid, then
in water.   Then let it fall in a fine spray from a cloth bag through

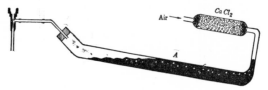

FIG. 16–14.   Cleaning mercury.

several meters of dilute nitric acid, then through several meters of
distilled water and dry it by evaporation at around 350° C.   A
" drip " tube is shown in figure 16–15.

Filtered mercury may be distilled in a vacuum with the
apparatus shown in figure 16–16 to obtain the cleanest mercury.

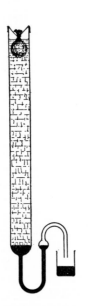

FIG. 16–15. Cleaning
mercury.

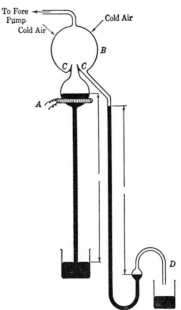

FIG. 16–16.   Distilling mercury.

The mercury is gently vaporized by the heater at A and condenses on the walls of the bulb B.   It then falls into the groove C and runs out at D.   About twenty pounds of mercury can be distilled in eight hours of continuous operation.

16–23.   Cathode Sputtering.—When the cathode dark space in a discharge tube is approximately half way to the walls of the tube and the discharge is run for some time, the walls become

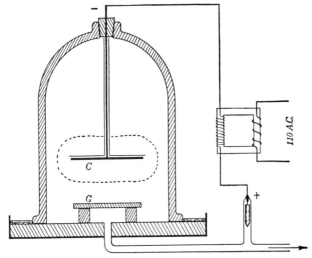

Fig. 16–17.   Cathode sputtering apparatus.

coated with a thin layer of the cathode metal.   If a glass plate G, figure 16–17, is supported in a bell jar at a distance of 7 cm. from the face of a 10 cm. platinum disc cathode C, and the air pressure is reduced to 0.004 mm. of mercury, a 10,000 volt transformer maintaining a potential difference of 5000 volts across the discharge sends a current of 10 milliamperes between the electrodes. This would be expected to deposit an opaque platinum mirror upon the glass in the course of two hours.   However, there are so many variable factors entering into the phenomenon that accurate predictions are difficult to make.   Other conditions remaining the same, the mass in grams deposited uniformly over unit area each second (the rate of sputtering) is directly proportional to the first power of the current and inversely proportional to the first power of the distance from the cathode C to the plate G.

Two kinds of particles leave the cathode. One kind consists of uncharged molecules or atoms of the cathode metal which diffuse in all directions so that the plate, and to some extent the jar, become coated with a thin film of the metal. The other particles are electrons which leave the cathode at right angles and travel with high velocity, causing considerable heating of the plate and jar. These electrons may be deflected by a small magnetic field (10 to 25 oersteds) so as to prevent overheating the plate. The sputtering is thought to be due to evaporation of the metal from small spots on the cathode surface which have been struck by ions falling through the large potential drop in the cathode dark space. The ions come from the gas in the jar. Metals which sputter with difficulty in the residual air can be made to do so if certain gases, such as argon, are used. Gold, platinum, copper, iron, tungsten, silver and nickel may be deposited with comparative ease in the residual air, while aluminum and silicon are difficult to sputter.

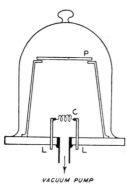

FIG. 16–18.   Evaporation apparatus.

If the cathode dark space touches the plate where the deposit is being formed, the cross gradient of potential sets up large currents in the thin metal, blistering it.

16–24. Evaporation Process.[9]—It is possible to deposit a coating of metal on the surface of a body with the apparatus shown in figure 16–18. In this simple evaporation apparatus, the material to be deposited is volatilized in the heating coil (C). Particles of the material travel out from C in straight lines and deposit on the lower surface of the plate (P). This method has the advantage that it is possible to deposit materials, such as aluminum, which are difficult, as well as those which are easy to sputter. Further, the body to be coated remains cool, and may even be a wax, provided its vapor pressure is low, such as Apiezon wax W. A large electrical current is required instead of the high voltage used in sputtering. The disadvantage is that the system must be highly evacuated (10^{-5} millimeter of mercury) and a fast pump must be used to remove the gases thrown out when the material is evaporating. The amount of material deposited per square centimeter is inversely proportional to the square of the distance between the source and the mirror and to the cosine of the angle of incidence of the particles upon the mirror, provided the distances are not excessively large.

In a particular evaporation apparatus, the coil (C) was located 15 centimeters below the plate (P) and consisted of 15 closely wound turns of 30 mil tungsten wire wound on a rod 5 millimeters in diameter. Aluminum pellets were boiled in nitric acid for approximately one-half of one minute, thoroughly washed in distilled water, dried and then placed inside the coil (C) (half filling it). The clean glass plate was placed on its tripod, the cover added and sealed with wax. The system was evacuated below the conducting stage (tested with a large spark coil). Then about 40 amperes (a.c.) were used to heat the coil for 5 seconds.

For greater distances between C and P, more of the material must be used. If the separation is too small, the aluminum deposit will be discolored or have a powdery surface. For very thick coats, or for large surfaces, several coils must be used and the separation must be increased if the deposit is to be uniform. An opaque film of aluminum is 10^{-5} to 10^{-6} centimeter thick. Blisters will occur if the glass was not thoroughly cleaned. Clean with soap, water, KOH, water, nitric acid, distilled water and rub with cotton. The surface does not need to be so clean if a thin chromium layer is first deposited. (See below.) The higher the vacuum, the harder and brighter the aluminum coating. Some workers evaporate the aluminum as rapidly as possible, relying on its " getter action " to assist the pumps; others use one or two minutes for the complete evaporation.

When the pressure is in the range from 2 to 5×10^{-3} mm., run a high voltage discharge (spark coil or small transformer) between an electrode in the top of the bell jar and the base plate. This tends to clean the surface and to form a coating which adheres more strongly.

A shield may be used between coil C and P for a brief time before permitting the metal to deposit on the plate. This avoids an impure underlayer and hence gives a more adherent surface. Aluminum wire may then be used in C without the nitric acid cleaning.

For chromium deposits, put the metal in a small spiral cone (tip down) of 4 or 5 turns of 30 mil tungsten, instead of the coil (*C* of figure 16–18) and heat as rapidly as possible with, say 40 amperes. If three heavy lead rods (*LL* of figure 16–18) are used in a triangular form, both a cone for chromium and a spiral for aluminum can be used in succession without re-evacuating the apparatus.

The cone is used to keep the melted copper from running away. A few grains of gold may be used in a coil.

A tungsten deposit may be obtained by heating a wire of this material very near to its volatilization point. A trial run can be made to determine a safe heating current. For example, an 8 mil wire of this material, $3\frac{1}{8}$ inches long, burned out with $7\frac{1}{2}$ amperes, and when heated with 7 amperes for one hour gave a three-quarter coat at a distance of one centimeter.

Experiment 16–1

METALLIZING MIRRORS AND FIBERS

(1) Sputter an opaque surface of gold on a piece of glass. (See section 16–23.) The glass must be cleaned, with soap, water, potassium hydroxide (KOH), water, then with nitric acid (HNO₃), washed with distilled water, dried and rubbed with cotton before sputtering if the deposit is to be uniform.

(2) Aluminize a glass plate by the evaporation process. (See section 16–24.) Clean the glass with soap, water, nitric acid, distilled water. Deposit a thin layer of chromium, then a layer of aluminum without admitting air.

(3) Metallize an electrometer fiber. Quartz fibers are prepared by heating the tips of two quartz rods to white heat in an oxygen flame and drawing one of them across the other. The flame blows the fine threads away. To catch them, place a piece of cardboard, stuck full of pins, at an angle in front and a little above. To prepare an electrometer suspension, choose a fiber of appropriate length and fasten a small lug and a square hook of fine tungsten wire to its ends by means of small drops of shellac and lampblack. The lampblack serves to insure electrical contact between the tungsten and platinum coating which is to be sputtered on. Mount half a dozen fibers parallel to each other between

the sides of a rectangle of stiff wire, holding them in place with drops of shellac or glyptal. The rectangle should have legs to support it in a horizontal position about one half an inch above the table. Place this in the sputtering apparatus about eight or nine centimeters from the cathode and reduce the pressure until the edge of the cathode dark space is about half way between the cathode and the fibers. Using a one-half kilowatt, ten thousand volt transformer, a conducting coat of platinum should be secured in about thirty minutes. For gold the time will be about half that for platinum.

REFERENCES

1. C. R. Burch, Nature, **122**, 729 (1928).
2. Sloan, Thornton and Jenkins, Rev. Sci. Inst., **6**, 80 (1935).
3. K. C. D. Hickman, Jr. Frank. Inst., **221**, 215 (1936).
   A. E. Lockenvitz, Rev. Sci. Inst., **8**, 322 (1937).
4. G. C. Dunlap and J. G. Trump, Rev. Sci. Inst., **8**, 37 (1937).
5. O. E. Buckley, Proc. Nat. Acad. Sci., **2**, 683 (1916).
6. Jaycox and Weinhart, Rev. Sci. Inst., **2**, 401 (1931).
   See also, J. B. H. Kuper, Rev. Sci. Inst., **8**, 394 (1937).
7. J. B. Hoag and N. M. Smith, Rev. Sci. Inst., **7**, 497 (1936).
8. R. M. Zabel, Rev. Sci. Inst., **4**, 233 (1933).
9. J. Strong, Astro. Jr., **83**, 401 (1936).
   F. Pearson, unpublished.
   H. W. Edwards, Rev. Sci. Inst., **8**, 451 (1937).
10. A. L. Hughes, Rev. Sci. Inst., **8**, 409 (1937).
11. Brown, DiNardo, Cheng and Sherwood, Jr. Ap. Phys., **17**, 802 (1946).

GENERAL REFERENCES

A.—S. Dushman, *The Production and Measurement of High Vacuum.* General Electric Co. (1922).

B.—L. Dunoyer, Translated by J. H. Smith, *Vacuum Practice.* Bell & Sons (1926).

C.—F. H. Newman, *The Production and Measurement of Low Pressures.* D. Van Nostrand Co. (1925).

D.—G. W. C. Kaye, *High Vacua.* Longmans, Green & Co. (1927).

E.—J. Yarwood, *High Vacuum Technique.* John Wiley & Sons, Inc. (Second Edition, 1945).

F.—Strong, Neher, Cartwright, Whitford and Hayward, *Procedures in Experimental Physics.* Prentice-Hall (1938).

CHAPTER 17

SMALL CURRENT TECHNIQUE

17–1. Introduction.—Special instruments are used to measure electrical currents which are too small to be detected with galvanometers. These currents, which are of the order of magnitude of 10^{-8} to 10^{-17} ampere, are often encountered in work with radio-active substances, x-rays, etc., and consist of streams of comparatively large numbers of charged particles. Their measurement will be discussed in this chapter while those cases where there are so few moving charges that the particles may be observed individually will be dealt with in chapter 18.

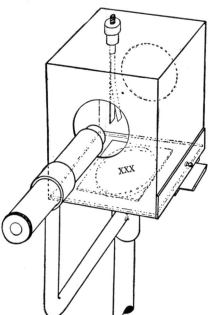

Fig. 17–1. An electroscope.

ELECTROSCOPES

17–2. Principle of the Electroscope.—A given sample of radio-active substance sends out a definite number of alpha, beta or gamma particles. The number of ions which these can produce in air or other gas at a fixed temperature and pressure is directly proportional to the number of particles. If saturation voltages are applied across the gas, all ions produced will be drawn out. Hence, the ionization is directly related to the number of grams of radio-active substance. In an electroscope such as that of figure 17–1, the case acts as one plate of an ionization chamber, the leaf as the other plate. The usual electroscopes require several hundred volts between the leaf and the case to deflect the leaf 30 to 50 degrees from the vertical. This is suffi-cient to insure saturation. The ions which reach the leaf neutralize its charge and cause it to fall at a rate proportional to the amount of active substance producing the ionization. Thus, the rate of fall of the leaf of an electroscope is a measure of the *intensity* of a radioactive substance.

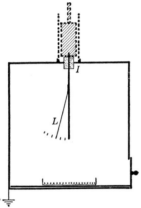

Fig. 17–2. An alpha ray elec-troscope.

17–3. Various Forms of Electro-scopes.—Electroscopes have special designs according to the type of ray to be measured, the condition (solid, liquid or gas) and the strength of the active material. The insulators (I) in all electroscopes must be of the best and must be kept clean. Amber is most commonly used.

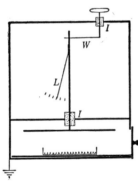

Fig. 17–3. An alpha ray electroscope of large capac-ity.

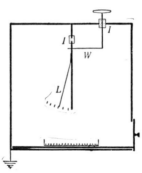

Fig. 17–4. An alpha ray electroscope of small capac-ity.

In the *solids* electroscope[1] of figures 17–1, 2, 3, and 4, the active substance is placed at *xxx*, ionizing the gas immediately above. When all three rays are emitted, they all contribute to the ionization current but, since the alpha rays are by far the strongest ionizers, the instrument is spoken of as an *alpha ray* electroscope.

In figure 17–3, the leaf system L is entirely enclosed in the upper metal box and the ionization chamber is in a separate compartment below.   The leaf is charged by means of the fine wire W which is then rotated to touch the grounded case.   The capacity of the leaf and the lower metal plate, with respect to the case, is comparatively large in this type of instrument, perhaps several hundred e.s.u.   Therefore, a comparatively *strong* radioactive substance is needed to discharge the leaf at a sufficient rate for accurate timing.

The electroscope of figures 17–1 or 2 usually has a capacity of approximately 10. to 60 e.s.u.   If the leaf is found to drop more rapidly than desired for accurate timing, due to the use of a strong source, add a condenser of several hundred e.s.u. capacity in parallel with the leaf and case.   This may consist of a small concentric cylinder condenser, as in the dotted lines of figure 17–2 or an auxiliary condenser built with excellent insulation and connected with a shielded lead wire to the leaf and case.   The natural leak of the instrument will be altered by the addition of the condenser.

For measuring *feeble sources*, the capacity of the leaf system with respect to the ground must be small; 2 or 3 e.s.u. as shown in figure 17–4.

Figure 17–5 shows the Wilson tilted electroscope, a form which is particularly *sensitive* because of its small capacity and the position in which the leaf is used for observation. The leaf is attracted to the charged plate P and takes up

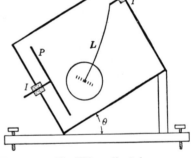

Fig. 17–5.   The Wilson tilted electroscope.

a position of equilibrium which approaches instability under the influence of gravity and the attraction to P.

In the Zeleny[2] electroscope, the insulated leaf is attracted by electrostatic induction to a metal plate whose potential, with respect to the case, is kept constant at 50 to 200 volts. When the leaf touches, it acquires a charge of the same sign as that of the plate and is vigorously repelled. Ions formed in the gas around the leaf neutralize its charge until it is again attracted to the plate. The number of *oscillations* of the leaf each second is a measure of the strength of the ionizing source.

Beta ray electroscopes are similar to those of figure 17–1 and 2, except that an aluminum sheet about 0.006 centimeter thick is placed over the active material to cut off all alpha rays. The ionization in the leaf chamber is then due to the beta and gamma rays together. The former, however, are much better ionizers than the latter, so that the fall of the leaf is largely due to the beta activity.

For measuring *gamma ray* activity alone, the electroscope must be built of or completely surrounded by lead two or three millimeters thick in order to cut off all alpha and beta rays. If the source is very strong, the active material may be placed several feet from the electroscope. When comparing two sources (one of which may be a standard) whose activities are quite different, each may be placed at a convenient distance, so that the rate of fall of the leaf permits accurate measurement. Correction is made using the inverse square law. For example, if the rates of fall of the leaf are R_1 and R_2 when the sources are at d_1 and d_2, respectively, figure 17–6, then the intensities I_1 and I_2 are in the ratio

$$I_1/I_2 = R_1 d_2^2 / R_2 d_1^2. \tag{17-1}$$

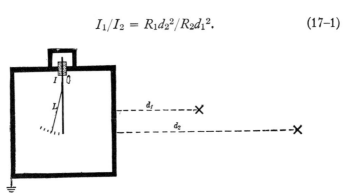

FIG. 17–6. A gamma ray electroscope.

For determining the activity of a gas, an *emanation* electroscope as in figure 17–7 may be used. The ionization chamber C is carefully cleaned and evacuated, then filled with gas. The leaf system *EL* is charged by the wire *W* and draws ions of opposite sign to the collecting electrode *E* which results in a movement of the leaf proportional to the intensity of the emanation.

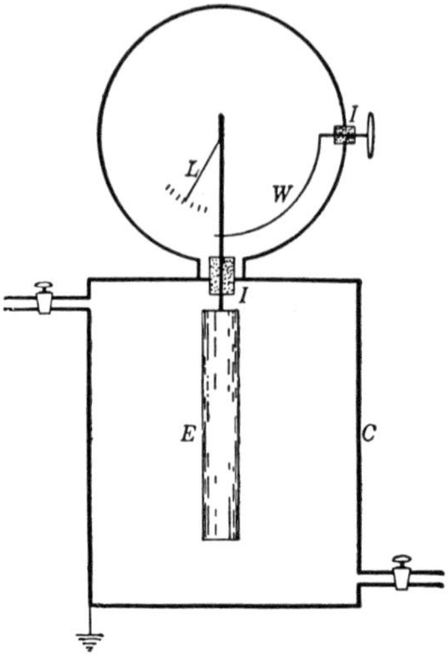

Electroscopes for measuring cosmic radiation have been devised by Millikan and Neher. In this unit the sensitive element consists of a quartz fiber on which gold has been evaporated to render it conducting. Instead of using gravity to provide the restoring force, torsional force in the quartz fibre is used. This provides a rugged system which can be operated in any position and is amazingly free from vibrational disturbances. The electroscope can, therefore, be operated for example in a moving airplane.

Fig. 17-7.

An emanation electroscope.

The sensitive element from the cosmic-ray electroscope has also been adapted to a small portable unit, called the Lauritsen electroscope. The entire unit is built into a housing the size of a fountain pen. The device can be carried around by a person working in an x-ray or radioactive laboratory, and will serve as a warning device to inform him when he is getting a dangerous amount of exposure to radiation. See figure 17-8A.

Fast neutrons eject protons from paraffin. The ionization of a gas by the recoil protons can be used as a measure of the neutron intensity. The *neutron electroscope*[3] of figure 17-8 consists of a sensitive electroscope in a cylindrical chamber (*A*) of, perhaps, 8 centimeters length and 5 centimeters diameter. The inner walls of the chamber are coated with paraffin (*B*) approximately one millimeter thick, over which

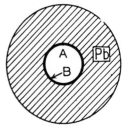

Fig. 17-8. A neutron electroscope.

a wire gauze is placed. A heavy shield of lead, say 5 centimeters
thick, is placed around the chamber to screen out less penetrating
radiations, such as x-rays. The observing telescope is mounted
inside a hole in the lead and covered with a lead plug except when
readings are made.

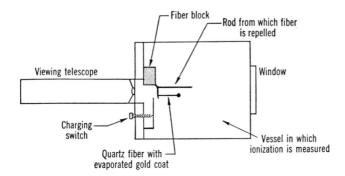

Fig. 17-8A. Simplified diagram of a Lauritsen electroscope. The position of the
quartz fiber is viewed through the viewing telescope with the aid of light admitted
through the ground-glass window. When the electroscope is charged, the fiber
stands away from the rod, and then approaches the rod as ions are collected. The
time-rate-of-change of position of the fiber is proportional to the amount of ionizing
radiation passing through the vessel.

Slow neutrons can also be detected by the electroscope technique. Since slow neutrons do not produce recoils of appreciable
energy, another principle must be used. In this case, use can be
made of the fact that slow neutrons produce disintegrations. The
nuclei of B^{10} will capture slow neutrons efficiently, i.e., the reaction
has a large cross section. The nucleus then disintegrates and an
alpha particle is emitted. The alpha particle will ionize very
heavily along a short track, and is therefore admirably adapted to
detection by electroscope technique. In order to provide enough
boron nuclei, two procedures are possible. The electroscope may
be filled with a boron gas, such as boron trifluoride. In this case,
the disintegrations take place in the gas of the chamber. Alterna-
tively, the walls of the electroscope may be lined with boron, in
which case, the disintegration alpha particles are ejected from
the walls.

The electroscope is essentially a potential measuring instrument. The *Braun voltmeter* of figure 17–9 is used to measure potentials from 0 to 10,000 volts. The potential is applied between *A* and *B* causing the comparatively heavy aluminum needle *L* to move over the calibrated scale *S*. The instrument does not draw an appreciable amount of current for its operation.

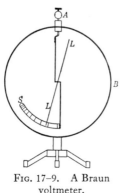

17–4. Adjustment of an Electroscope.— Keep the fingers off the insulator at all times.

The case of an electroscope should be grounded in order to reduce irregularities in its operation.

Fig. 17–9. A Braun voltmeter.

One of the simplest methods for charging the leaf of an electroscope is to stretch a rubber band, then touch it to the charging rod and slowly move it along until the deflection is of the desired amount. If the deflection is too great, flick the corner of a small piece of paper across the charging rod. Each movement will remove only a small amount of electricity and the leaf may be brought down very close to the desired position.

Adjust the telescope until only the edge of the leaf is sharply in focus. Use the same small irregularity on its edge as a reference mark in all work. The divisions in the eyepiece of the telescope should be parallel to the edge of the leaf at the center of the scale. Care must be taken to avoid parallax.

It is customary to use the same range of divisions, say from the tenth to the twentieth division. This is necessary since the deflections of the leaf are not always strictly proportional to the deflecting voltage.

17–5. The Natural Leak of an Electroscope.—The leaf of an electroscope will fall back slowly to the uncharged position even though there is no known radioactive substance nearby. The number of divisions which the leaf passes over each second, or more usually, the reciprocal of the time to pass over the chosen range of scale divisions, is called the natural leak.

The natural leak should be measured occasionally during an experiment and its average value subtracted from the activities observed during these intervals.

The natural leak should be such that it is only a small percentage of the activity being measured. Usually this means that the natural fall of the leaf can just be seen, amounting to, perhaps, one small division per minute in an electroscope of the type shown in figure 17-1. It is due to leakage across the surface of the insulator, local radioactive contaminations and cosmic rays.

To reduce the natural leak: (1) Clean the insulator with ether or alcohol and wipe with a clean lint-free cloth. In extreme cases, the surface of the insulator may be scraped with a razor blade or a sharp knife. Only a thin layer need be removed. (2) Sandpaper the metal parts, wash with ether or alcohol and wipe with a clean cloth. (3) When first used, the natural leak will be large, as the insulator "soaks up a charge." It should decrease exponentially and be sufficiently constant that measurements may be made after one-half to one hour. (4) It may be necessary to place a small metal cap over the top of the charging rod, where it projects above the instrument. The cap is removed to charge the leaf and must always be replaced in exactly the same position. (5) With humid conditions, it is useful to place a drying agent in the electroscope. Calcium chloride, phosphorous pentoxide or sulphuric acid are suitable. (6) If the natural leak is still high, move to another location, as there is probably some contaminating material in the room.

17-6. Inserting a New Leaf.—Aluminum leaf is easier to handle but gold leaf is steadier in operation.

Clean the supporting metal strip with ether or alcohol and wipe with a clean, lint-free cloth. Spread a *very small* amount of soft beeswax over the upper end of the support, down to the transverse scratch in the metal which serves as the hinging line for the leaf.

Cut a piece of foil to the proper size, keeping it between two of the sheets of paper that it comes in. A razor, freshly cleaned with ether or alcohol, is used. Do not press down too hard on the guiding ruler or the foil will stick to the paper. Carefully remove the top paper and place the waxed end of the support strip on one end of the foil. Only a touch is needed to make them stick together. Invert carefully and press the foil gently into the wax in order to insure good electrical contact and to define the hinging line of the foil. Now place the leaf in its case.

17-7. Calibration of an Electroscope.—*Voltage Calibration.*—
When the leaf is charged, its potential is raised to a fixed value.
Connect a battery or other source of potential of, perhaps, 200 to
600 volts between the leaf and the case. Change the potential so as
to bring the leaf to the different divisions of the scale and plot a
curve of the deflections *vs.* volts. A resistance of 10,000 to 100,000
ohms may well be used in series with the battery as a protection
against a short circuit of the leaf to the case. The voltmeter should
be connected across the battery at the time the readings are taken,
unless it is of very high resistance or is of the electrostatic type
requiring negligible current in its operation. It will be found that,
at least over a limited number of scale divisions, deflections are
directly proportional to the applied voltage. Since the capacity between the leaf system and the case is only approximately constant,
the deflections are not, in general, strictly proportional to the
voltages. For accurate comparisons of ionization currents, the rate
of fall of the leaf should be observed over the same divisions or
correction made for the non-linearity of the scale.

Capacity of the Leaf System.—The capacity (C) of the "leaf
system" consists of that of the leaf, its support and any conductors connected thereto, with respect to the surrounding grounded
casings. It is found by adding a small standard condenser (C_o) in
parallel with it, as indicated by the dotted lines of figure 17-2, and
observing the fall of the leaf as compared with that of the leaf system alone. (1) Measure the natural leak with and without the
additional capacity. (2) Insert a radioactive material so that the
leaf falls across ten divisions rapidly; for instance, in five or ten
seconds when C_o is absent. Let this time be t'_1 seconds. (3)
Repeat (2) with C_o added. Let this longer time be t'_2. (4) Subtract the corresponding natural leaks from the reciprocals of t'_1
and t'_2 and again take reciprocals. These corrected times are to be
called t_1 and t_2. (5) Find the capacity (C_o) of the standard condenser. If this is made of concentric cylinders,

$$C_o = \frac{l}{2 \log_e b/a} \qquad (17\text{-}2)$$

where l is the length of the shorter cylinder in centimeters; b, the
inside radius of the outer cylinder and a, the outside radius of the
inner cylinder in centimeters. It is highly important that the two

cylinders be coaxial; i.e., uniform spacing between them all around. If the spacing is small compared to the radii of the cylinders, correction for end effects will be negligible. From the equation above, C_o will be in "centimeters" (= e.s.u.). Dividing by 900,000 will give micro-farads or by 9×10^{11} will give farads.

(6) The current (i) due to the active material is the same whether the capacity is C or $C + C_o$, and is equal to the rate of flow (q/t) of quantity (q) of electricity. Thus,

$$i = q/t = C \cdot \Delta V/t_1 = (C + C_o)\Delta V/t_2 , \qquad (17\text{--}3)$$

where ΔV is the voltage change of the leaf system, which is the same in both cases since observations were made over the same divisions in the eyepiece of the telescope. It follows that the capacity C of the leaf system can be computed from the equation. Thus

$$C = C_o \frac{t_1}{t_2 - t_1}. \qquad (17\text{--}4)$$

This will be in the same units as C_o.

Ionization Current.—From the voltage calibration curve, one may determine the drop of potential ΔV corresponding to the movement of the leaf over a definite number of divisions. Substitution of 17–4 in 17–3 gives

$$i = \frac{C_o \cdot \Delta V}{t_2 - t_1}. \qquad (17\text{--}5)$$

The same units are used on both sides of the equation.

Number of Ions per Second, n.—This is equal to the ionization current i divided by the charge (e) on each ion. Thus,

$$n = i/e \qquad (17\text{--}6)$$

For example, assume that when a given radioactive substance is placed in an electroscope the leaf falls at a rate which, on calibration of the instrument, proves to be due to a current of 10^{-12} amperes or 3×10^{-3} e.s.u. Then, the charge of each ion being 4.8×10^{-10} e.s.u., the number of ions formed each second was 6.2×10^6.

Alpha Particle Activity.—From other studies it is known that each alpha particle produces a total of approximately 1.74×10^5 ions. Hence, if all the energy of the alpha particles was utilized in the ionization process, their number is equal to $n/1.74 \times 10^5$. In the example above, 37 effective alpha particles were emitted each second, or 37 atoms disintegrated in unit time. From the definition given in section 11–3, the activity $\mathscr{A}$ was 10^{-6} millicuries. Thus, $\mathscr{A} = n/(1.74 \times 10^5)$ (3.71×10^7) millicuries. This is the activity observed by the electroscope. Other atoms may have disintegrated: atoms whose alpha particles were absorbed in the radioactive material. A comparison of the activities of a known and unknown material requires their use in approximately equal areas and thicknesses and that they be placed in the same position in the electroscope. Usually, very thin layers of the active substance are used.

ELECTROMETERS

17–8. Principle and Use of the Quadrant Electrometer.—This instrument is used to measure currents and voltages. It operates on the principle of electrostatic repulsion. Essentially, there are three parts: two fixed conductors, called the quadrants, and a suspended conductor, called the needle. As ordinarily used, the needle is charged to a high fixed potential (100 volts) and a difference of potential is applied between the quadrants. The needle is attracted toward one of the quadrants and repelled by the other. The rate at which the needle moves is a measure of the current and the final deflection is a measure of the difference of potential between the quadrants.

The quadrant electrometer is generally used to measure currents ranging from about 10^{-8} ampere (the usual limit of the ordinary wall type galvanometer) to 10^{-15} or 10^{-16} of an ampere (such as produced in a gas by the action of radioactive substances, x-rays or ultra-violet light). It can be adapted for measurements of larger currents but is not as convenient as the galvanometer or ammeter. It will measure potential differences from 10^{-5} to 10 volts and, in the special Kelvin form, it will measure many thousand volts, a.c. or d.c.

17-9. Description of the Instrument.—The Dolezalek is the most common of the many forms of electrometers (figure 17–10). The needle is made of aluminum, flat and figure-eight-shaped, suspended by a gold, phosphor bronze or platinized quartz fiber between the quadrants. The quadrants consist of a pill-box-shaped brass chamber split into four parts. Opposite quadrants are connected together with wires, each pair serving as one fixed conductor. The needle and quadrants are supported with amber or quartz since great care must be taken with extremely small currents to minimize any leak of the electricity. The apparatus is surrounded by a grounded metal case, not shown in the figure, which cuts off air currents and stray electro-static effects or charges. The rotation of the needle is observed with a scale and a telescope focused on a small mirror fastened to the suspension.

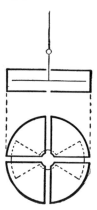

Fig. 17–10. The Dolezalek electrometer.

17-10. Electrometer Connections.—Figure 17–11 shows the *heterostatic* connection for use in measuring the voltage v. The needle N is kept at a high potential (30 to 160 volts) by the battery V. One pair of quadrants is grounded and the other is raised to the potential (v) which is to be measured. A protective resistance P of large value (a radio resistor, 10^4 to 10^6 ohms) must be used to prevent burning out the battery and suspension in case the needle should accidentally touch one of the quadrants.

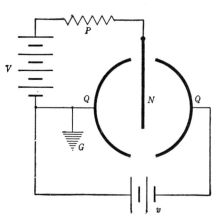

Fig. 17–11. "Heterostatic" voltage connection of an electrometer.

The ground G (such as a water pipe) serves to prevent surrounding objects from inducing charges and may be made at any point in the connections, provided the entire apparatus is carefully shielded.

Figure 17–12 shows the *idiostatic* connection for measuring the voltage *v*. Here the needle and one of the quadrants are

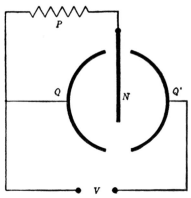

raised to the same potential (with respect to the other quadrant *Q'*). The applied voltage may be either alternating or direct in this case since the needle is attracted (rotated) in the same direction whether it is positive and the free quadrant *Q'* negative or vice versa. It is to be noted that the instrument does not use any current when operated in the heterostatic or idiostatic manner.

Fig. 17–12. "Idiostatic" voltage connection of an electrometer.

Figure 17–13 shows the connection for measuring a small current passing between the plates *A* and *B* by the so-called *rate of deflection method*. Charges of electricity formed in the gas between *A* and *B* (by a radio-

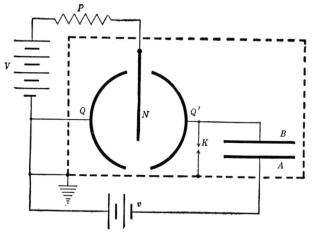

Fig. 17–13. Measurement of a small current with an electrometer by the rate of deflection method.

active substance, x-rays, ultra-violet light, etc.) are driven to plate *B* by the accelerating potential *v*. As the charge builds

up on B and Q', the needle is deflected at a rate depending on
the strength of the current from A to B. K is a grounding key
short circuiting the quadrants and is only opened at the time
readings are being taken. This
key should be closed when the
battery v is first connected,
to prevent the large induced
charge on B from reaching the
quadrant. It is important that
the quadrant Q', the key K
and the plate B be *carefully
shielded* at all times with a
grounded metal case in order
to prevent the addition of induced charges to those collected from between the plates A
and B. This is indicated in figure 17–13 by the dotted lines.

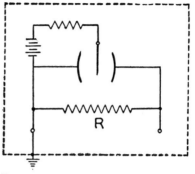

Fig. 17–14. Measurement of a small
current with an electrometer by the
constant deflection method.

The *constant deflection method* of measuring small currents is
more convenient than the preceding method but is not as sensitive.
It is satisfactory down to approximately 10^{-13} ampere. As shown
in figure 17–14, the unknown
current i passes through the
high resistance R (10^6 to 10^{10}
ohms) producing a potential
drop (iR) which is measured in
terms of the deflection of the
electrometer needle. As in all
small current work, great care
must be taken to insulate the
ungrounded quadrant and its
associated conductors and to
shield all parts against stray
ions and electric fields.

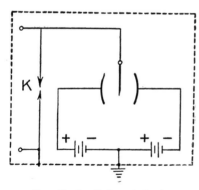

Fog. 17–15. Balanced circuit.

In the *balanced circuit* of
figure 17–15, the unknown potential is applied to the needle and
ground. One of the quadrants is raised to a fixed positive potential, the other to an equal negative potential, with respect to the
ground. The grounded point or one of the batteries is varied

slightly, until, with K closed, a zero deflection is obtained. Either of the methods for current measurement may then be used.

17–11. Calibration for Voltage Measurements.—The procedure to be used in the adjustment and voltage calibration of an electrometer is given in experiment 17–1.

There are three things to be considered in calibrating an electrometer for voltage measurements; first, the voltage sensitiveness or number of millimeters deflection on a scale one meter away caused by one volt across the quadrants; second, the variations of the sensitiveness with deflection and with needle potential; third, the period of free swing. It is desirable that the sensitiveness be constant over the entire scale and that it be high when dealing with small differences of voltage, even at a sacrifice of the range of the instrument. Further, the period must not be too great for convenience in making the readings.

The curve showing the deflections at increasing voltage across the quadrants (constant needle potential) is not, in general, a straight line. In other words, the voltage to cause a deflection from 0 to 3 centimeters is not the same as that from 3 to 6 centimeters, etc. The elementary theory (Starling, " Electricity and Magnetism," p. 157, 4th Edition) of a Dolezalek electrometer leads to the following equation for the deflection θ (radians rotation of the needle),

$$\theta = K(v_1 - v_2) \left(V - \frac{v_1 + v_2}{2} \right) \qquad (17\text{–}7)$$

where K is a constant, v_1 and v_2 are the potentials of the quadrants with respect to the ground and V is the potential of the needle with respect to the ground.

With the idiostatic connection, the needle is connected directly to one of the quadrants, and $V = v_1$ so that equation 17–7 reduces to

$$\theta = \frac{K}{2} (v_1 - v_2)^2 = \frac{K}{2} v^2, \qquad (17\text{–}8)$$

stating that the deflection is proportional to the square of the potential difference between the quadrants. Thus the Kelvin multicellular electrostatic voltmeters are provided with a " squared " scale.

With the heterostatic connection, the needle potential V is great compared with the potentials of the quadrants, i.e., $V > \dfrac{v_1 + v_2}{2}$ so that equation 17–7 reduces to

$$\theta = KV(v_1 - v_2) = KVv \qquad (17\text{--}9)$$

where
$$v = v_1 - v_2 \qquad (17\text{--}10)$$

and the sensitiveness is
$$S = \frac{\theta}{v} = KV \qquad (17\text{--}11)$$

stating that the deflections are linearly proportional to the quadrant voltage. This is found to be nearly true in practice but for accurate work it is necessary to calibrate the scale in terms of volts or to use a small part of the scale near the zero reading.

Equation 17–11 also indicates that the deflections are directly proportional to the potential of the needle. This is far from true in practice. In the elementary theory, the electrostatic field between the needle and quadrants is assumed to be uniform. Obviously there is a distortion of the lines of force at the edges of

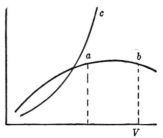

Fig. 17–16. Sensitiveness of an electrometer with various needle potentials.

the conductors which is different with different positions of the needle. This *electrostatic distortion* * introduces a couple, sometimes aiding and sometimes opposing the restoring couple of the twisted suspension. The direction of this couple depends on the construction and adjustment of the instrument. Results obtained experimentally are shown in figure 17–16. Curve ab is for the case where the electrostatic distortion couple aids the mechanical restoring couple and shows that between points a and b the needle

* The theory is discussed in Chapter I of Makower and Geiger's " Practical Measurements in Radioactivity." This leads to the corrected form for sensitivity given by

$$S = \frac{\theta}{v} = \frac{K_1 V}{K_2 + K_3 V^2}$$

for the case where the electrostatic distortion couple aids the mechanical restoring couple. The K's are constants. See also reference 5.

potential may vary considerably without appreciably affecting the sensitiveness. Curve c is for the case where the two couples oppose each other and shows that very high sensitivity may be obtained. When the electrometer is in this condition, a very small change of needle voltage causes large variations of the sensitiveness and may even throw the instrument into an unstable condition.

17–12. Calibration for Current Measurements.—*Constant Deflection Method.*—It is assumed that the resistance (R) of figure 17–14 is known. The voltage drop ($v = iR$) across R is determined from the deflection-quadrant voltage curve of the preceding section. Then,

$$i = v/R. \qquad (17\text{–}12)$$

Rate of Deflection Method.—The quadrant electrometer is generally used *to compare different currents* but may be used in an absolute determination. In the former case, the rate of deflection of the needle, taken over a given part of the scale and with fixed needle potential, is measured for the different currents. If this is not too large, it is directly proportional to their relative strengths. This linearity can be seen from the following considerations. The current i is that due to a flow of q units of electricity (usually in e.s.u.) between the plates of the ionization chamber (A and B of figure 17–13) in a time t. If the capacity of the upper plate and quadrant (B, Q') is C and its voltage increase is Δv, then

$$i = \frac{q}{t} = \frac{C \cdot \Delta v}{t}. \qquad (17\text{–}13)$$

Now, in the discussion of voltage calibration, it was shown that the deflection may be considered as roughly proportional to the voltage increase on the quadrant. Hence we have

$$i = \frac{C}{S'} \frac{\Delta\theta}{t} = K' \frac{\Delta\theta}{t} \qquad (17\text{–}14)$$

where $\dfrac{1}{S'}$ is the constant of proportionality. Now K' will not be a constant if the capacity C varies with the needle position or if

S' changes in any way. Both of these quantities do change somewhat and S' is a complicated function of the needle potential.* This is due to four couples; first, the electrical couple of attraction and repulsion of the electrical charges; second, the mechanical restoring couple; third, the electrostatic distortion couple, and fourth, an additional damping effect caused by the reaction of the charges set up on the quadrants by the motion of the charged needle, known as the *inductional electrostatic control*. This last is analogous to the damping effect of a loop of wire on the moving coil of a galvanometer. Thus, in order that the rates of deflection of the needle of the quadrant electrometer may be taken as proportional to the currents to be compared, it is necessary to use the same part of the scale and to keep the needle potential fixed.

To measure a current in *absolute units* (e.s.u.), observe the time t_1 for a deflection of $\Delta\theta$ centimeters (about 10) on the scale. This was caused by a charge of amount q_1 e.s.u., collecting on the quadrant. If C is the capacity (e.s.u.) of the insulated quadrant and all connected apparatus with respect to the ground, then

$$q_1 = it_1 = C\Delta v = K''\Delta\theta \qquad (17\text{-}15)$$

where Δv is the increase in voltage due to charge q_1. This may be obtained from the voltage-deflection calibration previously discussed. Now connect a small standard condenser of capacity C_0 (10–50 e.s.u.) in parallel with ionization chamber. It will now require a longer time, t_2, for the same current i to give the same deflection $\Delta\theta$. Then

$$q_2 = it_2 = (C + C_0)\Delta v = K\Delta\theta \qquad (17\text{-}16)$$

Whence

$$i = \frac{C_0\Delta v}{t_2 - t_1}. \qquad (17\text{-}17)$$

The standard condenser may consist of two long concentric metal cylinders of nearly the same radius. Its capacity can be computed from equation 17-2.

$$* S = \frac{\theta}{v} = \frac{K_1 V}{K_2 + K_3 V^2 + \dfrac{K_4}{C} V^2}$$

17–13. Capacity of the Quadrant System.—This includes the capacity of the insulated quadrant, the connecting wires and the insulated collector in the associated ionization chamber, or other auxiliary equipment, with respect to the grounded casings. A procedure identical with that just given for measuring the absolute value of a current may be used. Equations 17–15 and 17–16 give

$$C = C_0 \frac{t_1}{t_2 - t_1}. \tag{17-4}$$

The inductional method of Harms[4] offers greater accuracy in determining the capacity of an electrometer than that just described. Although simple in operation, its discussion is too detailed to be included here.

17–14. Measurement of Quantity of Electricity.—If a quantity of electricity (q) is placed on an insulated quadrant system having capacity (C), the needle will be deflected to a voltage (v). Then

$$q = Cv \tag{17-18}$$

where all values are measured in the same units. Here, v is obtained from the voltage-deflection curve.

17–15. Various Forms of Electrometers.—The previous discussion has centered about the Dolezalek type since it is one of the most widely used of the various forms. Many other types have been designed, some using only two quadrants, others as many as six sectors in place of the usual four of the quadrant form. In some, the potential, current or quantity to be measured is applied to the quadrants while, in others, the needle is used and the quadrants are raised to a fixed potential. In the following paragraphs, a note is given on each of the principal types.

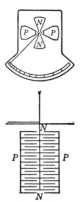

Fig. 17–17. The Kelvin electro-static voltmeter

The needle N of the *Kelvin* electro-static voltmeter of figure 17–17 is constructed of several thin, figure-eight-shaped aluminum plates suspended horizontally at their centers at equal distances along a vertical suspension. These move toward and between the two sets of fixed plates PP (one for each end of the needle) like the rotor plates of a variable condenser in a radio set. One set of fixed plates and the needle are connected to one terminal of the instrument while the other set of fixed plates is joined to the second binding post, so that the meter operates idiostatically. The instrument is rugged in construction and covers a wide range of voltages (zero to many thousand) either a.c. or d.c. Unlike the D'Arsonval type meters, it does not use any current for its operation. It requires leveling before being used.

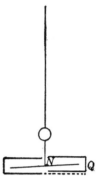

Fig. 17–18. The Compton electrometer.

If the needle of a Dolezalek electrometer is tilted slightly along its axis, the electro-static and mechanical restoring couples oppose each other. This means that a smaller needle voltage is needed to produce a given deflection than if the couples aid each other, and that the instrument will have a high sensitivity. In the *Compton* electrometer[6] of figure 17–18, the needle is tilted and also one quadrant is displaced a little above or below the plane of the other three. These changes, together with the reduced size of the quadrants and needle (giving smaller capacity) make the instrument unusually sensitive. A sensitivity of 15,000 millimeters per volt has been obtained without unduly sacrificing the uniformity of the scale deflections or the rapidity with which readings can be taken. The instrument is more difficult to handle in its highly sensitive state than the Dolezalek type.

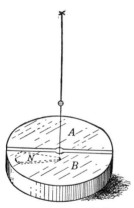

Fig. 17–19. The Hoffmann electrometer.

The *Hoffmann* electrometer of figure 17–19 uses a needle suspended in a small pill-box-shaped metal chamber which has been cut into two parts. For this reason, it is sometimes referred to as a binary or duant electrometer, as contrasted with the quadrant form cut into four parts. These binants (halves) *AB* are raised to a small fixed potential (1–12 volts) and the charge to be measured is applied to the needle N. This needle is an extremely thin platinum sheet suspended at one end (instead of the middle) and located symmetrically with respect to the two halves, close to the lower plates. The binants are surrounded with a heavy metal sheath to help maintain a constant tempera-

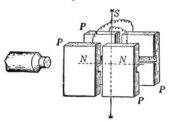

ture. The instrument has a voltage sensitiveness about equal to that of the Dolezalek type but, in view of its small capacity (about 5 e.s.u.), it is able to record much smaller quantities and currents of electricity. For example, it has been used to measure the ionization produced by a single alpha particle.

FIG. 17–20. The Lindemann electrometer.

In the *Lindemann* electrometer[8] of figure 17–20, the suspension S is clamped at both ends and the needle N (which is really needle-shaped) has its center fixed at the center of the suspension (forming a cross) and each end is situated between two metal plates. These four plates $PPPP$ are connected in pairs and act in the same fashion as the quadrants of the Dolezalek electrometer. The motion of the needle is observed with an ordinary microscope. The end of the needle can be made to move about three-quarters of a millimeter per volt so that with an X20 eyepiece in the microscope a sensitivity of around 500 divisions per volt can be attained. The capacity is from 1 to 3 e.s.u. and the needle takes up its final posi-

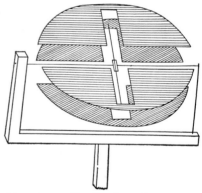

FIG. 17–21. The Dershem electrometer.

tion in from one-fifth to one second (the smaller value for a smaller sensitivity). Further, in view of the method of suspension, the instrument may be tipped in any desired position.

The *Dershem* electrometer of figure 17–21 is a modification of that of Lindemann. A mirror is used at the center of the needle, with consequent magnification of the movement and ease of reading on a large scale The needle can never touch the quadrants, eliminating the need for a series protective resistance and increasing the life of the instrument. Provision is made for the adjustment of the quadrants and the tension and orientation of the needle. In the instruments now available, the dimensions are approximately one and one-half those in the Lindemann electrometer. The suspension is of quartz, metallized by the evaporation process. The unknown voltage is applied to the needle, in a balanced circuit (see figure 17–15) with 20 to 40 volts each side of center for the quadrants (a total of 40–80 volts). The instrument may be tipped in any position. The capacity is approximately 5 to 7 e.s.u.; the period is less than one second. The maximum sensitivity for stable operation is about 4000 milli-meters per volt, at one meter. The usual operating sensitivity ranges from 500 to 1000. It is greater when a fine suspension is used and increases very rapidly with increase in quadrant voltage so that the supply batteries must be accurately constant, especially at the higher sensitivities. When operated in the less sensitive condition a few volts may be required to give a deflection of one millimeter at one

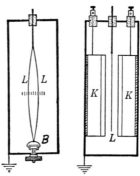

Fig. 17–22. A bifilar electrometer.

Fig. 17–23. A single fiber electrometer.

meter. The scale is uniform up to a rotation of about ten degrees, beyond which the sensitivity falls off. Currents of 10^{-15} ampere can be measured to within one per cent, currents of 10^{-16} ampere to about ten per cent and currents of 10^{-17} ampere can be detected.

The Wulf string or *bi-filar* electrometer[9] of figure 17–22 is constructed with two long (6 centimeter) platinized quartz fibers *LL* joined together at both ends and suspended by an amber plug. The fibers are stretched from the lower end by a small weight or from the center of a bow-shaped quartz fiber *B* in case the instrument is to be moved about. On applying a charge, the fibers separate from each other by an amount which, observed at their center by a microscope, is directly proportional over a wide range to the voltage applied. The capacity (2 or 3 e.s.u. in operation)

and the period of such a system are very small.   See, also, figure
15–2.

The *single fiber* electrometers[10] of figure 17–23 use a fiber
hanging or stretched between two metal knife edges which are
usually charged to a relatively high fixed potential.   Motion of
the fiber is observed with an ordinary microscope.   The capacity
is small (1 to 10 e.s.u.).   The sensitiveness can be made as high
as 300–1000 divisions per volt and a wide range of voltages (0.001
to 100) may be measured.   This instrument, like the Wulf,
Lindemann and Dersham electrometers, has the great advantage
of quick response and absence of oscillations.

The preparation of quartz fibers for use in electrometers is
described in experiment 16–1.

D. C. Amplifiers

17–16.   D. C. Amplifiers.—The F. P. 54, or " electrometer
tube " is a space charge tetrode which has been constructed so as

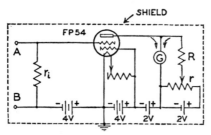

Fig. 17–24.   A simple d.c. amplifier.

to have an unusually high
input resistance.   The tube
may be used as a d.c. am-
plifier of any small current
applied across a fixed resistance between its grid and
cathode. Very small changes
in plate current may be observed by " balancing out "
the comparatively large d.c.
plate current.   A simple circuit of this type is shown in figure
17–24.   The fixed resistance R is to be large (say 3000–5000 ohms)
in comparison with that of the galvanometer G.   Before a voltage
is applied across the input terminals AB, the potentiometer r (say
400 ohms) is adjusted until there is no deflection of the galvanometer.   It is possible to do so since the plate current of the tube
flows through G in the opposite direction to that from the balancing battery in the lower right hand corner.   A small current
through r_i will now alter the grid potential, which changes the
plate current and destroys the balance.   The deflection of the galvanometer will then be directly proportional to the input current

if the tube is operated on the straight portion of its plate current-grid voltage characteristic curve.

Soller[11] has replaced the batteries of figure 17–24 by two batteries and a series of resistors, as in figure 17–25. By suitable choice of the resistances, it is possible not only to supply the proper voltages to the tube, but also to make the balance much more stable, i.e., free from small voltage changes of the battery, etc.

Various improvements of the Soller circuit have been made to secure greater stability of balance, one of the best of which is shown[12] in figure 17–26, where the space-charge-grid currents are used to assist in overcoming battery and emission changes.

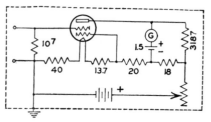

FIG. 17–25. The Soller circuit.

Currents of the order of 10^{-14} can be measured with comparative ease with these tube circuits. By enclosing the tube and that most critical portion of all tube circuits, the grid lead, in an evacuated chamber, it has been possible[13] to measure currents of the order of 10^{-17} amperes, such as supplied by the ionization due to a proton in a shallow chamber. By way of comparison with a Hoffmann duant electrometer of sensitivity 20,000 millimeters per volt and a period of 30 seconds, the tube circuit has a sensitivity of 250,000 millimeters per volt and a period (of the galvanometer) of 5 seconds.

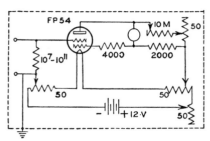

FIG. 17–26. A stable d.c. amplifier.

The electrometer triode of Philips consists of two metals plates, one the grid, the other the plate, mounted parallel to each other in the tube. The filament is located between and parallel to the plates. Practically all of the electrons emitted by the filament go to the plate. Potentials on the grid cause only small changes in the plate current. The structure is such, however, that the input resistance is sufficiently high for use in small current measurements.

It is also possible to employ inexpensive receiving tubes as electrometer tubes. It will be appreciated that two characteristics are required of a tube to be thus used. First, it must have a high grid resistance, and second, it must "float" in a semi-conducting state, i.e., when the grid is not connected to anything it must acquire a bias such that the tube is neither fully conducting nor fully cut off. In this state, any change in the grid potential will produce a change in the plate current. The type 38 tube fulfills the above requirements, as does, to a lesser extent, the type 89. Neither of these tubes has quite as high a grid resistance as has the FP54, but high resistances are to be found, especially if one carefully selects his tube from a large batch. The operation is improved if the potentials applied are all well below those for which the tubes are normally rated. Thus the 6.3 volt heater may be run at 4 volts, while $22\frac{1}{2}$ volts on the screen and 45 on the plate will give lower grid currents and better over-all performance than the higher voltage encountered in radio applications.

Ionization Chambers

17–17. Ionization Chambers for Use with X-rays.—The measurement of the intensity of an x-ray beam by means of an ionization chamber has been discussed in the chapter on x-rays, particularly in section 9–4. Ionization chambers are shown in figures 9–6, 9–7 and 9–10, while some details of their construction have been given in experiment 9–3. In addition, we may add the following notes.

In designing a chamber, be sure that an electric field exists over the region where the beam is absorbed. If a soft x-ray beam enters the chamber and is almost all absorbed in the first few centimeters of gas, then the collecting rod must also be located in the front end of the chamber.

For the usual wave-length range, a chamber of 20 centimeters length will serve to absorb practically all radiation if the proper gas is used, and 15 centimeters is satisfactory for most uses. Now, there are sudden kicks observed in the electrometer, even when no x-rays are present. These are mostly due to alpha particle emission from the walls of the chamber. The number of these spurious impulses is greater with long chambers. There is a further factor, indicating the use of short chambers. Consider a chamber of a given length, having capacity C between the collector and the walls, which absorbs 50 per cent of the incident radiation. The current produced will be $i = Q/t = CV/t$. A similar chamber twice as long will absorb 75 per cent of the radiation, an increase of 50 per cent, as we know from the exponential absorption law. However, it will have twice the capacity, an increase of 100 per cent. It follows that the output current of the longer chamber will be only 75 per cent that of the shorter one. Actually, the capacity to be considered is not only that of the chamber but also includes the fixed value of the measuring circuit, so that the current from the longer chamber is not so small as the value just computed. Also, if the radiation which is absorbed by the short chamber is but a small percentage, say one per cent, of that in the original beam, then greater length does help materially.

The *diameter* of the chamber depends on the area of the x-ray beam. The beam should not strike the inner walls nor the collector. For fluorescent x-rays, where the rays diverge from their source, a conical chamber may be used.

The *collector* should be such as to keep the capacity as small as possible. It is possible to obtain *saturation* (withdrawal of all ions produced) with moderate voltages even when fine wires are used. For example, with a tube 20 centimeters long, 5 centimeters in inside diameter and with a number 40 copper wire collector, the potential needed for saturation is about 50 volts. With a similar tube and a sixteenth inch nickel wire, the saturation potential is about 25 volts. Higher potentials, from 100 to 200 volts, are frequently used.

Concerning the choice of *metals* to be used in the construction of the chamber and the collector; copper is more likely to be free from radioactive contaminations than brass; lead is very likely to be contaminated; tin, rather than lead solder should be used. The contaminations are largely on the surface of the walls and may be reduced by sandpapering or by rolling sand around inside, on a lathe. In the following comparison[14] of the number of alpha particles emitted from a given area of material per unit time, the smaller the number, the more suitable the material for use in chambers: cold rolled steel 12, commercial brass 15, pyrex glass 16, commercial platinum foil 29, commercially electroplated nickel 31, commercial aluminum foil 34, electroplated copper (CuCN) 37, and commercial tin foil 47.

For practical purposes, there is no observable effect of the *polarity* of the applied potential; the collector may be either positive or negative.

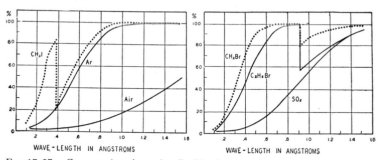

FIG. 17–27. Comparative absorption (in %) of x-rays of different wave-lengths by various gases.* In all cases the absorbing layer is 20 centimeters thick. Air and argon at a pressure of 3 atmospheres. CH_3I and C_2H_5Br vapor pressure at 20° C. CH_3Br and SO_2 at 1 atmosphere.

Amber, covered with ceresin wax, is used as the *insulation* for the lead wire from the collector. The use of a *guard ring* will reduce the leakage a great deal. There is the central lead wire, some amber, the surrounding metal guard ring, then a good insulator such as bakelite or hard rubber. The guard is grounded.

The *window*, where the x-ray beam enters the chamber, should be as thin as possible, yet strong enough not to burst under the pressure difference on its two sides. Cellophane 0.008 centimeter thick or aluminum 0.025 centimeter thick will serve for a window of area $\frac{1}{8}'' \times \frac{5}{8}''$.

It is advisable to use a one-sixteenth inch lead *sheath* around the chamber to avoid x-rays from the rectifier tubes, etc.

The choice of the *gas* to be used in the chamber depends on the wave-length of the x-rays. A comparison of the absorption of different gases for different wave-lengths is given in figure 17–27.

* The data for these curves were very kindly computed for the author by Dr. E. Dershem.

The choice of the pressures of the gases has been made from practical considerations.   The curves are not extended above 1.5 angstroms since longer wave-lengths are greatly absorbed in air and a vacuum spectrograph is required.   One can observe the copper lines in air at approximately 1.5 angstroms but they are very weak.

With *air*, greater pressures than one atmosphere can be used, say two or three.   The window will blow out with too high a pressure while if it is thicker, it will cut off too great a percentage of the x-rays.

Argon is frequently used and is many times as effective as air for most x-rays (as used in diagnostic work).   It is not so useful for the shorter wave-lengths as it is for longer rays.   Pressures of two or three atmospheres may be used, the limit being set by the window, as in the case of air.

Xenon is best and *krypton* is very good but these gases are expensive.   The krypton absorption curve (not shown in figure 17–27) is practically the same as that for CH_3Br, except that the critical K absorption occurs at 0.864A. instead of 0.918A.

Methyl iodide (CH_3I) is useful over a wide range of wave-lengths, especially for the harder x-rays, since its critical K absorption occurs at 0.374A.   It is a liquid at room temperatures and atmospheric pressure.   Connect the bottle containing the liquid, through a P_2O_5 tube (the gas *must not* contain water vapor) to an evacuated ionization chamber, and allow the pressure to rise to approximately 30 centimeters of mercury.   At higher pressures some of the gas will liquefy and ruin the insulation.   With this gas, it is necessary to take the chamber apart and clean the insulation every three months or so.

Ethyl bromide (C_2H_5Br) is most useful between 0.4 and 0.9A.   The same technique is used as with methyl iodide, i.e., it must be dry, the chamber must be cleaned occasionally, and the pressure must be below the point where the vapor condenses.

Ethyl iodide (C_2H_5I) and *methyl bromide* (CH_3Br) have also been used but are not common.   Helium is useless as it is too light.   It is desirable to have heavy molecules at high pressures, no liquids and freedom from chemical reactions with the chamber itself.

X-ray beams of the same wave-length may be compared directly with a given chamber.   With different wave-lengths, certain corrections must be made. The measurement of the absolute intensity of an x-ray (photons per square centimeter per second) is a still more elaborate process.

17–18. Ionization Chambers for Use with Gamma Rays.— The construction is similar to that used with x-rays except that the size of the chamber is of greater significance. This is due to the fact that the secondary particles ejected by the gamma rays have higher energies, produce many ions and eject charged particles from the walls of the chamber. Use high pressure. The kind of gas used is not as important as with x-rays.

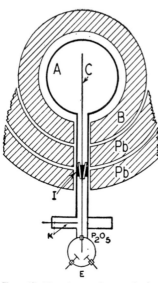

FIG. 17–28. A cosmic ray ionization chamber.

17–19. Ionization Chambers for Use with Cosmic Rays.— Ionization chambers used with cosmic rays are discussed briefly in chapter 15 and a simple form is described in experiment 15–1. Because of the small intensity of cosmic rays, their chambers must have: large volume, gas at high pressure, careful insulation, and shields to cut out the less penetrating local radiations.

In the Compton form,[15] shown in figure 17–28, the chamber (*A*) consists of a steel sphere with a wall thickness of 3 millimeters, diameter 10 centimeters, volume 425 cubic centimeters, filled with argon at a pressure of approximately 30 atmospheres and surrounded with 2.5 centimeters of bronze (*B*, to cut off beta rays from the lead) and two lead shields each 2.5 centimeters thick. The collector (*C*) was a steel rod 1.6 millimeters in diameter supported by a tapered plug fitting tightly into a conical amber bushing (*I*). The gas pressure in the chamber serves to tighten this joint. The electrometer is indicated at *E*, the charging key at *K* and the drying agent at P_2O_5 and the circuit is given in figure 15–4. A potential of approximately 150 volts is applied between the chamber (*A*) and the collector (*C*) to draw out the ions produced by the cosmic rays as they pass through the chamber.

When the pressure of the gas in an ionization chamber is increased, the recombination of ions is greater and the withdrawal of all ions becomes increasingly difficult.

The ratio of the ionization in argon to that in air is about 1.6 at atmospheric pressure, 13.8 at 30 atmospheres and 67 at 50 atmospheres.

Other cosmic ray meters are described by Kolhörster,[16] Hoffmann,[17] Regener,[18] Millikan and Neher,[19] and Compton, Wollan and Bennett.[20]

In order to test a chamber to determine whether it will withstand a given pressure or not, fill it with liquid and compress, measuring the pressure with a gauge. If the chamber should break, the liquid will squirt out without serious damage. If a gas were used in the test, and a break should occur, the gas would continue its expansion, driving parts of the chamber ahead and possibly doing serious damage.

Experiment 17-1

A STUDY OF A QUADRANT ELECTROMETER

The purpose of this experiment is to study the adjustment and to measure the voltage sensitiveness of a quadrant electrometer under various conditions. When first using an electrometer it will be well to use a comparatively coarse suspension. A 0.0015'' or 0.0007'' gold galvanometer suspension will serve.

Adjustment.—1. Carefully raise and suspend the needle as nearly as possible in the center of the quadrants. Two of the quadrants should lie entirely on one side and two on the other side of a line joining the center to the middle point of the scale.

2. The adjustment of the electrometer requires leveling so that the needle will remain in its symmetrical position when the needle potential is applied. Connect as in figure 17–11 with a needle potential (V) of about 100 volts (it may be positive or negative), with the quadrant voltage (v) = 0 and with the quadrants both grounded.

3. Charge and discharge the needle. If the needle swings to one side, the leveling may be altered so as to make it return to the zero position. It will usually be found that one leveling

screw is more effective than the others in making the adjustment. It will be found difficult to level the instrument so that there will be *no* deflection when the needle voltage is applied, particularly if the needle is tilted or bent out of shape. In practice, the deflections are reduced to as small a value as possible, say a fraction of one millimeter on a scale one meter away.

If the zero position keeps changing (drifts), tighten the suspension screws, resolder the suspension joints or put in a new one.

4. Apply a small voltage to the quadrants ($v = 1$ volt). If the deflection creeps back to zero, clean the insulators with ether.

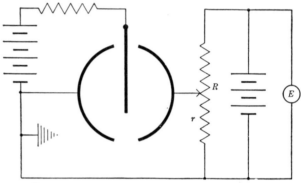

Fɪɢ. 17–29.   Voltage calibration of an electrometer.

Voltage Calibration.—1. A convenient arrangement for applying various potentials is indicated in figure 17–29. Four or five dry cells are connected across a high resistance box (10,000 ohms or more). The total voltage E is read on a voltmeter. A plug is used to tap off a known voltage, $v = rE/R$.

2. Observe the deflection obtained for various potentials applied to one quadrant, with a fixed needle potential (say 15 volts). Deflections up to 20 or 25 centimeters on each side of the zero position should be used.

3. Repeat (2) using, in each case, needle potentials of 30, 60, 120 volts.

4. Plot the various values of quadrant potentials, positive and negative, as abscissae and the deflections from zero as ordinates for the different needle potentials. Draw all curves on the same chart with the zero point in the center of the page. Note the

range over which the deflections are directly proportional to the quadrant potentials.

5. Plot deflections as the ordinates and needle potentials as the absicssae, maintaining a definite potential on the quadrants (say 2 volts). Note the deviation from a straight line and state on the curve whether the distortion couple is aiding or opposing the mechanical couple.

6. Compute the voltage sensitiveness of the instrument under the most favorable condition, recording its value on the chart of part 5.

Precautions.—See that the various parts of the electrometer are connected so as to have definite relative potentials.

Do not fail to include the protective resistance in all of the connections as indicated.

REFERENCES

1. Reference A. Chapter II.
2. Zeleny, Phys. Rev., **32**, 581 (1911). See also R. Barton. Rev. Sci. Inst., **2**, 217 (1931).
3. Crane, Lauritsen and Soltan, Phys. Rev., **45**, 507 (1934).
4. Harms, Phys. Zeit., **5**, 47 (1904).
5. R. Beatty, The Electrician, **65**, 729 (1910); **69**, 233 (1912).
6. A. H. and K. T. Compton, Phys. Rev., **14**, 85 (1919).
7. Hoffmann, Phys. Zeit., **13**, 481 (1912).
8. Lindemann, Phil. Mag., **47**, 577 (1924).
9. Wulf, Phys. Zeit., **10**; 251 (1909); **15**, 250 (1914).
10. W. F. G. Swann, Jr. Opt. Soc., **11**, 375 (1925).
11. Soller, Rev. Sci. Inst., **3**, 416 (1932).
12. Dubridge and Brown, Rev. Sci. Inst., **4**, 532 (1933).
13. L. R. Hafstad, Phys. Rev., **44**, 201 (1933).
14. J. N. Sayler, Phys. Rev., **48**, 472 (1935).
15. See A. H. Compton and J. J. Hopfield, Rev. Sci. Inst., **4**, 491 (1933).
16. W. Kolhörster, Phys. Zeit., **27**, 62 (1926); Zeits. f. Phys. **47**, 449 (1928).
17. G. Hoffmann, Zeits. f. Phys., **42**, 565 (1927).
18. E. Regener, Phys. Zeit., **31**, 1018 (1930).
19. R. A. Millikan and H. V. Neher, Phys. Rev., **43**, 381 (1931).
20. A. H. Compton, E. O. Wollen and R. D. Bennett, Rev. Sci. Inst., **5**, 415 (1934).

GENERAL REFERENCES

A.—W. Makower and H. Geiger, *Practical Measurements in Radioactivity.* Longmans, Green and Co. (1912).
B.—Strong, Neher, Cartwright, Whitford, and Hayward, *Procedures in Experimental Physics.* Prentice-Hall (1938).

CHAPTER 18

THE DETECTION OF PARTICLES*

18–1. Introduction.—The ionization currents measured in the preceding chapter represent statistical averages of a comparatively large number of individual processes. However, small variations around the mean value can be observed if the detecting apparatus is sufficiently sensitive and rapid in response. Further, when the ionizing source is very weak and the apparatus very sensitive, impulses or discontinuities will be observed. For example, the ionization due to a single alpha particle can be detected with certain instruments. It is the purpose of this chapter to discuss the ionization and expansion chambers, counter tubes, etc., used to detect and measure the impulses due to single (or, at least, only a small number of) elementary processes.

Shallow Ionization Chambers

18–2. The Principle of Shallow Chambers.[1]—In figure 18–1, a heavy particle such as an alpha particle, proton or a nucleus projected during a disintegration process, ionizes the gas between

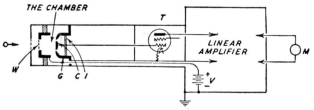

Fig. 18–1. A shallow ionization chamber and amplifier.

two conducting plates (W and C). A voltage (V) between W and C drives positive ions upon the collector C and hence upon the grid of the first tube (T) of the amplifier; after which the ions

---

* The word "particle" as used here includes photons as well as charged particles.

436

leak away to the ground. The pulse on the first tube is amplified in such a manner that the deflection of the output meter (M) is in direct proportion to the input voltage and hence to the ionization produced in the shallow chamber (WC). When the instrument has been properly constructed, the output meter registers one count for each particle which enters the chamber. When an oscillograph is used, records like those in figure 18–2 will be obtained.

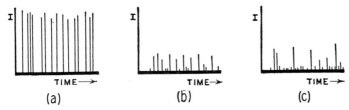

TIME⟶   TIME⟶   TIME⟶

(a)   (b)   (c)

Fig. 18–2. Intensity-time records with the apparatus of figure 18–1.

In (a), several alpha particles of nearly the same energy entered the chamber along parallel lines to produce nearly equal numbers of ions. In (b), the lines were caused by protons which had a wide variety of energies and directions, producing varying amounts of ionization. In (c), the longer lines were produced by recoil nuclei from the gas atoms in the chamber, when bombarded by neutrons, and the intermediate lines are due to recoil protons from neutron bombardment of a slab of paraffin in front of the chamber. The very short lines in (b) and (c) are due to gamma rays. These identifications have been confirmed with expansion chambers and magnetic fields. With a thyratron and counter-meter instead of an oscillograph, it is possible to adjust the bias voltage so as to identify the ionizing particle; the ratio of the impulses in (a) and (b) of figure 18–2 amounting to approximately five to one.

18–3. Construction of Shallow Chambers.[2]—(1) The *capacity* of the collecting system should be as small as possible; a few micro-microfarads. (2) The *insulation* must be of the very best (natural amber) and reduced to mere skeleton forms. (3) Complete metallic *shielding* is essential, but the walls should be thin near the chamber. (4) The *collector* may be made of thin copper and should be provided with a *guard ring* (G, of figure 18–1). Both C and G should have bevelled edges. (5) The *window* (W), which serves as one plate of the chamber, may consist of mica coated with gold foil or sputtered with silver or of thin metallic foil (e.g., aluminum several microns thick). The equivalent air thickness of the window for the particles should be as small as possible consistent with rigidity. Mechanical vibration of W will change the capacity of the chamber and give " microphonic " impulses in the meter. The window may be 2 centimeters in diameter. (6) Extreme care must be taken in cleaning, and in keeping *clean*, all parts of the chamber. Sandpapering or machining fresh surfaces will make it possible to reduce the residual count to one per hour. (7) The *depth* of the chamber should be between 0.2 and 1.5 centimeters depending on the range of the incident particles. It is desirable to have the peak of ionization, near the end of the range of the particle, lie within the chamber. For protons, the chamber should be not less than approximately 0.4 centimeter deep. (8) The *potential* across the chamber should be such as to produce a field of from 100 to 1000 volts per centimeter. The lead wire from W to the positive terminal of this voltage supply should be enclosed in a separate grounded tube.

For *neutrons*, a paraffin block may be placed in front of the chamber so that projected protons ionize the gas inside, or better, the walls of the chamber may be lined with paraffin, over which a light, conducting coat of graphite is brushed. A chamber lined with paraffin and containing methane may also be used. A lithium or boron lined chamber uses the ionization of alpha particles ejected by the neutrons and is very efficient, particularly for slow neutrons.

For single *beta particle* detection, use a chamber ten centimeters deep, containing a heavy gas such as methyl bromide.

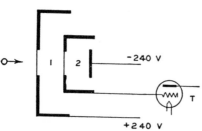

Fig. 18–3.   A differential chamber.

18–4. Differential Chambers. — If an alpha particle stops in the first chamber, (1) of figure 18–3, the grid of the amplifying tube (T) will receive a positive impulse. If the alpha particle produces its maximum ionization (near the end of its range) in chamber (2), the grid will go negative. It is thus possible to separate particles whose ranges are nearly equal to each other. In one construction,[3] the chambers are each 0.25 centimeter deep and the windows are of thin gold foil with a stopping power of 0.4 millimeter.

18–5. Notes Concerning the Linear Amplifier.[2]—This is of the resistance-capacitance coupled type. Unusually *careful shielding* is necessary all through the amplifier and *excellent filtering* is essential. The first tube is by far the most critical. This tube must be non-microphonic, must have a fairly high input resistance and a low effective or input capacity. It is usually operated with sub-normal voltages in order to reduce the noise level. Inasmuch as the charge on the grid of the first tube leaks to the ground through the grid resistance or natural leakage of the tube itself, the time constant (RC) for this stage is comparatively large. The " sharpening " of the impulses is best done by making the time constant of the second stage sufficiently small. The product RC for the remaining stages is made large to prevent oscillations, but not so large as to cause " blocking " or " motor boating."

The voltage supply may be stabilized [4] by passing its current through a tube whose grid voltage is supplied, in part, by an *ir* drop produced in a resistance by the current itself. Then, an increase in the supply voltage gives more current, which increases the bias on the stabilizer tube, increases its plate resistance and lowers the output current to the desired value.

18–6. Scale-of-Two Counter Circuits.[5]—Even the most delicately constructed mechanical counters can not respond to impulses above a definite frequency. The inverter circuit of Hull has been modified by Wynn-Williams in such a manner that the counter (M of figure 18–4) is operated by every other impulse. The counts per second registered by the meter are doubled to give the input rate.

At the start, the gas-filled triode (thyratron) (1) is conducting; and tube (2) is inoperative. The plate current of (1) has produced an *ir* drop in resistance r_1, charging condenser C, with positive on the bottom plate.

An impulse, applied across AB, with A positive, does not alter the plate current of (1) but does start (2) by raising its grid potential above the striking point. (See section 8–14.) The plate current of (2) operates the meter (M) and sets up an *ir* drop across resistance r_2, positive at the top and negative below. This potential drives a current into C, through resistance r_1. Then the voltage drop in r_1 is so great that it equals that of the plate battery. Since these voltages are in opposition the net voltage on the plate of tube (1) is zero or negative and this tube shuts off. Condenser (C) is now charged, with positive on the top plate.

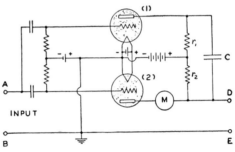

FIG. 18–4.   A " scale-of-two " counter.

A second impulse, positive on A, starts tube (1) and, in the process of reversing the polarity of C, shuts off tube (2), resetting meter M. Thus, the meter counts every other impulse.

The terminals D and E may be connected through a resistance or an amplifying tube[6] to the input terminals of a similar scale-of-two counter. The meter (M) of the latter circuit will count every fourth impulse. In the scale-of-eight counter, three circuits like that in figure 18–4 are used in series with each other.

The thyratron scaling circuit is limited in the rapidity of its response by the inherent de-ionization time of the thyratron, of the order of 10^{-4} second. The circuit will, therefore, not operate on pulses following one another by less than this interval. However, scaling circuits employing vacuum tubes have been developed in recent years which, since no positive ions are present, are free from this limitation and indeed may speed up operations by a factor of 100. Many units with high-speed characteristics and nine or more stages (scale-of-512) high are in use at the present time. The vacuum-tube scaling circuit differs slightly from figure 18–4 in that the grids and plates are cross-connected by a resistance-capacity network. Such scaling circuits are basically outgrowths of the Eccles-Jordan trigger circuit in which two triodes are so connected as to have two stable modes of operation and the pulse flips the pair from one stable state to the other.

COUNTER TUBES

18–7. The Principle of Counter Tubes.—The Geiger-Müller[7] counter tube consists of a fine wire mounted along the axis of a metal tube which contains a gas at a pressure of a few (2 to 10) centimeters of mercury. As in figure 18–5, a voltage (300 to

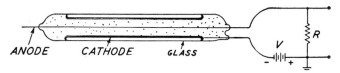

FIG. 18–5. A Geiger-Müller counter tube.

2000) is applied in such a manner as to make the metal tube negative with respect to the wire. The voltage (V) is greater than a certain critical or *threshold* value but less than that which would cause a discharge of electricity to occur through the gas. A slight ionization produced in the gas by the entrance of even a single particle will initiate a process of cumulative ionization between the two electrodes and a comparatively large current will flow through the external resistance (R). The potential drop across R rises quickly, the net voltage across the tube falls below the extinction voltage (in many cases equal, approximately, to the threshold voltage) and the current ceases to flow.

An inherent and valuable characteristic of counter tubes is the large *internal amplification* due to the cumulative ionization initiated by each ionizing particle. The currents in ionization chambers are usually of the order of magnitude of 10^{-10} to 10^{-15} ampere and require sensitive instruments or high gain amplifiers for their detection. With counter tubes, on the other hand, the currents (through R of figure 18–5) are sometimes as great as 10^{-5} amperes. A two stage amplifier connected across R is often sufficient to operate a counter-meter.

The *number of voltage impulses* produced across the load resistance (R) each second is directly proportional to the number of particles incident on the tube in unit time, provided the individual ionizing events do not occur so rapidly that the discharge in the tube can not cease in the brief interval between successive events.

18–8. Types of Counter Tubes.—Different types of counter tubes are used for the detection of different kinds of particles. When constructed in the manner shown in figure 18–5, with comparatively thick walled cathodes, they are useful for the more penetrating radiations, such as X and gamma rays. In these cases, secondary particles ejected from the cathode contribute appreciably to the initial ionization of the gas. It follows that the thickness and surface condition of the cathode must be considered in the preparation of these tubes. They usually consist of thick walled or fine mesh copper tubes.

When the intensity of the radiation is small, as in the case of cosmic rays, large tubes are used in order to increase the number of primary ions produced in the tube. The cathode walls should be thin, smooth and of light metal, in order to reduce the local gamma rays as much as possible.

In the so-called " quantum " counters, a window is provided so that light may reach the inner surface of the cathode. This surface is sensitized as in photoelectric cells and emits electrons which ionize the gas.

For less penetrating radiations such as alpha and beta particles, very thin aluminum or glass (bubble) windows are used to permit the particles to enter and ionize the gas directly. It is advantageous to use small tubes with thin walled cathodes to reduce the background of counts due to more penetrating radiations.

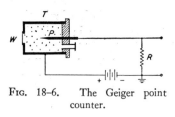

FIG. 18–6.   The Geiger point counter.

The Geiger point counter shown in figure 18–6 is usually used to detect alpha particles. It has a smooth fine point (P) or a small ball on the end of a fine wire, supported inside a tube (T) by an insulating plug. It is operated with dry air at atmospheric pressure, the particles entering through a thin foil window (W). The potential (1000 to 2000 volts) is usually applied so as to make the tube positive with respect to the point. If the voltage is reversed and properly adjusted at a critical low value, the magnitude of the pulse across R is proportional to the number of ions originally created by the incident particles. Inasmuch as heavy radiations, such as alpha particles and protons, produce many more ions than do beta or gamma radiations, the voltage set up across the external resistance is greater in the former than in the latter cases. Thus, with a *proportional counter*,[8] it is possible to count alpha particles even in the presence of a comparatively strong background of gamma rays.

18-9. Counter Tube Circuits.—A counter tube may be coupled to an amplifier through a small condenser, as in figure 18-7. The resistance (R) should be between 10^8 and 10^{10} ohms; the

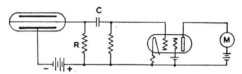

Fig. 18-7.   A simple counter tube circuit.

capacity (C), approximately equal to that of the counter tube, say 10 micro-microfarads, and should have unusually good insulation. An impulse will make the upper end of R negative by 10–200 volts (approximately the "over-voltage") and will, therefore, shut off the plate current of the amplifier tube, as noted on the meter (M) or by the operation of a relay or counter mechanism. In practice, in this and the following circuits, the vacuum tube is of the screen grid or pentode type in order to prevent feed back. If desired, a second amplifier tube may be added to invert the phase; i.e., drive the second grid positive and cause an increase, rather than a decrease, in the output plate current. The second tube may also be a grid-controlled gas-filled tube (a thyratron) with a mechanical or self-stopping circuit. These tubes can deliver a greater output than that given by a high vacuum tube. For rapid counting, a scale of two, four or eight circuit (section 18-6) may be used. The design of a direct-reading counting-rate meter is described in reference 9.

The impulses may be made visible by the flashes of light from the neon glow lamp, N of figure 18-8. The resistance r is so adjusted that the voltage drop across the glow lamp is less than its striking potential. An impulse shuts off the plate current, the drop in r disappears and the lamp lights up. But, since the current through the lamp must flow through r, a large ir drop is set up, the net potential across the lamp drops below the extinction voltage and the lamp goes out. Thus, one flash of light is seen for each impulse.

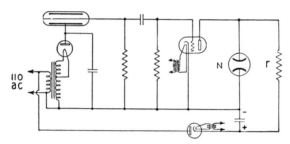

FIG. 18–8.   Visual counting circuit.

The circuit[10] of figure 18–9 is capable of unusually high counting rates since the total resistance, $R = R_g + R_p$, through which the tube discharges, is from one one-hundredth to one one-thousandth of the load resistance used in the preceding circuits.

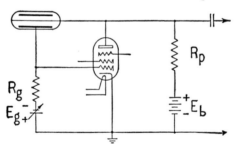

FIG. 18–9.   The Neher-Harper circuit.

In one case, using a 57 or 6C6 vacuum tube, R_p was 2 megohms and R_g ranged from 1 to 50 megohms, the larger values for smaller (larger capacity) counter tubes. The grid bias (E_g) (0 to 15 volts, in the case above) must be adjusted critically for a given value of R_g; if too small, the potential drop across R_p lowers the voltage supplied by E_b to a value below the threshold of the counter tube and, if too large, a blocking action occurs. When E_g has been properly adjusted, the current through R_p is small and a large part of the battery voltage ($E_b > V_t$) is applied to the counter tube and also to the vacuum tube. When the gas in the counter tube is ionized, a current flows out of E_b, through R_g and R_p. Due to the resultant potential drop in R_g, the grid of the vacuum tube becomes less negative and a comparatively large plate current flows through R_p. The drop in R_p is then so great as to reduce the potential across the counter tube below the extinction voltage, causing the discharge to cease and the initial conditions to be re-established. The impulse across R_p is applied to the grid of a low gain amplifier through a coupling condenser.

One purpose of the circuit is to " quench " the discharge in the counter. The circuit accomplishes this by dropping the voltage across the counter below the value necessary to sustain a discharge. When positive ions are collected on the counter cylinder, the grid receives a positive pulse, the tube conducts and acts as a partial " short-circuit " of the counter, lowering the potential between wire and cylinder. After the positive ions are collected, current flows through R_g, and the whole arrangement returns to normal and is again sensitive for the next event. A variety of other " quenching circuits " have also been developed which all perform substantially the same function.

The principle of the coincidence counter circuit[11] of Rossi, may be understood from figure 18–10. At the start, the grid of

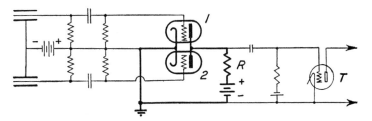

Fig. 18–10. A coincidence counter circuit.

the tube (T) (preferably a gas-filled triode) is highly biased so that its plate current is zero. The vacuum tubes in the center of the diagram are operating in a normal manner. When an ionizing particle passes through only one of the counter tubes, say the upper one, the plate current in tube 1 is momentarily interrupted. The potential drop in R is then decreased, the upper end becoming less negative, although this is partially compensated for* by the increased plate current through tube 2 which results when its plate voltage is increased. Since the grid of T was adjusted well below its starting voltage, the impulse across R proves insufficient to start the plate current of T. If, however, ionization takes place at practically the same instant in both counter tubes, due perhaps to the passage of a single particle through them, then, the plate currents of both tubes, 1 and 2, are temporarily shut off and the drop in R disappears. The upper end of R then becomes more positive than it was. As a result of this change, the grid of T is raised above the striking voltage and a plate current flows through the recording mechanism to give a coincidence count. This coincidence arrangement can be extended to any number of counters by simply connecting together all the plates of each vacuum tube connected to each counter.   Fivefold coincidence circuits are now common and twenty-fivefold coincidence units have been built.   Pentodes are frequently used in place of the triodes shown in figure 18–10 because of their cut-off characteristics.

18–10.   The Background Count.—Let a counter tube with its amplifier and counting mechanism be placed in a room which is as free as possible from known radioactive substances. A certain background or residual count will be observed, just as a natural leakage current is found to take place in electroscopes and electrometers.   These counts are due to cosmic rays and to radioactive substances distributed in the walls of the room, the air, the earth and in the tube walls, electrodes and gas.   The average background counting rate (B) is obtained by dividing the total number of counts observed over a comparatively long time interval (say 15 minutes or more) by the total time.   If the chosen time interval is too small, successive values of the background rate will not all be the same but will fluctuate around the average value. If the counter apparatus is sufficiently rapid in its recovery at each count, there will be one count for each incident particle. (Then, $B \equiv \bar{b}$ of section 11–11.)

If the voltage on a counter tube is increased, the observed background (B) will also increase.   In other words, the apparatus becomes more sensitive and weaker radiations are detected. This is shown in curve B of figure 18–11.

* This is true for triodes but not for screen grid tubes.

As an example, the residual or background count amounted to 6 to 15 counts per minute, according to the applied voltage, for a Geiger-Müller tube whose cathode was 6 centimeters long and 1 centimeter in diameter (sectional area of 6 square centimeters). This amounts to 1 to $2\frac{1}{2}$ counts per minute per square centimeter. In a second tube, 12 centimeters long and 2 centimeters in diameter (area 24 cm.^{2}), B varied from 35 to 45, i.e., from $1\frac{1}{2}$ to 2 counts per minute per square centimeter. In general, a tube which has been prepared so as to be essentially free (itself) from radioactive contaminations and is placed in an "uncontaminated" room will have a background of approximately one to three residual counts per minute per square centimeter.

If two tubes are placed a few centimeters apart, with their axes parallel and in a horizontal plane and connected in a coincidence circuit, chance or *accidental* counts will occur which are not due to the passage of a single particle through both tubes[12] or to a shower of cosmic-ray particles originating in matter above the counters which sprays one or more ionizing particles through each counter.

18–11. The Counting-rate Voltage Curve.—Let a radioactive source of moderate and constant intensity be placed near a counter tube and the average number of counts per minute (N) be obtained from readings taken over a comparatively long time interval. Then,* the average activity (N_0) of the source is

$$N_0 = N - B, \tag{18-1}$$

where B is the average background counting rate.

Figure 18–11 shows a typical curve of counting rates when different voltages are applied to the counter tube. The *operating voltage* (V) is usually set somewhere within the range $\overline{PP}$, since, over this *plateau* the applied voltage may vary without causing large changes in the counting rate. The width of the plateau depends (among other factors to be discussed later) in an approximately linear manner with the load resistance (R of figure 18–5)

---

* It is here assumed that N is large compared with B. The case of a *weak source* is discussed in sections 18–12 and 11–11 and the case of a *very strong source* is treated in section 18–13. Unless the counter apparatus is sluggish, equation 18–1 is identical with equation 11–23 ($\bar{n} = \bar{a} - b$, where $\bar{n}$ is the activity of the source).

and may amount to 300 volts, although it is usually only a few score of volts.

The *threshold voltage* (V_t), where impulses are first obtained, varies from 300 to 2000 volts, as discussed in the section on the manufacture of a tube.   The difference between the operating and the threshold voltages $(V_0 = V - V_t)$ is called the *over-voltage* and varies in practice from ten to several hundred volts.

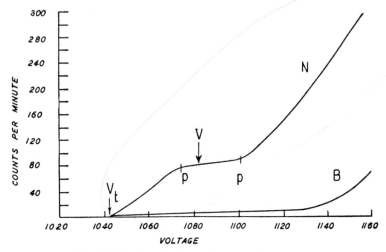

Fig. 18–11.   A typical counting rate-voltage curve.

18–12.   The Sensitivity of Counters.—Every instrument has a lower limit; it cannot be used to measure quantities of lesser amount.   In the case of counter tubes, this sensitivity is set by the background or residual counting rate.   Further, when the source is so weak as to add comparatively few additional counts above the background, it becomes necessary to consider statistically the fluctuations which occur around the average or "long time" value.

Now read Section 11–11.

The relative sensitivity, as defined by equation 11–26, varied from 0.6 to 1.8 for a tube designed for the detection of feeble gamma rays.[13]   The cathode was 12 centimeters by 2 centimeters and was made of 100 mesh copper gauze.   The relative sensitivity was a maximum when the tube was filled with dry air at 6.5 centimeters of mercury, the over-voltage was 170 and the circuit was of the type shown in figure 18–7.

18–13. The Efficiency of Counting.—The efficiency of counting (E) is defined as the ratio of the number of observed counts per unit time (N_0) to the number of ionizing particles ($\bar{n}$) which passed through the counter tube during that time. Thus,

$$E = N_0/\bar{n}. \qquad (18\text{--}2)$$

If 1000 particles pass through and only 900 are recorded, the efficiency is 0.9 or 90 per cent.

Let three counter tubes be placed one above the other, with axes parallel, and connected in a triply coincidence circuit. The over-all efficiency would then be

$$E_t = E_1 E_2 E_3 = N_t/\bar{n}, \qquad (18\text{--}3)$$

where E_1, E_2 and E_3 are the respective efficiencies of the individual counters and N_t is the observed triple counting rate. If, now, the center tube be disconnected (but left in place), the efficiency of the double coincidence circuit will be

$$E_d = E_1 E_3 = N_g/\bar{n}, \qquad (18\text{--}4)$$

where N_d is the observed double counting rate. From the last two equations, we see that

$$E_2 = N_t/N_d. \qquad (18\text{--}5)$$

The efficiency of a counter tube may, therefore, be determined[12] by placing it as the center tube in a triple counter and observing the counting rates, corrected for accidentals, when the tube is connected to its amplifier (N_t) and when it is not (N_d). In similar manner, by interchanging the tubes, E_1 and E_3 may be determined.

The *inactive* time (σ) of a counter is defined as the time interval during which it is insensitive to ionizing particles. With a high speed circuit and a rapid counter-meter, σ is (probably) largely the time required for the restoration of the voltage across the counter tube after its discharge. If N_0 is the number of counts observed in one minute (corrected for background), then $N_0\sigma$ is the inactive portion of that minute and $(1 - N_0\sigma)$ is the active time. Now, during the time available, N_0 counts were obtained, whereas, if the full minute had been useful, the total number of particles ($\bar{n}$) capable of initiating a discharge would have been counted. Therefore

$$E = \frac{N_0}{\bar{n}} = \frac{1 - N_0\sigma}{1} \qquad (18\text{--}6)$$

from which it is seen that the efficiency* of a counter depends on the counting rate (N_0) and on the inactive time (σ).

The inactive time, sometimes called dead time or recovery time, of a counter can be measured by appropriate circuits, and is found to be of the order of 10^{-4} to 10^{-3} seconds. Hence, most counters will not count effectively at higher counting rates than 1000 per second and indeed are already missing an appreciable number of counts when operating at 100 per second.

Approximately seven per cent of the length of the usual Geiger-Müller tube, near each end, is inefficient. The effective region of a Geiger (point) counter consists of the cone made between the point and the window.

18–14.   The Manufacture of Geiger-Müller Counter Tubes.— It is comparatively easy to make a reasonably good gamma ray counter tube of *small* dimensions. There is some disagreement among the various experimenters as to the manufacturing details but, if the following technique is used, most of the tubes will have sufficient sensitivity and stability and low background count for classroom work. A copper tube several centimeters long and about one centimeter in diameter, is flared at the ends and has a tungsten lead wire welded to it. It is cleaned with grit-free soap solution, thoroughly washed and dried. A 3 to 10 mil, thorium free, tungsten anode wire is cleaned by passing it slowly through a hot solution of potassium nitrite, then thoroughly washed and dried. The copper tube is slipped inside a pyrex tube and stabilized with several glass dimples around the ends. The anode wire is then mounted along the axis as accurately as can be judged by eye (see figure 18–5). The inside of the tube is washed with cleaning solution (potassium dichromate and sulphuric acid); immediately and thoroughly rinsed with distilled water and dried by pumping for several hours with a fore pump. It is then filled

---

* A statistical treatment of the relationship between the observed and true counting rates, together with a graphical solution when only one counter is used, has been given by Volz and extended by Schiff.[14]

to a pressure of approximately six centimeters with air which has passed very slowly through a drying tube or (better) has been stored for several days over P_2O_5 or $CaCl_2$. The tube is then sealed off and is ready for use.

If, on the other hand, it is desired to make counter tubes which are *consistently* sensitive, stable and of low background count and particularly if they are of *large* size (a foot or more long and several inches in diameter) for the detection of feeble radiations, then a more elaborate procedure is necessary. One such method* is as follows. A seamless copper tube, say 15 inches long, $\frac{9}{16}$ inch in diameter, with walls 8 mils thick is flared at the ends, carefully washed with grit-free soap and distilled water. The tube is assembled in its pyrex container with a 3 mil tungsten anode. It is washed with cleaning solution, water, ammonium hydroxide, water, 5 per cent nitric acid for 10–15 minutes and then water. It is evacuated with a diffusion pumping system and baked at 500° C. for 15 hours (over night). The tungsten wire is flashed very brightly (at 2600–3000° C.) for 30 seconds. Dry air is admitted to atmospheric pressure through a P_2O_5 tube and a CO_2 trap. The tube is then heated in an oven at 500° C. from 1 to 1.5 hours (until the copper is heavily oxidized). The tube is removed from the pumping system, the oxide coat is washed off with 5 per cent nitric acid (perhaps one-half hour) followed by a thorough washing in distilled water. The tube is then re-evacuated and baked as before for 15 hours. When cool, dry air (or hydrogen) is admitted to a pressure of approximately 7 (or 10) centimeters of mercury ($V_t \doteq 1100$ volts). When operated at an overvoltage of 150, the residual count will be about 135 counts per minute.

The threshold voltage is higher when the gas pressure is higher and when the anode is of larger diameter. Typical curves[15] are shown in figure 18–12 for the case of dry air and argon in tubes of oxidized copper 3 centimeters long and one centimeter in diameter. The anodes were tungsten wires whose diameters were 3, 5 and 10 mils., as indicated in the figure. The tubes were operated with gamma rays. It is to be noted that lower voltages may be used with argon than with air.

* The author is indebted to F. R. Shonka for this technique. The necessary rigor of the various steps is unknown at present. The procedure can probably be shortened with further study.

In general, any gas can be used in a counter. On the other hand, it is well to avoid oxygen, water vapor and the halogens because these gases favor the formation of negative ions and spurious counts. Low-operating potentials are achieved with the rare gases, argon, neon and helium being the inexpensive representatives. It is necessary to use a mixture in order to avoid troubles with metastable states formed in the discharge. For example, neon-hydrogen and argon-helium mixtures have been found successful.

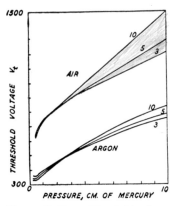

FIG. 18–12. Threshold-voltage pressure curves of a counter tube. The numbers 10, 5, 3 refer to the central wire diameter in mils.

The addition of an organic vapor to the gas in a counter will cause the discharge to terminate due to an internal process, and hence such counters are called " self-quenching " counters. The quenching circuit, such as the Neher-Harper circuit (figure 18–9), is eliminated, and the quenching resistance R and condenser C in figure 18–7 may be omitted. The self-quenching counters will operate satisfactorily on a resistance of a megohm or even less. Hence, a faster recovery time is secured and faster counting can be achieved. Typical vapors used include ether, alcohol, xylene, amyl acetate and ethyl acetate. These are added, in an amount of one to two cm. pressure, to a filling of some gas which constitutes the main ingredient. For example, one cm. ether plus seven to 12 cm. argon is a good filling mixture.

EXPANSION CHAMBERS

18–15. The Principle of Expansion Chambers.—A simplified diagram of an expansion chamber (that of C. T. R. Wilson, used in 1911) is shown in figure 18–13. A large cylinder of glass G (10–20 centimeters diameter) is closed at one end by a glass window (W) and at the other end by a piston (P) to form the chamber. A trace of water in the chamber keeps the air saturated. When the piston is suddenly pulled down, the temperature in the chamber drops below the dew point. Then, small drops of water form on condensation centers such as dust particles or ions. The cloud of water droplets is illuminated by light (L) from the side and viewed or photographed through the window from above. The droplets may be allowed to settle slowly to the bottom of the chamber or, since they are usually formed on charged particles, be removed quickly by means of an electric field between the metal piston and the metal ring (R).

When all condensation centers have been removed, an expansion will fail to form a new cloud. If, at this stage, a radio-active source, such as polonium located at x, sends out even a single alpha particle, new ion pairs will be created in the chamber. Then, a sudden expansion will precipitate droplets along the path of the particle. The importance of direct observation of the drop-

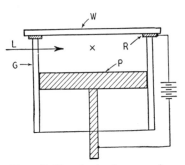

Fig. 18–13. A simple expansion chamber.

track of a *single* ionizing particle in the study of the nature of the particle and its collisions with other particles is immediately obvious.

It is easier to secure good tracks of the heavily ionizing radiations, such as alpha particles, than of the less ionizing radiations, such as electrons. The chamber need not be as clean nor the illumination as intense for alpha tracks as for electron tracks.

In order to secure fine, sharp tracks: (1) the gas must be saturated and at a constant, uniform temperature before the expansion, (2) the particles must pass through the chamber at approximately the time of the expansion and (3) the expansion must occur quickly and be of a definite amount.

18–16. The Design and Operation of Expansion Chambers.[16-24]—*The Expansion Ratio.*—The ratio of the final to the initial volume V/V_0 of the chamber is called the isothermal expansion ratio (R). When a simple piston of the type shown in figure 18–13 is used, R is given as the ratio of the depth of the chamber after the expansion to the depth before the piston moved out. In machines, such as those using a flexible diaphragm piston, where it is difficult to determine the volumes, R can be obtained from the pressures of the gas in the chamber and the application of Boyle's (isothermal) law. Thus, the gas is compressed and allowed to attain a constant temperature (in approximately one minute). Then, the total pressure of the gas and vapor is measured with a manometer. Subtracting the vapor pressure at the existing temperature gives the initial gas pressure (P_0). The chamber is then expanded and allowed to reach thermal equilibrium, when the manometer reading is taken and corrected for the vapor pressure to give the final gas pressure (P). Then

$$R = V/V_0 = P_0/P. \qquad (18\text{-}7)$$

If good tracks are to be obtained, the expansion ratio must be accurately adjusted to a particular value for each gas-vapor combination. This is especially true for electron tracks. The table below shows optimum values of R as observed experimentally by different workers. It is seen that the volume increase for the argon-alcohol combination is about ten per cent.

The Gas and Vapor.—The gas-vapor combination should have as small an expansion ratio as possible in order to shorten the expan-

Gas	Vapor of	Optimum R
Air	water	1.35
Air	*n*-propyl alcohol	1.185
Nitrogen, 2 atmospheres	3 parts ethyl alcohol, 1 part water	1.125
Argon	*n*-propyl, or ethyl or *iso*-propyl alcohol	1.117
Argon at 100 cms	85% ethyl alcohol plus 15% water	1.09
Argon, 2 atmospheres	3 parts ethyl alcohol, 1 part water	1.08

sion time and to reduce the distortion of the tracks caused by the shock of stopping the piston at the end of its stroke. Air and alcohol are commonly used.

Argon is better than air since it has a higher specific ionization and a smaller expansion ratio. The initial pressure should be greater for the more penetrating rays and less for those which produce short tracks.

Alcohol is better than water since the expansion ratio is smaller, there is better scattering of light from the droplets and photo-nuclei are not produced even with an intense light source.   Only a small amount of liquid need be placed in the chamber.   Uniform and rapid saturation of the chamber is essential and may be accomplished by distributing the liquid over the floor of the chamber by means of a cloth or a wick system.

The *size of the chamber* is determined by the nature of the radiation to be studied; it is small for short-range particles and vice versa.

The *sliding piston* (figure 18–13) is rarely used today, chiefly because of the leakage around its edges.   Instead, the piston is permanently sealed to the chamber walls by means of a rubber ring or a metal bellows (sylphon).   The piston is moved between stops by mechanical devices, electromagnets or by air pressure. Wilson[16] has shown that a thin rubber diaphragm may be used between stopping surfaces, provided turbulence of the gas in the chamber is avoided with a gauze or a perforated disc between the diaphragm and the chamber.   Air pressure is used to expand these diaphragms.

The *operation* of a chamber may be carried out manually or by means of a mechanism driven by a motor.   The various steps (field off, expansion, light on, etc.) are given their proper sequence, for example, by cams on the shaft of the driving mechanism.   A chamber may be placed between two counter tubes connected in a coincidence circuit (see figure 18–10).   If the output of this circuit is used to start an expansion, the particles recorded will be, for the most part, those which have passed through the chamber in line with the counter tubes.

Continuously active cloud chambers have been devised but have not yet proven of practical value.

The *electrical field* used to remove the ions is not critical and may range from 20 to 300 volts.   It is removed or reduced to a small value during the expansion.   If a strong field is used during the expansion, it is possible to separate the positive and negative ions to such an extent that each track is doubled.   From the separation of the tracks and the mobilities of the ions, it is possible to compute the age of the track.   Older tracks are wider.[24]   The "sweep" field is often applied between the piston and a ring of metal or colloidal graphite (Aquadag) around the top of the chamber.   It is better to use wires or plates on insulating supports so as to avoid distortion of the tracks by surface charges on the chamber walls.

The time during which an expansion takes place should be short. This is necessary, not only to secure a sufficient drop in temperature to cause condensation of the vapor on nuclei but also to prevent the continued motion of the gas from distorting the newly formed track. The *expansion time* is usually of the order of magnitude of 0.01 second,[23] although as long as 0.25 second has been used.[22] Flexible diaphragms and metal bellows can be moved quickly whereas heavy pistons and water surfaces are comparatively sluggish.

If a particle passes through the chamber appreciably before the expansion takes place, the tracks will be broad and dense. If the ions are formed in the chamber too late, the tracks are thin. The *sensitive time*, during which reasonably sharp tracks can be formed, is usually a fraction of a second, although in one design[22] it amounted to 1.5–2 seconds.

A suitable time interval must be used between *successive expansions*. A certain period of time must be allowed for the old drops to be removed by the electric field or by precipitation, some of the liquid must re-evaporate and thermal equilibrium must be restored. This requires approximately one minute, but may be reduced[20] to one-quarter of a minute if, after an expansion, the gas is partially compressed, then slightly expanded, then fully compressed. It is left in each of these three conditions for about 5 seconds.

With a particular counter-controlled chamber, a particle passed through the chamber, the electric field was removed, and the expansion took place in 0.015 second. The light was turned on 0.035 second later and a photograph of the tracks was secured during the following 0.1 second. The electric field was turned on and, 30–60 seconds later, the gas was compressed. After 30–60 seconds more, the chamber was in thermal equilibrium, ready for the next expansion.

Extraneous Droplets.—Dust particles must be removed by repeated expansions when the chamber is first assembled. Even then, a general fog results from over-expansion; never from under-expansion. With the optimum expansion ratio, extraneous droplets may appear if there is too much liquid, above that needed to saturate the gas. It is thought[21] that the impact of the piston at the end of an expansion may also cause undesired droplets. Leakage currents set up by the sweep field may electrolyze alcohol and give general fogging. Photo-ionization of the vapor (water, but not alcohol) by the intense light may give undesired tracks. The photo-nuclei are mostly uncharged and cannot be removed with an electric field, but must slowly settle to the bottom of the chamber. Photo-electrons from the metal parts of the chamber may be eliminated by painting with colloidal graphite. This also reduces the number of alpha particles emitted by contaminations in the walls. The chamber walls, gas and liquid must be as free from radioactive contaminations as possible. Aluminum should be paraffined, varnished or covered with bakelite. Cellophane may be used to prevent the condensation of drops on the walls and window.

Distortion of the Tracks.—There must be no convection currents of the gas in the chamber either from temperature gradients or small leaks, otherwise the tracks will be badly distorted. Paper gaskets with Vulcalock cement are used. Freshly machined castings leak badly and should be varnished or coated with bakelite. The latter is not effected by alcohol while varnish is.

Turbulence of the gas during and after an expansion is a source of considerable distortion of the tracks, particularly near the walls of the chamber. Rigid pistons should have a uniform motion in a smooth cylinder of as nearly the same diameter as possible. Baffles or gauzes above the piston are very effective in reducing turbulence and are essential when using flexible diaphragms. A gauze made of 31 gauge wires, 6 per centimeter, has been used. When 18 wires per centimeter was tried it was found to slow down the expansion too much. Metal plates, closely drilled with holes 1.5 to 6 millimeters in diameter, have also been used. Unequal tensions in stretching a rubber diaphragm will give unequal movements and expansions.

Oscillations and bumping at the end of the piston stroke must be reduced to a minimum. A quiet expansion is desirable. Some of the devices used for this purpose are as follows: dash pots of oil or air, electromagnetic damping, mechanical catches, leather pads, wool wound around the grooves of a metal bellows, small expansion ratio, long expansion time and, in the pneumatic type, a small amount of copper wool in the port hole to reduce air oscillations.

The droplets fall under the force of gravity. Argon has a higher viscosity than air and reduces the free fall velocity. In one case, the entire chamber was allowed to fall after an expansion. Short photographic exposures are desirable. The camera lenses may give a fictitious curvature to the tracks.

If the source of the particles is located inside the chamber, it should be placed along the path of the piston's movement. If projecting in from the side, eddy currents will occur around it.

A black *background* may be secured by placing velveteen over the piston or gauze. Use the type of velvet which has a short nap and is silk and not cotton backed. For vertical use, the cloth is glued in place. A gelatin and lamp-black background moulds unless there is a trace of $CuSO_4$ present.

An *intense light source* should be used for a short time only, in order to avoid unequal heating of the chamber with consequent distortion of the tracks and also to secure a photograph of a sharply defined track (before it has widened with age or become distorted). Ordinary lamps are used at double their rated voltage for a short period. Capillary arcs are operated from a condenser discharge or by short circuiting an impedance in series with them.

Usually, two cameras are used to take *stereoscopic pictures* in order that the tracks may be seen in three dimensions. For weak tracks, photographs are taken with the light scattered in the forward direction, since this is more intense than that at right angles to the beam.

18–17. Some of the Features of Drop-tracks.—In *general:* See figure 12–18. Heavy, slow particles produce broad, densely packed, straight line tracks with an occasional sharp, small angle bend, especially near the end. Light, slow particles produce narrow, beaded, tortuous tracks. Fast particles, both light and heavy, produce narrow, beaded, straight tracks. At lower pressures, the tracks are longer but retain the characteristics of a given kind of particle.

Alpha Particles.—Read Section 12–6. The tracks are straight and comparatively broad, their width depending, among other factors, on the square root of the time interval from the passage of the particle to the formation of the droplets on the ions. The ionization is very intense along the track so that it appears as a continuous line. If the droplets were formed on the ions at such a late time that they were able to diffuse over an appreciable width, the track would appear "fuzzy" and individual droplets could be seen. Alpha tracks are comparatively short (the range of these particles at the existing gas pressure) and are slightly heavier near their ends. When the gas pressure in the chamber is comparatively low, the tracks have a beaded character along their sides, due to secondary electrons (delta rays).

Protons.—The tracks of low-energy protons look like alpha tracks but are approximately ten times longer (for equal energies). Proton tracks are slightly narrower than alpha tracks of the same age. The tracks of protons of moderate energy have a beaded appearance; they look like fast electron tracks, but are denser and wider. As the energy of the protons increases, the tracks become narrower and the individual droplets are seen more frequently. Protons of energy greater than 5×10^8 volts have about the same ionizing power as electrons. Tracks of still faster protons have the same appearance as those of fast electrons.

Electrons.—For energies in excess of approximately 2 Mev, and for pressures in the chamber below 1 or 2 atmosphhres, electron tracks are straight and beaded, the individual droplets often appearing in doubles or triples. The primary ionization at one atmosphere is about 20 ion pairs per centimeter of path. Secondary electrons are produced with ranges from 0.01 to 0.1 millimeter, giving the dotted or beaded appearance of the track. There are about 40 ion pairs, total, per centimeter of path. When electrons with energies in excess of approximately 2 Mev pass through a gas at a pressure of 2 or more atmospheres, they suffer an occasional small angle deflection. The probability of such a deflection is directly proportional to the pressure. Since, also, the number of individual nuclear deflections is inversely proportional to the square of the energy of the electrons, 200–300 Kev electron tracks are found to have many curves. The curves are generally gradual, since they are made up of many small deflections (which are more probable than large angle deflections). For electrons of energies of 100 Kev or less, the tortuous tracks are heavier, are thick near the ends, and show more beads at the points of curving. Sharp bends are common.

X and γ Rays.—The ionization is largely due to secondary (photo-) electrons ejected by the primary rays. Consequently, the individual tracks, for the most part, have the bearded, tortuous appearance of slow electron tracks. The space ionized by the secondary electrons is much larger than that occupied by the primary rays.

18–18. Photographic Emulsions.—It has been found that ionizing particles, such as protons, alpha particles and electrons leave tracks in photographic emulsions, which become evident when the emulsion is developed. A whole new detection technique is thus available. Because of the short ranges, the tracks are short, and must be measured under a microscope. Special emulsions, thicker than the usual ones, have been developed to assist this process. In the study of cosmic rays, plates have been exposed at various elevations, and have been carried aloft in balloon flights. In nuclear physics applications, the beam of particles from an accelerating machine may be allowed to fall on a plate for a brief time, or neutrons may be used to cause reactions with materials added to the emulsion. The tracks of heavily ionizing particles are much denser than those of electrons, and the nature of the particle producing the track may be inferred from the density and length of the track. Neutrons are detected by impregnating the emulsion with some substance, such as boron or lithium, which has a large capture cross-section for slow neutrons and which emits an alpha-particle producing dense ionization. Fast neutrons may be photographed by placing near the emulsion some paraffin or other hydrogen-rich substance from which recoil protons are ejected into the emulsion.

REFERENCES

1. C. E. Wynn-Williams and F. A. B. Ward, Proc. Roy. Soc., **A131**, 391 (1931).
2. J. R. Dunning, Rev. Sci. Inst., **5**, 387 (1934).
3. Rutherford, Ward and Wynn-Williams, Proc. Roy. Soc., **A129**, 211 (1930).
4. Street and Johnson, Jr. Frank. Inst., **214**, 155 (1932).
   R. D. Evans, Rev. Sci. Inst., **5**, 371 (1934).
5. C. E. Wynn-Williams, Proc. Roy. Soc., **A136**, 312 (1932).
6. W. G. Shepherd and R. O. Haxby, Rev. Sci. Inst., **7**, 425 (1936).
6'. E. C. Stevenson and I. A. Getting, Rev. Sci. Inst., **8**, 414 (1937).
   H. Lifschutz and J. L. Lawson, Bul. Amer. Phys. Soc., **12**, 7 (Nov. 1937).

7. H. Geiger and W. Müller, Phys. Zeit., **29**, 839 (1928); **30**, 489, 523 (1929); Naturwiss, **16**, 617 (1928).
8. Geiger and Klemperer, Zeits. f. Physik, **36**, 364 (1926); **49**, 753 (1928).
9. Gingrich, Evans and Edgerton, Rev. Sci. Inst., **7**, 450 (1936).
10. Nehrer and Harper, Phys. Rev., **40**, 940 (1936).
    See T. H. Johnson, Jr. Frank. Inst., **215**, 239 (1933).
11. Also J. C. Mouzon, Rev. Sci. Inst., **7**, 467 (1936).
12. Street and Woodward, Phys. Rev., **46**, 1029 (1934).
13. R. D. Evans and R. A. Mugele, Rev. Sci. Inst., **7**, 441 (1936).
14. L. I. Schiff, Phys. Rev., **50**, 88 (1936).
15. C. L. Haines, Rev. Sci. Inst., **7**, 411 (1936).
16. C. T. R. Wilson, Proc. Roy. Soc., **A142**, 88 (1933).
17. P. M. S. Blackett, Proc. Roy. Soc., **A146**, 281 (1934).
18. P. M. S. Blackett, Jr. Sci. Inst., **4**, 433 (1927).
19. P. M. S. Blackett, Jr. Sci. Inst., **6**, 184 (1929).
20. P. M. S. Blackett, Proc. Roy. Soc., **A123**, 613 (1929).
21. G. L. Locher, Rev. Sci. Inst., **7**, 471 (1936).
22. J. A. Bearden, Rev. Sci. Inst., **6**, 256 (1935).
    See also Crane and Mouzon, Rev. Sci. Inst., **8**, 351 (1937).
23. J. C. Street and E. C. Stevenson, Rev. Sci. Inst., **7**, 347 (1936).
24. Brode, MacPherson and Starr, Phys. Rev., **50**, 581 (1936).

GENERAL REFERENCES

A.—Strong, Neher, Cartwright, Whitford and Hayward, *Procedures in Experimental Physics*. Prentice-Hall (1938).

B.—E. Pollard and W. L. Davidson, Jr., *Applied Nuclear Physics*. John Wiley & Sons (1942).

C.—S. A. Korff, *Electron and Nuclear Counters*. D. Van Nostrand Co., Inc. (1946).

CHAPTER 19

NOTES ON HIGH VOLTAGE TECHNIQUE

(See also the chapters on X-rays and the Acceleration of Ions.)

The Measurement of High Voltage

19–1. Sphere Gaps.—When the separation between two charged spheres is gradually reduced, a critical distance between their closest surfaces will be found where the air will break down and a spark occur. This distance or gap depends on the voltage difference between the spheres. Values will be found in table 3, together with the conditions under which the measurements are to be made. Foreign bodies, whether insulators or conductors, in the neighborhood of the gap will distort the electro-static field and alter the values. For accurate work the spheres should be freshly polished. When a spark takes place in a sphere gap, sparks may occur in distant parts of the room. If these occur between current carrying wires, an arc may form, burning out motors, lamps, etc. Use fuses or circuit breakers in all power lines.

19–2. Resistance Types.—Another method of determining high voltages consists in measuring the potential drop across a portion of a very high resistance connected across the line. As an alternative method, a small current meter may be placed in series with a known, high resistance across the line and Ohm's law applied. Such resistances are available on the market, sometimes with corona shields.[1] "Metallized" resistors have a very thin metallic film on an insulating rod in a protective casing. A large number of smaller resistances in series with each other may be used as in figure 19–1. In this figure, a large number (800) of resistors,[2] each of 10 megohms, are placed end to end in contact with each other in

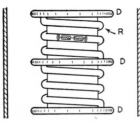

Fig. 19–1. Mounting of high resistances for use at high voltages.

clean, dry, rubber tubes, making a total of 20 strings of 40 units each. The rubber tubing (R) is wound around insulating spacers between metal discs (D). The latter are used as corona shields and must have smooth, rounded edges. Corona can be reduced by placing the entire unit in a sealed glass or textolite cylinder together with an open dish of carbon tetrachloride (CCl_4). The discs may be about one foot in diameter, spaced one-half foot apart. A microammeter is used in series with the resistors and can be calibrated to read volts directly, by means of Ohm's law.

Resistance ribbon consists of a fine wire woven back and forth at right angles to the supporting cotton threads; the latter running lengthwise of the ribbon. The currents in adjacent wires are in opposite directions so that the inductive effects are at least partially neutralized.

Tubes of various liquids may also be used as high resistances. Alcohol (any form) may be added to xylol to lower its resistance to the desired value, say 100,000 ohms per cubic centimeter. The following solution[3] has a constant resistance at various temperatures: 121 grams manite, 41 grams boric acid, 0.06 gram KCl, one liter water. Polarization at the electrodes causes changes in the resistance and hence in the calculated voltages. Amalgamated zinc electrodes in a solution of saturated zinc sulphate give non-polarizable electrodes.

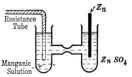

FIG. 19–2. Non-polarizing electrode for high resistances.

(See figure 19–2.) Cadmium iodide in amyl alcohol, using amalgamated cadmium electrodes, is also satisfactory for these high resistances. (One meter length and one millimeter diameter gives approximately 100 megohms.) The glass tubing containing these liquids should have a sufficiently large cross-section to prevent overheating with the power used. Extremely high resistance may be obtained by using a stream of water which breaks up into drops. For lower resistances, use ordinary water in a long rubber or glass tube. For large power, the water should be circulated. Seventy-five feet of three-eighths inch tubing full of water has a resistance of approximately 15 megohms. Such resistances in series with an oscillograph allow the study of the wave form of high potentials.

19-3. Generating Voltmeters.—Figure 19-3 shows one form of a generating voltmeter.[4] Two half-cylinders on a common shaft are rotated in an electro-static field. As shown, A_1 is charged with a quantity of electricity equal to CV, where C is the capacity between A_1 and the high potential electrode B, and V is the desired voltage. When A_1 has rotated to the position of A_2, in the figure, it will be shielded by A_2 and will have discharged its electricity to A_2 through the galvanometer (G) by way of the commutator C. Thus, for each revolution, a quantity of electricity $2CV$ will pass through the galvanometer. If the cylinder rotates n times per second, the current through G will be $I = 2CVn$, and

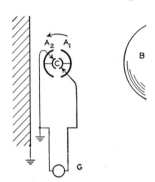

Fig. 19-3.   A generating voltmeter.

$$V = KI \qquad (19\text{-}1)$$

When the instrument is in a fixed position and rotated at a given speed, K is a constant and the voltage is directly proportional to the current generated. This has been verified experimentally. The instrument may, therefore, be calibrated at low voltages and used at high values. These voltmeters do not draw energy from the source, are easily calibrated and can be used to measure the wave form of the applied potential. For the latter purpose, the driving motor is operated from the same power source as that used to produce the high voltage. The motor and cylinder are shifted as a whole through various angles so as to establish the condition shown in figure 19-3 (A_1 on the right) at different times in the cycle of the high potential.

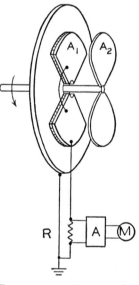

Fig. 19-4.   A generating voltmeter.

In the modified form [5] of the generating voltmeter shown in figure 19–4 (where there is no commutator), the fixed and insulated quadrants (A_1), are alternately shielded and exposed to the electrostatic field by the rotor plates (A_2). The alternating current which is then generated flows through the resistance R, creating a potential drop which is amplified, rectified and then observed on the meter (M). By the use of several values of resistance at R, a wide range of voltages may be measured with the same meter.

19–4. Miscellaneous.—A series of condensers may be connected across the high voltage line and measurements made of the potential drop across one of them by means of a high resistance voltmeter. In this " capacity potentiometer," the total voltage is calculated from the known values of the capacities. From the relation $Q = CV$, it may be seen that the larger potential drops occur across the smaller capacities. These condensers must, therefore, have better insulation than those of large capacity.

High voltages may also be determined from the step-up ratio of the transformer [6] and by means of electrostatic repulsion instruments operating on the principle of the Braun voltmeter (figure 17–9). The latter, however, must be especially constructed to avoid corona or break down, as in the attracted disc type.[7]

19–5. Indirect Measurement of Voltages.—Indirect measurements of high voltage may be made by observing the magnetic deflection of ions previously accelerated by the unknown voltage. Also, the absorption or range of ions in various materials may be used to determine the voltage used in their acceleration. The voltage applied to an x-ray tube may be measured from the intercept of an isochromat with its axis.[8] (See X-ray Chapter.)

SOME PROBLEMS OF INSULATION

19–6. Corona.—If a potential is applied at the end of two parallel wires and gradually increased, a voltage, called the *disruptive critical voltage*, is reached at which wattmeters in the circuit begin to register a loss of energy. A hissing noise is heard and streamers and glow points may be seen (if it is dark) issuing from dirt and surface irregularities along the wires. The energy which is lost increases gradually as the potential difference between the wires is raised until, at the *visual critical voltage*, a comparatively bright illumination appears all along the wires and the noise increases noticeably.   It is impossible to give a general value for this voltage, where corona begins, since it depends on many factors, but to give the reader a rough idea, one may say that for a particular transmission line and for certain conditions it amounted to a value between 100 and 200 kv.   With still higher voltages, the intensity of the light increases, an odor of ozone and nitrous oxide is noticed and the power losses increase rapidly.[9]   The breakdown occurs first near the surface of the conductor, since the electric field intensity is greatest there.   Since ionized air is conducting, the size of the conductor is effectively increased and the electric gradient in air nearby is reduced below the breakdown point.   The discharge, then, extends to a definite distance from the wire at a fixed voltage.   When the voltage is sufficiently high, a spark-over occurs at some chance place between the conductors. If the wires are sufficiently close together, spark-over will occur first and visible corona never appears.   With the wires far apart, the corona forms first.   Due to the differences of mobilities of the ions, the corona losses are usually greater between a small and a large conductor when the latter is negative than when it is positive.

To reduce corona losses, high voltage machines should be used in a dry, warm room, free from dust.   Rounded corners and smooth surfaces on all conductors are imperative.   Pans and kettles of metal (aluminum is very good) which were intended for kitchen use are useful in high voltage installations.   The voltage at which corona starts may be raised by increasing the diameter of the conductor;   the greater the radius, the lower the field gradient near the wire and the less the chance of breakdown (in direct proportion, for parallel wires).   The disruptive gradient of air between cylindrical conductors is 21.1 kilovolts (effective) per centimeter at 25° C. and 76 centimeters pressure.   For several hundred kilovolt lead-wires, 2-inch brass tubes may be used.   Corona can be reduced by placing the machine in air at high pressure.   Carbon tetrachloride and the gases used in refrigerators, such as freon, are also useful.

19–7.   Dielectrics.—Various synthetic compounds such as " textolite," are used as dielectrics as well as glass, porcelain, etc. Bakelite is not satisfactory with vacuum systems as it has a high vapor pressure.   For supports, in comparatively field-free regions, paraffined wood is satisfactory. The wood should be well dried and then boiled gently in paraffin for several days, until, on sectioning, it is found that the paraffin has completely penetrated the wood. Large leakage occurs with ordinary wood due to the moisture inside and on the surface.

The ionization of the air in small closed spaces inside of insulators is often the seat of an early break down. These are removed by oil impregnation under high pressure.

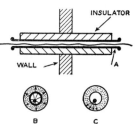

FIG. 19-5. A bushing.

19-8. Transition Regions. — The most important simple rule to prevent breakdown is to keep the electrical field away from those regions in which the structural materials change, as in bushings, metal to glass joints or wherever the dielectric constant changes.

High voltage bushings are frequently provided with a metal tube fitting snugly into the insulator, as at *A* in figure 19-5. The tube forms an equi-potential surface and distributes the field uniformly through the dielectric, as at *B*. Without out the tube (*C*), the insulation may break down in the regions where the field is concentrated.

FIG. 19-6. Potential gradients in insulators.

Consider two charged metal plates near and parallel to each other. With a uniform dielectric such as air between them, the potential increases linearly from the negative to the positive plate, as at *A* in figure 19-6. If one adds a slab of insulating material of greater break down strength, such as glass (shaded area), with the intention of preventing a rupture, he alters the potential gradient or field intensity, as at *B*. Under the increased electrical stress, the air may become ionized. Then, a large gradient occurs in the glass and it may well be punctured.

The potential difference between two concentric cylinders is not distributed uniformly in the space between them; i.e., the field intensity is not constant, even through a homogeneous dielectric. Instead, a large part of the potential drop occurs near the inner cylinder, as shown at C in figure 19–6. Thus,

$$G = \frac{dV}{dx} = \frac{V}{x \log_e (R/r)} \text{ volts/cm.,} \qquad (19\text{–}2).$$

where V is the applied potential, G is the field intensity or gradient of voltage x centimeters from the axis, R is the inner radius of the outer cylinder and r is the outer radius of the inner cylinder.

In the so-called *gradient insulators*, a material of fairly high dielectric constant is placed around the inner cylinder, as at D in figure 19–6, in order to lower the electric stress in this region. This is surrounded with an insulator of lower dielectric constant, etc.

19–9. X-ray Filament Transformers.—Step-down transformers for heating the filaments of the rectifying tubes such as used with x-ray tubes may be constructed in the following manner. Secure ten strips of a good grade of transformer iron, each one and one-half inches wide, one-sixteenth inch thick and eight feet long. Bend these into a circular core whose inside radius is about one foot. Wind with two layers of friction tape for insulation. This

must bind tightly or the transformer will hum badly. Around this ring wind a layer, 300 turns, of number 18 D.C.C. wire. This is the primary and is connected through a 48 ohm, 3.2 ampere rheostat to the 110 volt a.c. supply. The secondary coil, which passes through the primary ring with approximately one-foot spacing at all points, is made of 50 turns of number 14 D.C.C. wire (radius

Fig. 19–7. Filament transformer for high-tension lines.

one foot) with taps every fifth turn after the thirty-fifth turn. No iron is used in the secondary, the ring being held together with friction tape. The secondary potential will be 6 to 15 volts. Support the two coils with paraffined wood.

A tube of textolite or other high-voltage insulation material about half an inch thick may be used between the primary and secondary windings of a step-down transformer to provide sufficient insulation for use in high potential x-ray circuits (up to 40 kilovolts). This gives a more compact unit than that described in the preceding paragraph. It may be immersed in transformer oil for the higher voltages.

REFERENCES

1. See L. S. Taylor, Bur. Stds. Jr. Research, **5**, 609 (1930).
2. Hafstad, Heydenburg and Tuve, Phys. Rev. **50**, 504 (1936).
3. Pohl and Pringsheim, Ver. der d. Phys. Ges. **15**, 175 (1913).
4. P. Kirkpatrick and I. Miyake, Rev. Sci. Inst. **3**, 1 (1932).
   P. Kirkpatrick, Rev. Sci. Inst. **3**, 430 (1932).
   R. Gunn, Phys. Rev. **40**, 307 (1932).
   H. A. Thomas, Rev. Sci. Inst. **8**, 448 (1937).
5. Van Atta, Northrup, Van Atta and Van de Graaff, Phys. Rev. **49**, 770 (1936).
6. J. R. Meador, Elec. Eng. **53**, 942 (1934).
7. E. H. Bramhall, Rev. Sci. Inst. **5**, 18 (1934).
8. P. Kirkpatrick and I. Miyake, Rev. Sci. Inst. **3**, 4 (1932).
9. F. W. Peek, Jr., *Dielectric Phenomena in High Voltage Engineering*, McGraw-Hill Book Co. (1929), page 296.

PROBLEMS

1-1. What voltage is needed to balance an oil drop carrying 5 electrons when located between the plates of a condenser which are 5 mm. apart? The mass of the oil drop is 3.119×10^{-13} gram. (*19.1 volts*)

1-2. What is the velocity of fall of an oil drop of density 0.98 and radius 10^{-4} cm. in air of viscosity 0.0001826 and pressure 76 cm. of mercury. Use both the corrected and uncorrected laws of fall.
(*Corrected 0.0126 cm./sec. Uncorrected 0.0117 cm./sec.*)

1-3. 31.5 volts applied to two parallel plates 1 cm. apart give a charged oil drop between them an upward velocity of 10 divisions in 10 seconds (50 divisions = 1 mm.). The drop falls freely under gravity with a velocity of 10 divisions in 100 seconds. The coefficient of viscosity of air = 0.00018. Density of the drop = 0.9. Neglect the density of air. Pressure = 76 cm. Hg. How many electrons does the drop carry? (*one*)

1-4. In a determination of Avogadro's number N from Brownian movements, the average-squared-distance of Brownian displacement through which the particle moves in 30 seconds is found to be 3.70×10^{-5} cm. The temperature = 21° C.; the pressure = 74.4 cm.; the density of the oil = 0.92 gr./cm.^{3}; and the average time to fall freely over a distance of 0.944 mm. is found to be 100.8 sec. Find N.

1-5. The angle θ through which an x-ray beam ($CuK_{\alpha 1}$ line = 1.54 Å) is diffracted from a crystal of rock salt (molecular weight = 58.45, density = 2.163 g./cc.) is 15° 54' (first order). Find the value of e.

2-1. 1000 volts are applied to the plate of a two-electrode tube. What is the velocity of the electrons when they reach the plate?
(*1.88 × 10⁹ cm./sec.*)

2-2. What accelerating voltage is needed to give cathode particles a velocity of 3.763×10^9 cm. per second? (*4004 volts*)

2-3. Compute the ratio of the masses of two electrons accelerated with 4000 and 1000 volts, respectively. (*1.006*)

2-4. Find the strength of the magnetic field necessary to cause an electron of energy 1000 e.v. to move in a circular path of radius 5 cm.

2-5. Find the potential in volts between two plates of a cylindrical condenser necessary to cause an electron of energy 1000 e.v. to move in a circular path of radius 5 cm.

2–6. A field of 25 oersteds is applied perpendicularly to a cathode ray whose electrons have a velocity of 1.88×10^9 cm. per sec. What will be the radius of the circle into which they will be bent? *(4.25 cm.)*

2–7. What voltage is needed to return the spot of light in Thomson's e/m experiment to its original position if the magnetic field is of strength 30 oersteds, the velocity of the electrons 2.66×10^9 cm. per sec. and the plates 1 cm. apart? *(798 volts)*

2–8. In a Kirchner e/m experiment, when only one spot is observed, the accelerating voltage is 300 volts and the distance between the condensers is 50 cm. Using $e/m = 1.76 \times 10^7$ e.m.u./g., find the frequency of the oscillator.

2–9. The cathode ray tube used in the measurement of e/m by the "helical" method has X and Y deflection plates at distances from the screen of 14 and 16 cm., respectively. Measurements are to be made over a range of magnetic field values which will produce one, two, and three spirals with the X plates, and over a corresponding range with the Y plates. The accelerating potential will be held constant at 1000 volts. What is the largest magnetic field which will be required?

2–10. From the relation, $\mathscr{E} = mc^2$, calculate (a) the energy corresponding to the mass of one electron, (b) the energy corresponding to one mass-unit and (c) the energy corresponding to one millimass-unit.

2–11. How many electron volts are needed to accelerate (a) a proton, (b) an α-particle, to the same velocity as that of an electron accelerated by one electron volt?

2–12. An electron is accelerated by V volts and bent into a circular path of radius r cm. by a magnetic field of strength H oersteds. Show that $Hr = 3.37\sqrt{V}$.

2–13. One ampere is passed through a single turn of wire of radius 13 cm. Compute the field intensity at a point 6.5 cm. off the axis and 3 cm. out from the center of the coil. Compare with the intensity on the axis at the same distance out and at the center of the coil.
(0.051, 0.045, 0.048 oersted)

2–14. Compute the mass of an electron and of the hydrogen ion in solution.

2–15. Calculate the force on the plate of a two-electrode tube when bombarded by electrons accelerated by 200 volts, the plate current being 6 milliamperes and $e/m = 1.77 \times 10^7$ e.m.u./gram, assuming that all of their momentum is given up when they strike the plate. *(0.029 dyne)*

3–1. What wave-length is to be associated with an electron of velocity 9×10^9 cm. per sec. to give its observed diffraction pattern? Include the relativity correction for mass.

(0.077 Å)

3–2. Calculate the constant relating the wave-length of an electron in angstroms with its accelerating potential in volts. Neglect the relativity correction.

3–3. What wave-length is to be associated with an electron accelerated by 50,000 volts to give its observed diffraction pattern? Neglect the relativity correction.

(0.055 Å)

3–4. The wave-length associated with an electron is measured from the space lattice of a nickel crystal and found to be 0.0566 angstrom. The electrons were accelerated by 46,500 volts. Compute Planck's constant, assuming the mass of the electrons to be 9.0×10^{-28} gram and neglecting the relativity correction.

3–5. Given an electron with energy of 1000 electron volts and wave-length 0.389 Å outside the metal, nickel. What is the change in wave-length upon entering the metal, if the surface energy is 16 volts? Find the index of refraction of the metal for electrons of this wave-length.

3–6. The position of an electron is known to within 100 Å. What is the uncertainty in the determination of its velocity?

3–7. What wave-length is to be associated with a proton accelerated by 50,000 volts? Neglect relativity correction.

4–1. How many ergs of work are needed to remove an electron from the surface of sodium metal whose photo-electric long wave-length limit is 6800 angstroms? *(Greater than 2.89×10^{-12} erg = 1.82 volts)*

4–2. What potential must be applied across two zinc plates when one of them is illuminated by light of wave-length 2536 angstroms in order to repel the fastest electrons ejected? The work function of zinc is 3.89 volts. *(0.987 volt)*

4–3. If the work function of tungsten is 4.52 volts, how many ergs of work are needed to remove an electron from its surface?

4–4. Thirty foot-candles are received on a surface 2 feet from the source. What is the candle power? What will be the illumination at twice the distance?

4–5. What is the light flux in lumens passing through an area of 1 sq. in. at a distance of 2 ft. from the source of problem 4–4?

4–6. What is the total light flux in lumens from the source of problem 4–4? Assuming that the radiation is of maximum visibility, convert this flux to watts. If the source is a 60 watt lamp, what is its efficiency?

4–7. If the source of problem 4–4 is used to illuminate a photo-cell of 1 sq. cm. area and sensitivity of 40 microamps per lumen at a distance of 1 ft., what is the output of the cell in amperes?

4–8. What is the maximum frequency of x-rays from an x-ray tube having an applied potential difference of 100,000 volts?

5–1. What will be the root-mean-square value of the fluctuating current in the inductance-capacitance circuit in the plate circuit, as in the shot effect, if the effective resistance of the coil is 5 ohms, the capacity is 600 micro-microfarads and the plate current is 5 milliamperes?

(0.364 microampere)

5–2. If the work function of platinum is 6.27 volts, how many ergs of work are needed to remove an electron from its surface?

5–3. Compute the constant A in Richardson's equation (5–3) if the emission from each square centimeter of a tungsten filament at 2000° absolute is 4.2 milliamperes. The work function of tungsten is 4.52 volts.

5–4. What is the total current in amperes per sq. cm. from a tungsten filament at a temperature of 2000° K, where the field intensity is 2000 volts per cm. For A of Richardson's equation use 60.2 amps. per cm.^{2} per degree.^{2}

6–1. Compute the constant in the Child-Langmuir equation when the space-charge-limited current is 5.627 milliamperes and the plate potential is 180 volts.

6–2. A change of 10 volts in the plate potential of a three-electrode tube causes a change of 0.833 milliampere in its plate current. Compute the plate resistance of the tube. (12,000 ohms)

6–3. The mutual conductance of a three-electrode tube is 675 micromhos and the plate resistance is 12,000 ohms. What is the amplification constant? (8.1)

6–4. How many volts change on the grid of a three-electrode tube whose amplification constant is 8 and plate resistance is 12,000 ohms are needed to change the plate current by 4.0 milliamperes? (6 volts)

6–5. Find the " focal length " of a magnetic field of 30 oersteds making an angle of 5° with the electron beam, when the electrons have been accelerated by 1000 volts.

6–6. Find the focal length of a double-gauze lens, where the radius of curvature of the gauze is 10 cm., the incidence speed of the electrons is 1000 volts, and the voltage of the battery is 100 volts.

(+208 cms convergent; −19.3 cms, divergent)

6–7. Given: the focal length of a diaphragm-hole lens as 50 cm. The electrons pass through the field-free space in a parallel bundle and are then accelerated by a potential gradient of 100 volts/cm. With what potential were the electrons accelerated before they entered the field-free space? *(1250 volts)*

7–1. Compute the intercepting cross-section (radius in cm.) of neon atoms at 0.1 mm. pressure and 0° C. when a beam of electrons in passing through 10 cm. is reduced to 0.208 of its original value.

(1.18×10^{-8} cm.)

7–2. An electron beam of 1 ma., is reduced to 0.01 ma. after passing through 5 cm. of argon gas at a temperature of 20° C. and a pressure of 0.0429 mm. Compute the absorption coefficient (at 1 mm. pressure and 0° C.), the effective cross-section of the argon atoms for electrons, the mean-free-path of the electrons and compare with values given by the kinetic theory. The mean-free-path of argon atoms at 760 mm. and 0° C. is 8.84×10^{-6} cm.

7–3. Calculate the number of alpha particles scattered in a given time by a thin foil, at ten degree intervals from 10° to 180°, when their number is 10^6 at an angle of 10°.

7–4. One thousand alpha particles are scattered at a given angle in a given time by an aluminum foil. This foil is replaced by a gold foil of such thickness that the number of atoms (per unit area) is the same as for the aluminum. How many alpha particles will then be observed during the same time interval?

7–5. The ionizing potential of helium is 24.5 volts. What energy in ergs is required to extract an electron from its normal position in the atom? *(3.90×10^{-11} erg)*

7–6. Compute the constant relating radiation potentials in volts and the wave-length of the emitted light in angstrom units.

7–7. Compute the number of ergs in a photon whose wave-length is 0.710 angstrom.

8–1. In Erickson's method of measuring mobilities, ions of mobility 1.87 cm.-per-sec. per volt-per-cm. are introduced into an air stream whose velocity is 1704 cm. per sec. What voltage must be applied to the parallel plates, which are 10 cm. apart, in order that the ions shall be deflected 9.0 cm. vertically while being carried a distance of 16.4 cm. by the air? *(5000 volts)*

8–2. A current is first observed in the electrometer (E of figure 8–6) when the distance between plates B and C is 10 cm. and the potential difference between them is 41.6 volts. The commutator D makes 40 revolutions per minute. Find the mobility of the ions.

8–3. A discharge tube containing pure argon is placed in a horizontal position and viewed with a rotating mirror whose axis of rotation is parallel to the axis of the tube. The mirror rotates at 2400 r.p.m. and the striations are seen to be inclined at an angle of 56 degrees with the axis of the tube when viewed at a distance of 30 cm. from the mirror. What is the velocity of the striations? *(10,170 cm./sec.)*

9–1. Compute the constant relating the voltage applied to an x-ray tube and the wave-length of the emitted x-ray line in angstroms.

9–2. Compute the wave-length of the " modified line " of an x-ray beam whose wave-length is 0.558 Å ($K_{\alpha 1}$ line of silver). The scattered rays are observed at an angle of 46° with the direction of the primary beam. *(0.565 Å)*

9–3. The intensity of a homogeneous x-ray beam in passing through an absorbing medium of 10 cm. thickness is reduced to one-half its value. Find the absorption coefficient.

9–4. The wave-length of x-rays from molybdenum ($Z = 42$) is 0.71 Å. Use Moseley's law to find the wave-length of the radiation from a tungsten ($Z = 74$) target. (Use 1.13 for the value of the screening constant in both cases.)

9–5. In a Laue photograph, measurements give, for a certain spot, $r = 5$ cm. and $\phi = 33.5°$. The distance from the crystal to the photographic emulsion is 3.12 cm. What are the Miller indices of the corresponding plane?

10–1. If hydrogen positive rays continue to radiate light 4 cm. beyond the cathode and the red spectrum line (6563 angstroms) has a Doppler shift of 2.188 angstroms, what is the time duration of the light emission? *(4 × 10⁻⁷ sec.)*

10–2. In a Thomson parabola apparatus the plates are 1 cm. apart and 5 cm. long. They are 22 cm. distant from the screen. If the electro-static deflection due to a field of 100 volts/cm. is 0.11 cm. with protons, what must the magnetic field be to give an equal deflection?

10–3. Using the data in problem 10–2, calculate the electro-static and magnetic deflections for H^{++} and H_2^+ particles.

10–4. What is the minimum accelerating voltage that can be used on the apparatus of problem 10–3 so that the maximum deflections of H^+, H^{++}, H_2^+ will not exceed 4 cm.?

10–5. Plot a curve of the mass defects of the stable isotopes from mass number 0 to 20.

10–6. Assume that an alpha particle is composed of two neutrons and two protons. Compute the binding energy of the alpha particle.

11–1. Define the millicurie of radon and of polonium. What is the mass of one millicurie of polonium? *(0.0272 g.)*

11–2. What is the saturation current produced in an ionization chamber by 1 millicurie of polonium if all the alpha particles are completely absorbed? *(1400 e.s.u. = 4.6 × 10⁻⁷ amp.)*

11–3. The half-life period of thorium is 1.39×10^{10} years. What is its transformation constant and average life? 3.15569×10^{7} sec. = 1 yr.

11–4. How many days after uranium X_1 has been isolated before 90 per cent has changed to uranium X_2? The half period of uranium X_1 is 24.5 days.

11–5. The transformation constant for radium is 1.35×10^{-11} per second and its atomic weight is 226. The atomic weight of uranium I is 238. There are 3.44×10^{-7} gram of radium in equilibrium with each gram of uranium I. Calculate the half period of uranium I in years.

11–6. One gram of radium emits 3.71×10^{10} alpha particles per second. The transformation constant of radium emanation is 2.097×10^{-6} per second and its density is 0.00987 gm. per cc. The number of atoms per cc. of a monatomic gas is 2.705×10^{19}. Calculate the volume and mass of one curie.

11–7. There are 13.6×10^{10} alpha particles emitted each second by one gram of radium in equilibrium with its decay products. Calculate the volume of helium produced by one gram of radium and its products in one year. *(159 mm.³)*

11–8. The number of alpha particles emitted per gram of radium each second is 3.71×10^{10}. If the atomic weight of radium is 226, what is its half period in years? One year = 3.156×10^{7} sec.

11–9. Uranium I is freed from all its products and placed in a beta-ray electroscope. How many days before the rate of fall of the leaf of the electroscope reaches 50% of its maximum value? The transformation constant of uranium X_1 is 3.275×10^{-7} sec⁻¹.

11–10. If a person has one gram of radium today, how much will he have at the end of 10 years? Take the half-life of radium as 1590 years.

11–11. Equate the first derivative of equation 11–18 to zero and determine the time necessary to reach the transient equilibrium point in figure 11–5. $[(t_s = log_e (\lambda_1/\lambda_2)/(\lambda_1 - \lambda_2)]$

11–12. The number of counts per minute in a counter tube, as determined by measurements made over a long period of time, is 480 when the source is present and 60 when it is absent. Compute the probable error (in percentage) when the observation time is ten minutes. What is the relative sensitivity of the instrument?

12–1. A beta particle has an energy of 10^6 e.v. What is the corresponding value of Hr for this particle? Compare the relativistic and the non-relativistic values.

12–2. The ranges of the alpha particles from radium A and radium C′ are 4.69 cm. and 6.94 cm. respectively. If the velocity of those from radium A is 1.699×10^9 cm. per sec., what is the velocity of those from radium C′?

12–3. The range of the alpha particles from radium A is 4.69 cm. at 76 cm. mercury pressure and 15° C. What will the range be at 74 cm. and 22.7° C.?

12–4. The absorption coefficients of beta rays in aluminum for uranium X_1 and uranium X_2 are 460 and 18, respectively. What thicknesses of aluminum are necessary to reduce each to one one-hundredth of the original intensity?

12–5. The coefficient of absorption of a gamma ray is proportional to the density of the absorbing material. What thickness of cast iron will reduce the intensity of a gamma ray by the same amount as one inch of lead?

12–6. The absorption coefficients of beta rays in aluminum for radium C and C″ are 50 and 13. What will be the reduction in intensity of the *more* penetrating of these rays when passed through a sheet of aluminum which reduces the *less* penetrating to one one-hundredth of the original value?

12–7. What percentage of beta rays from uranium X_2 and of gamma rays from radium C will penetrate 0.12 cm. of aluminum whose absorption coefficients for these rays are 18 and 0.23 respectively?

12–8. 47.97 cm. of aluminum will reduce the gamma rays from thorium C″ to one one-hundredth of their original value. What is the coefficient of absorption?

13–1. Calculate the energy of the emergent protons in a small cyclotron whose field strength is 5000 gausses. The maximum radius of the ion beam is 5 cm. What is the oscillator frequency at resonance?
(29937 volts, 7.624 Mc.)

14–1. A proton beam of one microampere strikes a lithium target. A voltmeter across the accelerating tube reads 50 kilovolts. From the known yield curve (figure 14–11), how many alpha particles may be expected each minute?

14–2. Express equation 14–17 in Mev and also in milli-ergs.

14–3. Write the equations for the reactions described in the first paragraph of section 14–19.

17–1. The voltage sensitivity of an electroscope is 200 divisions per volt. Its capacity is 2 e.s.u. A certain current moves the leaf at the rate of 0.1 division per second. What is the value of this current in amperes? *(1.11 × 10⁻¹⁵ amp.)*

17–2. The leaf of an electroscope is found to pass over 10 divisions in 10 seconds when a radioactive substance is nearby. A standard condenser is placed in parallel with the instrument. The leaf then takes 50 seconds to pass over the same number of divisions. The standard condenser is made of two concentric cylinders of length 10 cm. The outside diameter of the inner cylinder is 2 cm. and the inside diameter of the outer one is 3 cm. What is the capacity of the electroscope?

(3.08 e.s.u.)

17–3. The voltage sensitivity of a quadrant electrometer is 1,000 scale divisions per volt. Its capacity is 50 e.s.u. A certain current causes a motion of 0.1 divisions per second. What is the value of this current in amperes? *(5.56 × 10⁻¹⁵ amp.)*

17–4. The voltage sensitivity of a quadrant electrometer is 600 divisions per volt and its capacity is 100 e.s.u. What charge, in coulombs, must be added to the system in order to produce a deflection of 20 divisions?

17–5. An ionization chamber alone has a capacity of $(C =)$ 20 e.s.u. With lead wires and electrometer, the capacity is 70 e.s.u. What is the effect on the output current of doubling the length of the ionization chamber? (i.e., $C = 40$ e.s.u.)

19–1. In the generating voltmeter of figure 19–3, the capacitance between A_1 and B is two e.s.u. If the current through the galvanometer is found to be three microamperes when the rotor is turning with a speed of 1800 r.p.m., what is the voltage V?

19–2. Given, 2 condensers, of 1μf. and $\frac{3}{4}\mu f$., in series. If an electrostatic voltmeter across the larger one reads 400 volts, find the total voltage, and also that across the smaller condenser.

19–3. A tube of one centimeter diameter, which will later be used as a Geiger-Müller counter tube, has a 3 mil (diameter) wire mounted along its axis. The voltage between the wire and the tube is 1200 volts (V). At what distance from surface of wire will the voltage be 80 per cent of V?

TABLE 1.—SOME WORK FUNCTIONS AND PHOTOELECTRIC THRESHOLDS

Surface (outgassed)	Photoelectric		Thermionic
	Threshold λ_0, Angstroms	Work function ϕ_3, volts	Work function ϕ_3, volts
Ag	2610 (20° C.) 2710 (600° C.)	4.73 4.56	4.08 (925° C.)
Au	2650 (20° C.) 2610 (740° C.)	4.82 4.73	4.42 (1050° C.)
Cu			4.38
Fe	2620	4.72	
Hg	2735	4.53	
Mo			4.41
Ni	2463	5.01	
Pd	2488	4.96	
Pt	1962	6.30	6.27
Rh	2500	4.57	4.58
Sn	2740 (β) 2820 (γ) 2925 (liq.)	4.50 4.38 4.21	
Ta	3050 (20° C.) 3150 (700° C.)	4.05 3.92	4.07
Th			3.35
W			4.52
		Minimum Values	
Th–W	4900	2.52	2.62
BaO–Pt	9200	1.34	1.05
Cs–CsO–Ag	>10,000	<1.23	0.65
Li–W	6700	1.83	
Na–Pt	5900	2.08	
K–Pt	7700	1.60	
Rb–Pt	7950	1.56	
Cs–Pt	8900	1.38	
Ba–Ag	7900	1.56	

From Hughes and DuBridge, *Photoelectric Phenomena*, pp. 75–86, McGraw-Hill Book Co. (1932). See, also, J. A. Becker, Rev. Mod. Phys. **7**, 123 (1935).

TABLE 2.—SOME CRITICAL POTENTIALS

V_i = minimum ionizing potential. V_r = resonance potential
m = meta-stable state.

See H. D. Smythe, Rev. Mod. Phys. **3**, 347 (1931); F. L. Arnot, *Collision Processes in Gases,*
Methuen & Co. (1933); *International Critical Tables*, McGraw-Hill Book Co. (1929).

	V_i	V_r		V_i	V_r
H	13.5	10.8	He	24.5	$\begin{cases} 19.77\ m \\ (20.55) \end{cases}$
H₂	15.9	11.5			
N	14.5	....	Ne	21.5	16.58
N₂	16.3	8.0	Ar	15.7	11.57
O	13.5	....	Kr	13.94	9.98
O₂	12.8	7.9	Xe	12.08	8.39

	V_i	V_r		V_i	V_r
Mg	7.61	2.70	Li	5.37	1.84
Ca	6.08	1.88	Na	5.12	2.09
Zn	9.35	4.02	K	4.32	1.60
Cd	8.95	3.78	Rb	4.16	1.55
Hg	10.39	$\begin{cases} 4.68\ m \\ (4.86) \end{cases}$	Cs	3.88	1.38

	V_i		Volts
CO.....................	14.1	$H_2 \rightarrow H + H$	4.4
CO₂.....................	14.4	$N_2 \rightarrow N + N$	9.1
H₂O.....................	13.1	$O_2 \rightarrow O + O$	5.1

TABLE 3.—SPARKING POTENTIALS

The voltages given are *peak values* (not the usual root-mean-square voltages) which will just break down non-ionized air at a pressure of 760 mm. and temperature 25° C. Needle gap voltages at a relative humidity of 80%. Sphere gap values practically independent of humidity. Adapted from values in the Handbuch der Physik (Geiger and Scheel), Vol. 16, p. 407, 1927. 1 and 2 cm. sphere values from Kaye "X-rays," p. 102, 1923.

Gap in cm.	Needle Points A	Kilovolts. A = Electrodes ungrounded. B = One electrode grounded									
		Diameter of Spheres									
		1 cm.	2 cm.	6.25 cm.		12.5 cm.		25.0 cm.		50.0 cm.	
		A	A	A	B	A	B	A	B	A	B
0.25	3	10	10	9	9	9	9				
0.50	5	17	17	17	17	17	17				
1.00	12	27	31	33	33	33	33				
1.50	17	32	40	45	45	45	45				
2.0	23	36	48	59	59	59	59	60	60	60	60
3.0	33	42	58	82	79	85	85	86	86	86	86
4.0	42	45	65	100	93	109	109	91	91	93	93
5.0	49	47	71	114	103	131	130	139	139	140	136
6.0	56		77	127	111	151	147	163	160	164	163
7.0	61					169	159	184	182	192	188
8.0	66					185	171	206	203	218	214
9.0	71					200	181	226	222	243	238
10.0	75					214	191	245	240	269	264
12.0						237	208	278	272	318	312
15.0							226	325	311	381	371
17.5								362	338	432	420
20.0								392	360	475	461
22.5								418	379	515	497
25.0								440	396	555	531
30.0								480	425	633	598

Below.—Average values for 75 cm. (diameter) spheres. C values for positive sphere grounded. D values for negative sphere grounded.

From Meador, E. E. **53**, 942 (1934); Bellaschi, E. J. **31**, 225 (1934) and Henderson, Goss and Rose, Rev. Sci. Inst **6**, 63 (1935).

Gap in cms.		5	10	15	20	25	30	35	40	45	50	55	60
Kilovolts (peak)	C	137	263	382	483	573	650	720	775	825	870	908	937
	D	137	263	382	495	597	685	757	818	872	920	960	995

TABLE 4.—NATURAL GROUPS OF ALPHA PARTICLES

v_0 = initial velocity. $\mathscr{E}_0$ = initial energy. V_0 = initial energy. V'_0 = initial kinetic energy of the recoil atom $(V'_0 = M\alpha V_0/M')$. R = mean range; r = extrapolated range; $\mathscr{I}$= total number of ion pairs produced. R, r and $\mathscr{I}$ in air at 760 mm. and 15° C.

Radioactive Substance	v_0 cm./sec. $10^9 \times$	$\mathscr{E}_0$ ergs $10^{-6} \times$	V_0 kilo-volts	V'_0 kilo-volts	R cms.	r cms.	$\mathscr{I}$ $10^5 \times$
Uranium I..........	1.420	0.666	4190	71	2.69	2.72	1.20
Uranium II.........	1.511	0.755	4740	81	3.24	3.28	1.36
Ionium.............	1.498	0.742	4660	82	3.15	3.19	1.34
Radium (1).........	1.519	0.763	4795	86	3.29	3.33	1.37
Radon.............	1.625	0.873	5488	100	4.04	4.08	1.57
Radium A..........	1.699	0.955	6001	112	4.64	4.69	1.72
Radium C (1).......	1.628	0.876	5508	105	4.06	4.11	1.58
Radium C'.........	1.922	1.222	7683	146	6.87	6.94	2.20
Polonium..........	1.597	0.843	5300	103	3.83	3.87	1.52
Actinouranium......	1.511	0.755	4740	82	3.24	3.28	1.36
Protoactinium......	1.569	0.814	5115	90	3.63	3.67	1.47
Radioactinium $\{(2)..$	1.701	0.957	6015	108	4.66	4.71	1.72
$\{(4)..$	1.663	0.914	5748	103	4.34	4.39	1.65
Actinium X (1)......	1.659	0.910	5720	104	4.31	4.36	1.64
Actinon (1)........	1.812	1.086	6826	127	5.68	5.74	1.95
Actinium A.........	1.884	1.174	7382	140	6.44	6.51	2.11
Actinium C (1)......	1.785	1.053	6621	128	5.42	5.48	1.90
Actinium C'........	1.892	1.184	7445	144	6.53	6.60	2.13
Thorium...........	1.446	0.691	4345	77	2.84	2.87	1.24
Radiothorium (1)....	1.615	0.862	5420	97	3.96	4.01	1.55
Thorium X.........	1.653	0.904	5681	103	4.26	4.31	1.63
Thoron............	1.739	1.000	6284	116	4.99	5.04	1.80
Thorium A.........	1.805	1.078	6775	128	5.62	5.68	1.94
Thorium C (3)......	1.707	0.964	6057	117	4.71	4.76	1.73
Thorium C'........	2.054	1.397	8779	169	8.53	8.62	2.51

(1) The fastest alpha particles, forming the most intense component (A) in the fine structure. (2) Weighted average for the group (A, B, C) of greatest energy. (3) Weighted average for the components A and B. (4) Weighted average for the group (H, I, J) of smallest energy. From *Radioactivité*, by Madame P. Curie, p. 533, published by Hermann & Co., Paris, 1935. See also, M. G. Holloway and M. S. Livingston, Phys. Rev., **54**, 36 (1938). In their article, mean range values are approximately 0.02 cm. greater than the values of R in the table above, except U I and U II which are 0.03 smaller in this more recent publication. Two values for the extrapolated range are given: those by ionization averaging 0.01 cm. smaller than in the table above; those by number-distance counting, greater by 0.05 cm. Standards given are: Th C', R = 8.570 ± 0.007, r(ionization) = 8.616; Ra C', R = 6.907 ± 0.006, r(ioniz.) 6.953; Ra F(Po), R = 3.842 ± 0.006, r(ioniz.) 3.870. A mean-range energy plot is given on page 31 of this article.

TABLE 5.—RANGE OF ALPHA PARTICLES IN VARIOUS SUBSTANCES

Extrapolated range = r. Gases at 76 centimeters pressure, 15° C. Solids and liquids at 15° C.

Values from *Radioactivité*, by Madame P. Curie, pages 218–220 (1935).

	r, cm.	r, cm.		r, microns	r, microns
Air............	3.87	6.96	Water.........	32.0	60.0
Oxygen........	3.64	6.60	Alcohol........	37.1	70.5
Nitrogen.......	3.89	7.0	Ether.........	43.0	
Hydrogen......	17.3	32.5	Benzene.......	36.3	70.0
Helium........	21.5	39.0	Photo-gelatin..	∼27	∼52
Argon.........	4.17	7.3			

For alpha particles whose range is 6.96 cm. in air at 76 cm. 15° C.

	r, microns		r, microns
Lithium................	129.1	Tin..................	29.4
Magnesium.............	57.8	Platinum.............	12.8
Aluminum.............	40.6	Gold.................	14.0
Calcium...............	78.8	Lead.................	24.1
Iron..................	18.7	Cadmium.............	24.2
Nickel................	18.4	Silver...............	19.2
Copper...............	18.3	Zinc.................	22.8

TABLE 6.—STOPPING POWER OF VARIOUS SUBSTANCES FOR ALPHA PARTICLES

S		s			
Relative stopping power (air at 15° C. and 76 cm.)		Relative atomic stopping power (relative to air of atomic weight 14.44 at 15° C. and 76 cm.)			
Air............	1.0	Air............	1.0	Aluminum...	1.45
Hydrogen......	0.21	Hydrogen......	0.22	Copper......	2.3
Helium........	0.17	Helium........	0.35	Silver.......	3.2
Oxygen........	1.07	Nitrogen.......	0.99	Tin.........	3.3
Neon..........	0.62	Oxygen........	1.06	Platinum....	4.2
Argon.........	0.98	Argon..........	1.90	Gold........	4.3
Aluminum......	1660.00			Lead........	4 4
		Water vapor....	1.5	Carbon......∼0.9	
		Alcohol vapor...	4.0		
		Water..........	1.6		
		Alcohol........	4.4		

S. From *Elements of Nuclear Physics*, by F. Rasetti, p. 48, Prentice-Hall (1936).
s. From *Radioactivité*, by Madame P. Curie, p. 223, Hermann & Co. (1935).

TABLE 7.—ALPHA PARTICLES

v_0 = initial velocity, $\beta = v_0/c$, c = velocity of light. $\mathscr{E}_0$ = initial kinetic energy in ergs, $= M_0c^2[(1/\sqrt{1-\beta^2}) - 1]$, M_0 = rest mass. V_0 = initial kinetic energy in electron kilovolts, $V_0 = 3\mathscr{E}_0/10e$. Hr (H = field in oersteds to curve particle into a circle of radius r, cm.), $Hr = (M_0v_0/e)\,(1/\sqrt{1-\beta^2})$. R = mean range in air at 760 mm. and 15° C. $\mathscr{J}$= total number of ions pairs produced in air by one particle.

v_0 cm./sec. $10^9 \times$	β^2 $10^{-3} \times$	$\mathscr{E}_0$ ergs $10^{-5} \times$	V_0 kilovolts	Hr oersted·cm. $10^5 \times$	R cm.	$\mathscr{J}$ $10^5 \times$
0.75	0.626	0.1857	1,167	1.555	0.55	0.33
0.80	0.712	0.2113	1,328	1.659	0.62	0.38
0.85	0.804	0.2385	1,499	1.763	0.70	0.43
0.90	0.901	0.2674	1,681	1.867	0.80	0.48
0.95	1.004	0.2980	1,873	1.971	0.91	0.53
1.00	1.113	0.3302	2,075	2.074	1.04	0.59
1.05	1.227	0.3641	2,288	2.178	1.18	0.65
1.10	1.346	0.3996	2,511	2.282	1.32	0.72
1.15	1.471	0.4368	2,745	2.386	1.48	0.79
1.20	1.602	0.4756	2,989	2.490	1.67	0.86
1.25	1.739	0.5161	3,244	2.594	1.87	0.93
1.30	1.881	0.5583	3,509	2.698	2.09	1.00
1.35	2.028	0.6022	3,785	2.802	2.33	1.08
1.40	2.181	0.6477	4,071	2.906	2.58	1.17
1.45	2.340	0.6948	4,368	3.010	2.86	1.25
1.50	2.504	0.7437	4,674	3.114	3.17	1.34
1.55	2.673	0.7941	4,991	3.218	3.50	1.43
1.60	2.849	0.8463	5,319	3.322	3.85	1.52
1.65	3.029	0.9002	5,658	3.426	4.24	1.62
1.70	3.216	0.9558	6,008	3.530	4.65	1.72
1.75	3.408	1.0129	6,367	3.635	5.09	1.82
1.80	3.605	1.0718	6,737	3.739	5.57	1.93
1.85	3.808	1.1322	7,117	3.843	6.08	2.03
1.90	4.017	1.1945	7,508	3.947	6.62	2.15
1.95	4.231	1.2584	7,910	4.052	7.20	2.26
2.00	4.451	1.3240	8,322	4.156	7.82	2.38
2.05	4.677	1.3913	8,745	4.260	8.48	2.50
2.10	4.907	1.4602	9,178	4.365	9.18	2.62
2.15	5.144	1.5309	9,622	4.469	9.92	2.76
2.20	5.386	1.6032	10,077	4.574	10.71	2.88
2.25	5.633	1.6772	10,543	4.678	11.54	3.02
2.30	5.887	1.7529	11,018	4.783	12.42	3.16
2.35	6.145	1.8308	11,504	4.888	13.43	3.29
2.40	6.410	1.9093	12,001	4.992	14.32	3.44
2.45	6.680	1.9901	12,508	5.137	15.35	3.58
2.50	6.955	2.0726	13,027	5.202	16.44	3.73

Selected from *Radioactivité*, by Madame P. Curie, p. 530, published by Hermann & Co. (1935). In computing this table the charge of the electron was taken as $e = 4.77 \times 10^{-10}$ e.s.u.

TABLE 8.—PROTONS

v_0 = initial velocity. $\beta = v_0/c$, c = velocity of light. $\mathscr{E}_0$ = initial kinetic energy in ergs. V_0 = initial kinetic energy in electron kilovolts. Hr (H = field to curve particles into a circle of radius r, cm., $Hr = M_H v_0/e(1/\sqrt{1 - \beta^2})$). R = mean range in air at 760 millimeters and 15° C.

v_0 cm./sec. $10^9 \times$	β^2 $10^{-3} \times$	$\mathscr{E}_0$ ergs $10^{-6} \times$	V_0 kilovolts	Hr oersted $\times$ cm. $10^5 \times$	R cm.
1.0	1.113	0.831	522	1.044	0.8
1.2	1.602	1.198	753	1.253	1.4
1.4	2.181	1.630	1,025	1.463	2.3
1.6	2.849	2.131	1,340	1.673	3.6
1.8	3.605	2.698	1,697	1.883	5.3
2.0	4.451	3.333	2,095	2.093	7.5
2.2	5.386	4.036	2,536	2.304	10.4
2.4	6.410	4.808	3,021	2.514	14.0
2.6	7.523	5.647	3,649	2.725	18.4
2.8	8.724	6.554	4,120	2.936	23.9
3.0	10.015	7.531	4,734	3.148	30.4
3.2	11.395	8.577	5,391	3.360	38.2
3.4	12.863	9.693	6,092	3.573	47.4
3.6	14.422	10.89	6,838	3.786	58.2
3.8	16.068	12.14	7,628	4.000	70.5
4.0	17.804	13.46	8,463	4.214	84.8
4.2	19.629	14.86	9,343	4.428	101.3
4.4	21.543	16.34	10,270	4.643	119.9
4.6	23.547	17.88	11,240	4.858	140.8
4.8	25.638	19.49	12,250	5.075	164.6
5.0	27.819	21.17	13,310	5.293	191.1

From *Radioactivité*, by Madame P. Curie, p. 536, published by Hermann & Co., Paris, 1935.

TABLE 9.—ELECTRONS

$\beta = v/c$, v = velocity of electrons, c = velocity of light. $\mathcal{E}$ = initial kinetic energy in ergs. V = kinetic energy in electron kilovolts. $Hr(H$ = field in oersteds to bend rays into a circle of radius r centimeters). λ = wave-length in x-units (= 10^{-11} centimeters). Relativity equations used throughout.

β	$\dfrac{1}{\sqrt{1-\beta^2}}$	$\mathcal{E} \times 10^9$ ergs	V kilovolts	Hr oersted·cm.	Radiated λ x-units
0.10	1.00504	4.095	2.574	171.2	4792
0.15	1.01144	9.295	5.842	258.4	2112
0.20	1.02062	16.75	10.530	347.7	1171
0.25	1.03280	26.65	16.75	439.8	736.4
0.30	1.04829	39.24	24.66	535.7	502.3
0.35	1.06752	54.86	34.48	636.4	348.7
0.40	1.09109	74.01	46.52	743.4	265.1
0.45	1.11979	97.33	61.17	858.3	201.7
0.50	1.15469	125.7	79.00	984	156.1
0.525	1.17494	142.1	89.34	1,051	138.0
0.550	1.19736	161.4	100.8	1,122	122.4
0.575	1.22226	180.6	113.5	1,197	108.6
0.600	1.25000	203.1	127.7	1,278	96.62
0.625	1.28102	228.3	143.5	1,365	85.96
0.650	1.31590	256.7	161.3	1,458	76.47
0.675	1.35534	288.7	181.5	1,559	67.98
0.700	1.40021	325.2	204.4	1,670	60.34
0.725	1.45190	367.2	230.8	1,793	53.46
0.750	1.51185	415.9	261.4	1,931	47.20
0.775	1.58237	473.2	298.4	2,089	41.47
0.800	1.66667	541.7	340.4	2,271	36.23
0.810	1.70523	573.0	360.2	2,353	34.25
0.820	1.74713	607.1	381.6	2,440	32.33
0.830	1.79287	644.2	404.9	2,535	30.46
0.840	1.84302	685.0	430.5	2,637	28.64
0.850	1.89831	729.9	458.7	2,749	26.89
0.860	1.95965	779.7	490.1	2,871	25.17
0.870	2.02818	835.4	525.1	3,006	23.49
0.880	2.10537	898.1	564.5	3,156	21.86
0.890	2.19317	969.5	609.3	3,325	20.24
0.900	2.29416	1,052	660.9	3,517	18.86
0.910	2.41191	1,147	723.0	3,739	17.11
0.920	2.55155	1,261	792.3	3,999	15.57
0.930	2.72064	1,398	878.7	4,310	14.04
0.940	2.93105	1,569	986.1	4,693	12.51
0.950	3.20256	1,790	1,125	5,182	10.97
0.960	3.57142	2,089	1,313	5,840	9.394
0.970	4.11344	2,530	1,590	6,797	7.758
0.980	5.02520	3,271	2,056	8,389	6.002
0.990	7.08883	4,947	3,109	11,950	3.967
0.995	10.0125	7,323	4,602	16,970	2.680
0.996	11.1915	8,282	5,204	19,060	2.370
0.997	12.9196	9,686	6,087	21,940	2.027
0.998	15.8193	12,042	7,568	26,890	1.630
0.999	22.3662	17,362	10,911	38,060	1.131

Selected from *Radioactivité*, by Madame P. Curie, p. 538, published by Hermann & Co., Paris, 1935.

TABLE 10.—ELECTRON VELOCITIES AT VARIOUS ACCELERATING POTENTIALS

Values calculated using the relativity equation

$$m_0c^2 \left(\frac{1}{\sqrt{1 - v^2/c^2}} - 1 \right) = \frac{Ve}{300}$$

where V = volts, v = velocity in cm. per sec. $e/m_0 = 1.77 \times 10^7$ e.m.u./g., $c = 2.998 \times 10^{10}$ cm./sec. The deviations from non-relativistic velocities ($\frac{1}{2}mv^2 = Ve/300$) are negligible to 300 volts, not over $\frac{1}{2}\%$ (smaller) to 3000 volts and not over 1% (smaller) to 7000 volts.

Volts	$\beta = \frac{v}{c}$	Velocity, $\times 10^{10} =$ cm./sec.	Volts	$\beta = \frac{v}{c}$	Velocity, $\times 10^{10} =$ cm./sec.
1	.001984	.00595	5,000	.1393	.418
5	.004438	.0133	6,000	.1523	.457
10	.006266	.0188			
20	.008875	.0266	7,000	.1644	.493
30	.01087	.0326	8,000	.1754	.526
40	.01255	.0376	9,000	.1858	.557
50	.01403	.0421	10,000	.1956	.586
60	.01537	.0461	20,000	.2727	.817
70	.01660	.0498	30,000	.3293	.987
80	.01774	.0532	40,000	.3751	1.12
90	.01883	.0564	50,000	.4138	1.24
100	.01984	.0595	60,000	.4474	1.34
200	.02806	.0841	70,000	.4771	1.43
			80,000	.5037	1.51
300	.03436	.103	90,000	.5277	1.58
400	.03967	.119	100,000	.5486	1.64
500	.04434	.133	200,000	.6966	2.09
600	.04857	.146	300,000	.7777	2.33
700	.05245	.157	400,000	.8289	2.49
800	.05607	.168	500,000	.8638	2.59
900	.05946	.178	600,000	.8888	2.66
1000	.06267	.188	700,000	.9073	2.72
2000	.08849	.265	800,000	.9215	2.76
			900,000	.9326	2.80
3000	.1082	.324	1,000,000	.9416	2.82
4000	.1248	.374			

TABLE 11.—ELECTRONS—RANGE AND SPECIFIC IONIZATION

R = range in centimeters in air at 760 millimeters and 15° C.

R' = range in aluminum in terms of the mass in grams per square centimeter required to stop the electrons.

$\beta = v/c$, v = velocity of electrons, c = velocity of light.

V = energy of electrons in kilovolts.

v = number of ion pairs (primary and secondary) produced per centimeter of path of electrons in air.

β	V kilovolts	R' gm./cm².	R cm.	v
0.024	0.15			7700
0.10	2.55	0.00005	0.04	2100
0.20	10.5	0.00027	0.23	1000
0.30	24.7	0.0012	1.0	400
0.40	46.6	0.0041	3.4	250
0.50	79.1	0.0087	7.3	180
0.60	127.8	0.0215	17.9	130
0.70	204.7	0.045	37.5	95
0.80	341.0	0.10	83.0	70
0.90	662.	0.26	217.	50
0.95	1127.	0.525	437.	45
0.98	2058.	1.03	860.	. . . .
0.99	3114.	1.57	1300.	41

From *Radioactivité*, by Madame P. Curie, p. 294, published by Hermann & Co., Paris, 1935.

TABLE 12.—ABSORPTION COEFFICIENTS OF ALUMINUM FOR BETA RAYS

Emitting Substance	μ (cm.⁻¹)	Emitting Substance	μ (cm.⁻¹)	Emitting Substance	μ (cm.⁻¹)
UX$_1$	460	Ra D	5500	MsTh2	40 to 20
UX$_2$	18	Ra E	45.5	RaTh	420
UY	⌣300	Pa	126	Th B	153
Ra	312	R Ac	175	Th (C+C'')	21.6; 14.4
Ra B	890; 80; 13	Ac B	1000		
Ra (C+C'')	50; 13	Ac (C+C'')	29		

From *Radioactivité*, by Madame P. Curie, p. 280, published by Hermann & Co., Paris, 1935.

TABLE 13.—ABSORPTION COEFFICIENTS FOR GAMMA RAYS

Emitting Substance	μ (cm. $^{-1}$) in aluminum				μ (cm. $^{-1}$) in lead
	I	II	III	IV	
UX$_1$	....	24	0.7	....	2.3
UX$_2$	....	..	....	0.14	0.72
Io	1088	22.7	0.41		
Ra	354	16.3	....	0.27	
Ra B	230	40	0.57	....	1.5
Ra C + Ra C″	....	..	....	0.23; 0.12	0.53
Ra D	....	45	1.17		
Ra E	....	..	....	0.24	
Po	2700	46	....	very feeble	0.96
R Ac	....	25	....	0.29	
Ac B	120	31	0.45		
Ac C + Ac C″	....	..	....	0.20	0.86
MTh2	....	26	....	0.12	0.62
Th B	160	32	0.36		
Th C + Th C″	....	..	....	0.096	0.46

From *Radioactivité*, by Madame P. Curie, p. 305, published by Hermann & Co., Paris, 1935.

TABLE 14.—SOME MASS ABSORPTION COEFFICIENTS FOR X-RAYS

	Wave-length in Angstroms						
	.100	.125	.150	.175	.200	.250	.300
Carbon	.143	.150	.156	.163	.175	.186	.202
Aluminum	.157	.180	.204	.228	.270	.395	.550
Iron	.275	.400	.611	.85	1.10	2.10	3.50
Copper	.340	.530	.810	1.12	1.59	2.97	4.70
	.350	.400	.500	.600	.700	.800	.900
Carbon	.224	.247	.316	.425	.582	.808	1.04
Aluminum	.770	1.08	1.92	3.20	5.02	7.66	10.4
Iron	5.20	7.50	14.2	23.7	36.8	55.0	74.0
Copper	7.00	10.0	19.0	32.0	49.2	71.5	98.0

Interpolated from Table I, pp. 801–802, A. H. Compton and S. K. Allison, *X-rays in Theory and Experiment*, D. Van Nostrand Co. (1935).

TABLE 15.—SOME STABLE ISOTOPES

Isotope of	Z = Atomic Number	Symbol	M = Isotopic mass	Relative abundance
Hydrogen	1	H^1	1.00812	99.98
		H^2	2.01472	0.02
Helium	2	He^3	3.01701	$\sim 10^{-5}$
		He^4	4.00388	100.
Lithium	3	Li^6	6.01690	7.5
		Li^7	7.01804	92.5
Beryllium	4	Be^9	9.01497	100.
Boron	5	B^{10}	10.01605	18.4
		B^{11}	11.01286	81.6
Carbon	6	C^{12}	12.00398	98.9
		C^{13}	13.00766	1.1
Nitrogen	7	N^{14}	14.00750	99.62
		N^{15}	15.00489	0.38
Oxygen	8	O^{16}	16.00000	99.76
		O^{17}	17.00450	0.041
		O^{18}	18.0047	0.20
Fluorine	9	F^{19}	19.00452	100.
Neon	10	Ne^{20}	19.99881	90.00
		Ne^{21}	21.00018	0.27
		Ne^{22}	21.99864	9.73
Sodium	11	Na^{23}	22.99680	100.
Magnesium	12	Mg^{24}	23.99189	77.4
		Mg^{25}	24.99277	11.5
		Mg^{26}	25.99062	11.1
Aluminum	13	Al^{27}	26.98960	100.
Silicon	14	Si^{28}	27.98639	89.6
		Si^{29}	28.98685	6.2
		Si^{30}	29.98294	4.2
Phosphorus	15	P^{31}	30.98457	100.
Sulphur	16	S^{32}	31.98306	95.1
		S^{33}	32.98260	0.74
		S^{34}	33.97974	4.2
Chlorine	17	Cl^{35}	34.98107	75.4
		Cl^{37}	36.97829	24.6
Argon	18	A^{36}	35.97852	0.307
		A^{38}	37.97544	0.061
		A^{40}	39.97504	99.632

Isotopic masses from E. Pollard and W. L. Davidson, Jr., *Applied Nuclear Physics*, John Wiley & Sons, Inc. (1942) p. 231. See also: E. Pollard, *Phys. Rev.*, **57**, 1186 (1940); W. H. Barkas, *Phys. Rev.*, **55**, 696 (1939); M. S. Livingston and H. A. Bethe, *Rev. Mod. Phys.*, **9**, 373 (1937). Relative abundances from G. T. Seaborg, *Rev. Mod. Phys.*, **16**, 1 (1944).

TABLE 16.—NATURAL RADIOACTIVE SERIES

y = years, d = days, h = hours, m = minutes, s = seconds

Atomic		Symbol	Substance	Radiation	Half Period T $T =$ 0.69315/λ	Transformation Constant λ, sec⁻¹
Wt.	No.					
			URANIUM—RADIUM SERIES			
238	92	U I	Uranium I	α	4.5×10^9 y	4.9×10^{-18}
234	90	UX₁	Uranium X₁	$\left\{ \begin{array}{l} 99.65\% \ \beta{\to}UX_2 \\ 0.35\% \ \beta{\to}UZ \end{array} \right\}$	24.5 d	3.275×10^{-7}
234	91	UX₂	Uranium X₂	$\beta{\to}$U II	1.14 m	1.013×10^{-2}
234	91	UZ	Uranium Z	$\beta{\to}$U II	6.7 h	2.87×10^{-5}
234	92	U II	Uranium II	α	2.69×10^5 y	7.2×10^{-14}
230	90	Io	Ionium	α	8.3×10^4 y	2.6×10^{-13}
226	88	Ra	Radium	α	1590 y	1.39×10^{-11}
222	86	Rn	Radon (Emanation)	α	3.825 d	2.097×10^{-6}
218	84	Ra A	Radium A	α	3.05 m	3.79×10^{-3}
214	82	Ra B	Radium B	β	26.8 m	4.31×10^{-4}
214	83	Ra C	Radium C	$\left\{ \begin{array}{l} 99.96\% \ \beta{\to}Ra \ C' \\ 0.04\% \alpha{\to}Ra \ C'' \end{array} \right\}$	19.7 m	5.86×10^{-4}
214	84	Ra C'	Radium C'	$\alpha{\to}$Ra D	1.5×10^{-4} s	$\sim 10^6$
210	81	Ra C''	Radium C''	$\beta{\to}$Ra D	1.32 m	8.75×10^{-3}
210	82	Ra D	Radium D	β	22 y	9.8×10^{-10}
210	83	Ra E	Radium E	β	5.0 d	1.60×10^{-6}
210	84	Ra F (Po)	Radium F = Polonium	α	140 d	5.73×10^{-8}
206	82	Ra G (Pb)	Radium G = (Lead)	....	stable	
			ACTINIUM SERIES			
235	92	Ac U	Actino-uranium	α	7.07×10^8 y	5.4×10^{-17}
231	90	U Y	Actinium Y	β	24.6 h	7.83×10^{-6}
231	91	Pa	Proto-actinium	α	3.2×10^4 y	6.7×10^{-13}
227	89	Ac	Actinium	β	13.5 y	1.6×10^{-9}
227	90	R Ac	Radio-actinium	α	18.9 d	4.24×10^{-7}
223	88	Ac X	Actinium X	α	11.2 d	7.16×10^{-7}
219	86	An	Actinon (Emanation)	α	3.92 s	0.177
215	84	Ac A	Actinium A	α	1.83×10^{-3} s	3.5×10^2
211	82	Ac B	Actinium B	β	36.1 m	3.21×10^{-4}
211	83	Ac C	Actinium C	$\left\{ \begin{array}{l} 0.3\% \ \beta{\to}Ac \ C' \\ 99.7\% \ \alpha{\to}Ac \ C'' \end{array} \right\}$	2.16 m	5.35×10^{-3}
211	84	Ac C'	Actinium C'	$\alpha{\to}$Ac D	5×10^{-3} s	$\sim 10^3$
207	81	Ac C''	Actinium C''	$\beta{\to}$Ac D	4.76 m	2.43×10^{-3}
207	82	Ac D = (Pb)	Actinium D = (Lead)	....	stable	
			THORIUM SERIES			
232	90	Th	Thorium	α	1.39×10^{10} y	1.2×10^{-18}
228	88	Ms Th¹	Meso-thorium 1	β	6.7 y	3.28×10^{-9}
228	89	Ms Th²	Meso-thorium 2	β	6.13 h	3.14×10^{-5}
228	90	R Th	Radio-thorium	α	1.90 y	1.16×10^{-8}
224	88	Th X	Thorium X	α	3.64 d	2.20×10^{-6}
220	86	Tn	Thoron (Emanation)	α	54.5 s	1.27×10^{-2}
216	84	Th A	Thorium A	α	0.158 s	4.78
212	82	Th B	Thorium B	β	10.6 h	1.82×10^{-5}
212	83	Th C	Thorium C	$\left\{ \begin{array}{l} 66.3\% \ \beta{\to}Th \ C' \\ 33.7\% \ \beta{\to}Th \ C'' \end{array} \right\}$	60.5 m	1.91×10^{-4}
212	84	Th C'	Thorium C'	$\alpha{\to}$Th D	3×10^{-7} s	$\sim 10^6$
208	81	Th C''	Thorium C''	$\beta{\to}$Th D	3.1 m	3.7×10^{-3}
208	82	Th D = (Pb)	Thorium D = (Lead)	....	stable	
40	19	K	Potassium	β	$\sim 10^9$ y	
87	37	Rb	Rubidium	β	6.3×10^{10} y	

For both natural and artificially radioactive substances, as well as stable isotopes, see G. T. Seaborg, *Rev. Mod. Phys.*, **16**, 1 (1944).

TABLE 17.—AIR EQUIVALENT OF FOILS FOR DEUTERONS.

Foil thickness = 0.001 inch.   Deuterons of 6 Mev.

Foil	Air Equivalent (cm.)
Aluminum	
(Diaphragm alloy)	4.6
Iron	10.8
Nickel	11.9
Copper	11.6
Molybdenum	11.2
Tantalum	14.0
Platinum	15.2

From F. N. D. Kurie, Rev. Sci. Inst., **10**, 202 (1939).

INDEX